THE GLOBAL WARMING DEBATE

The Report of the European Science and Environment Forum

Editor:

John Emsley

Committee:

Roger Bate
Frits Böttcher
John Emsley

ESEF

First Published in March 1996

by

THE EUROPEAN SCIENCE
AND ENVIRONMENT FORUM

Administrator: Lorraine Mooney
73 McCarthy Court, Banbury Street, London SW11 3ET

© ESEF

ISBN 0952773406

Copy Editor: B.W.H. Sweetman

Typography: Stuart Blade

Cover design: David Lucas

Printed in Great Britain by
BOURNE PRESS LIMITED, BOURNEMOUTH, DORSET
Set in Times New Roman 11 on 12 point

TABLE OF CONTENTS

Glossary 5

Publisher's Comments & Note for Contributors................. 6

An Economist's Foreword.............................Roger Bate.... 7

Introduction...John Emsley.. 22

SECTION 1: THE RÔLE OF CARBON DIOXIDE IN THE
        GLOBAL GREENHOUSE..................................... 27

Plant Responses to Rising Levels of Atmospheric Carbon
Dioxide ....Sherwood Idso.. 28

Carbon Dioxide: an Agricultural and Industrial Resource
.... John Emsley.. 34

The Distribution of CO_2 between Atmosphere,
Hydrosphere, and Lithosphere; Minimal Influence from
Anthropogenic CO_2 on the Global Greenhouse Effect
....Tom V. Segalstad.. 41

The Uncertainty of CO_2 Disposal and the Impact this May
have on Global Warming......................John McMullan.. 51

Do CO_2 Emissions Pose a Global Threat?..Jack Barrett.. 60

Carbon Dioxide Fluctuations Resulting from Climate
Change .... Piers Corbyn.. 71

SECTION 2: MEASUREMENT PROBLEMS............................. 79

What is a Global Temperature? The Over-Representation
of Temperate and Polar Zones
.......................Piers Corbyn & Manoucher Golipour.. 80

The Past is the Key to the Future...............Harry Priem.. 87

Reliability of Ice Core Records for Climate Prediction
....Zbigniew Jaworowski.. 95

Do Sulphates Cool the Greenhouse Debate?
....Robert Balling 106

European Temperature Variations Since 1525
.... **Gerd-Rainer Weber** .113

Random Natural Global Temperature Changes Superior
to Anthropogenic Signals .... **Asmunn Moene** 139

SECTION 3: MODELS, FORECASTS AND UNCERTAINTY 145

A Preliminary Critique of IPCC's Second Assessment of
Climate Change .... **S. Fred Singer** 146

Forging Consensus: Climate Modelling and Scientific
Review in the IPCC
.... **Patrick Michaels & Paul C. Knappenberger** 158

The Great Greenhouse Controversy .... **Fred Hoyle** 179

SECTION 4: THE SUN'S ROLE IN CLIMATE CHANGE.......... 191

Evidence from the Scandinavian Tree Line since the Last
Ice Age........ **Wijbörn Karlén & Johan Kuylenstierna** 192

Variations in the Energy Output of the Sun
.... **Genrik Nikolsky** 205

A Two-Century Comparison of Sunspot Cycle Length
and Temperature Change .... **John Butler** 215

A long-term Comparison of Sunspot Cycle Length and
Temperature Change from Zürich Observatory
.... **E Friis-Christensen & K Lassen** 224

SECTION 5: THE POLITICISATION OF SCIENCE 233

Political Pressure in the Formation of Scientific Consensus
.... **Sonja Boehmer-Christiansen** 234

Learning from the Past .... **Patricia Fara** 249

Climate Change: Forcing a Treaty........... **Frits Böttcher** 267

MISSION STATEMENT 286

ESEF members... 287

Glossary

CDIAC   Carbon Dioxide Information Analysis Centre at Oak Ridge, Tennessee.

CH_4 Methane. A greenhouse gas.

CO_2 Carbon Dioxide. A greenhouse gas.

EPA   Environmental Protection Agency. A US Federal body.

Firn   Glacier.

GCM   General Circulatory Model. A category of climate model, so called because they seek to model the full wind patterns of the planet.

GHGs   Green House Gases.

IPCC   Intergovernmental Panel on Climate Change.

N_2O Nitrous Oxide. A greenhouse gas.

NASA   National Aeronautical and Space Administration. A US Federal body.

ppm   Parts per million. A measure of concentration.

UKMO   United Kingdom Meteorological Office. The government agency involved in weather forecasting in the UK.

UNCED   United Nations Conference on Environment and Development.

UNFCCC   United Nations Framework Convention on Climate Change.

Publisher's Comments and Note for Contributors

As at 20 February 1996 ESEF has 54 members from 12 countries who, while sharing many different scientific views, are critical of and concerned about the premature certainty that exists among many organisations and politicians who seek to influence or make policy on environmental issues. The Forum is independent, non-profit making and is funded entirely by revenues from publications. Since this is the first publication we are particularly grateful to those people and companies that have bought copies in advance.

I would like to thank all those who have helped in the production of this book. Lisa Mac Lellan, Steve Berry, Barry Sweetman, David Lucas, Martin Summers and especially Lorraine Mooney for pulling it all together. So that we could attract the widest possible selection of authors, and given the limited time available for production, we did not adopt a house style for this publication. We shall for future publications and any contributors should follow the style of the paper submitted by Patricia Fara. It would be helpful if submissions (either papers or letters commenting on this first volume) were accompanied by a diskette version or were mailed electronically. Our address is 101627.2464@Compuserve.Com. Also, please include data on disk so that we can regenerate graphs and diagrams.

Roger Bate
20 February 1996

6

An Economist's Foreword[1]

Roger Bate
Director, Environment Unit,
Institute of Economic Affairs
2 Lord North St.
London

Summary

Global warming is a political issue. Information provided by scientists is used to inform policy. Decisions about whether to take action and what should be done are taken in the public arena. Such decisions are political; they are subject to the pressures of international diplomacy and the democratic process. Public choice theory recognises that participants in this process cannot help but bring with them their own, private aims and incentives. This is an unavoidable, but not unassailable, problem, except when it is forgotten; when it is assumed that political action is altruistic.

In this way, policies have been adopted in the name of averting damage to the planet from global warming, which will not have the desired effect, even if society complies fully, because the aims of those influencing and deciding policy were not those stated.

Acknowledgements
I would like to thank Lorraine Mooney and Julian Morris for commenting on earlier versions of this paper.

Introduction
This is a book about the science of global warming, to which economics can make a valid contribution. The aim of this foreword is to analyse the behaviour of the various participants in the global warming debate from the theory of the public choice school of economics.

---

[1] This foreword is adapted from a forthcoming paper. 'In Whose Interest is it Anyway? The Political Economy of Climate Change': London, Institute of Economic Affairs (IEA).

THE GLOBAL WARMING DEBATE

The most important idea in public choice theory is that individuals act in their own interest, whether in the public arena or as a private consumer[2]. It is conventional wisdom that political actors change moral hats between work and private life. It is expected that public servants apply their professional training and expertise in the public interest and not in their own; that government works on behalf of the people for the people.

Public choice theorists argue that this view is naïve. Evidence suggests that most people, most of the time, find it impossible to argue against their own manifest interests for any sustained period. Although one's self interest may include family interests and even community interest, it rarely goes any further. As Mitchell and Simmons conclude: "People may join civic organisations, churches, youth sports programs, or even run for local elected office out of a sense of community, but there is little evidence that a sense of community is what drives political participation outside the local community. There is, however, strong evidence that much political participation is based on a calculation of personal advantage" (1994, pp.24-5).[3]

Public choice theory takes as the basic unit of analysis the individual and the incentives he faces. Unlike much of political science it does not assume that organisations, and especially governments, can be treated as having special social mores. So, when the media reports that "the government attempted to implement global warming measures by imposing taxation on fuel", readers should be aware that what is really meant is that some individual person or members of a group made a particular decision. Neither governments nor nations think.[4]

---

[2] This concept is far from new, but rigorous analysis began with Professor James Buchanan who received the Nobel prize for economics in 1986 for his work on public choice. See Buchanan, J and Tullock G, (1962). There was significant early work by many political theorists such as Downs and Black, which there is no room to discuss here.

[3] This may appear a cynical analytical technique, but I contend that it explains the actions of various groups in the climate change debate.

[4] "The higher the political and economic stakes in international negotiations, the more likely are **nations to think** and act in terms of relative gains and losses", Leiv Lunde in Grubb and Anderson (1995) "Greenhouse burden-sharing after Berlin: economic ideals and political realities" (p. 52) (my emphasis).

"In the context of the FCCC process, as in general in the arena of international relations, independent, **selfish nations pursue their own self-interest** without the aid of a central authority to force them to co-operate with each other", Pascale D. Morand-Francis in

The public choice model of political decision-making divides society into four groups – voters, politicians, bureaucrats and interest groups. The actors are all assumed to want something from the system: individuals want benefits; politicians want votes; bureaucrats want security and budgets; interest groups want income. All bargainers (in this case in the global warming process) play within a game characterised by both shared and competing interests.

Politicians, bureaucrats and special interests have distinct advantages over the voters. All of them are professionals who will know more about their specialist subject than the average voter.

Attempts by voters to obtain good information on the panoply of issues that exist are too costly relative to the benefits that the voters, on their own, can capture. Voters remain "rationally ignorant" of much of the political process. As a result, the political process has a tendency to concentrate benefits on politicians, bureaucrats and special interests and to disperse costs on the much larger, but disorganised, uninformed voting public. As these concentrated benefits are worth fighting for, well-informed and articulate interest groups dominate the policy arena, contributing to constituencies and receiving political favours.

Climate Interest Groups

There are so many diverse interest groups that it is easy to suspect that, despite their rhetoric or early good intentions, many "form for the sole purpose of increasing their members' welfare and will strive to do so knowing full well that it comes at a cost to others. Because billions ... can be redistributed, interest groups are only too willing to make political investments of a substantial magnitude.... And although interest groups work on behalf of their members, their staffs have even greater interests to advance – their own" (Mitchell & Simmons p.62).

The result is a political process where rational pursuit of individual ends occurs within an institutional setting riddled with perverse incentives. Hence, politicians "find it highly rational to engage in obfuscation, play-acting, myth-making,[5] ritual, the

---

Grubb and Anderson (1995) "Lateral thinking and common measures" (p.68) (my emphasis).

[5] German Environment Minister, Angela Merkel, alarmingly stated in her opening speech at the Berlin Conference 1995: "The Greenhouse Effect is Capable of Destroying Humanity".

suppression and distortion of information, stimulation of hatred and envy, and the promotion of excessive hopes" (op cit. pp.63-4)[6].

The emission of carbon dioxide and its link to climate change involves everyone on the planet, but most individuals are not directly involved in the policy debate.[7] Those that have a direct interest include all significant industrial producers of CO_2 and those large sectors which are indirectly affected (insurance, banking, transport etc.); those whose entire *raison d'être* is the natural environment and its protection; and those with less overt incentives. I contend that these last interests are treated less critically by the media, as a result their influence may be overly significant.

Business Interests

Energy converters as well as related industries seem to have relatively obvious incentives. They are seen as being the cause of the majority of CO_2 emissions, and would just like to continue to do so because any restrictions would probably lead to a reduction in profits and they are accountable to their shareholders who want to make money. Everything about them is manifest. However, even these firms' employees have mixed motives. Individuals within a company will have conflicting incentives for survival, empire building and advancement, some of which may not be compatible with the aims of the firm as an entity. But individuals' actions will be constrained by the company's legal obligation to the shareholders.

Companies are also accountable for their actions. For example, when a company makes an exaggerated claim it is rightly censored. Adverse publicity and even expensive litigation can result. Companies are, therefore, in general careful of what they say and do.

---

[6] A satirical explanation is given by David Friedman:

"Special interest politics is a simple game. A hundred people sit in a circle, each with his pocket full of pennies. A politician walks around the outside of the circle, taking a penny from each person. No one minds; who cares about a penny? When he has gotten all the way round the circle, the politician throws fifty cents down in front of one person, who is overjoyed at the unexpected windfall. The process is repeated, ending with a different person. After a hundred rounds, everyone is a hundred cents poorer, fifty cents richer, and happy. Friedman, D, (1989) The Machinery of Freedom, 2nd ed. (La Salle, Ill.: Open Court, p.107)

[7] Most voters remain rationally ignorant because they are unlikely to benefit from any policy on global warming, and the cost to them of any policy will be minor relative to their other concerns.

Environmental Interests

Business interests have explicit agendas to make money whereas environmental interests have explicit agendas to save the planet. Perhaps this is why opinion surveys suggest that the public is more inclined to believe scientists from environmental groups than scientists from business.[8] However, as they get more successful environmental groups become more like business, and the incentives of the managers shift toward revenue raising and power. Clearly, at this point the aims of individuals begin to diverge from the stated aims of the group and the expectations of its members.

In many ways environmental groups are less accountable to their members than companies are to their shareholders as there are no objective criteria under which their success can be measured. For example, they are able to benefit from making currently irrefutable claims, without the attendant costs that might be borne by a company who lied to its shareholders about future profits[9].

Having said this, most groups have honest and earnest missions, but all have incentives and most will mislead, if the "ends justify the means".

Bureaucratic And Political Interests

International politics is an attractive option for many who are tired of the strictures of national legislation, entrenched special interests, and the voluminous existing statute book. By contrast, the international arena is a virtual *tabula rasa*.

While those sponsoring a new international treaty enjoy the spotlight, the responsibility, once ratified, falls across signatory countries. And although domestic governments come and go, international conventions and their accompanying institutions are never transient and always costly. As Dr Boehmer- Christiansen points out in her paper, it is evident that environmental treaties are rapidly occupying more of the world's bureaucracy than security measures.

The first intergovernmental meeting on climate change since the Rio summit in 1992 took place in Berlin in April 1995. No new commitments were agreed upon then but a 'Berlin Mandate' was

---

[8] That doesn't mean they are well-informed or on a noble mission.

[9] The Brent Spar oil rig fiasco provides an interesting case study of where even when it was shown that Greenpeace had made a mistake it hardly suffered any lasting adverse publicity.

adopted[10]. This mandate will lead to an increase in bureaucracy. Bureaucrats at international agencies therefore have an incentive to encourage evidence that shows that new stricter regimes, are required. Although international bureaus are non-profit, handsome rewards in terms of salaries and non-pecuniary benefits exist.

To obscure the extent of their influence, bureaucrats prefer to keep a low profile (as compared with some business and most environmental interests). Therefore, it is often easier to see their interest manifest itself when the efficacy of any programme is called into question. For example, The World Bank's Global Environment Facility (GEF) was originally due to cease functioning in 1994. However, it has a new lease of life as the interim funding agency (no longer on probation) for the climate change secretariat.[11] Threats to its closure led to recipients organising in defence of their benefit faster and more effectively than any greater gain could inspire diffused UN delegates, who individually do not bear the costs of the GEF. Its new role was assured and the GEF marches on[12]. History has shown that old programmes rarely disappear, in fact they often expand as their constituents devise new plans for implementation (see Sowell, 1995, Buchanan & Tullock, 1962 and Mitchell & Simmons, 1994 for examples).

One could paint similar pictures for many of the projects undertaken by international environmental bureaucracies. Their incentives become more obvious as research is conducted.

The IPCC was founded by UNEP and the World Meteorological Organisation. Both these organisations, like many others, are always on the look-out for useful funding possibilities, always looking for means to make their science 'relevant' and are subject to fashion as is everyone. One such change is outlined below.

---

[10] The Berlin Mandate concluded that the UNFCCC commitments were "inadequate" and that in 1997 parties to the convention would set targets for emissions reductions of greenhouse gases. Crucially these targets would only be for ANNEX 1 (OECD) countries; there was no commitment required for the developing world for the years 2005 and up to 2020.

[11] This Secretariat is still located in Geneva, but is supposed to be moved to Bonn, to aid those bureaucrats who didn't want to move to Berlin with Germany's change of capital – at least that was the justification for housing it in Bonn.

[12] 90% of the desired funding for a Climate Change Secretariat was forthcoming. In addition two subsidiary bodies were formed: one for Scientific and Technological Advice (SBSTA), the other on Implementation (SBI). The SBSTA will be the main link between the scientific world and the Convention Process.

"The cooling since 1940 has been large enough and consistent enough that it will not soon be reversed, and we are unlikely to quickly regain the 'very extraordinary period of warmth' that preceded it. Even this mild diagnosis can have 'fantastic implications' for present-day humanity" (Science editorial, March 1, 1975, quoting CC Wallen, then of the World Meteorological Organisation).

Environmental programmes are flourishing. Indeed, there has been a hearty acronym soup cooked up over the past few years. Alphabetically running from ACYS (the Arctic Climate System Study) to WOCE (the World Ocean Circulation Experiment) via groups such as the TOGA (Tropical Oceans and Global Atmosphere)[13].

Science Interests

Much 'big science' requires vast sums of money and competition for funding is intense. Having a high profile and apparent policy relevance help in the scramble for funds – climate change has both. Due to their success in capturing funding many climate scientists' careers now depend on global warming. As one journalist put it: "Imagine that you have been toiling away at atmospheric physics for 30 years and suddenly along comes global warming. Next thing you know the United Nations is paying you hundreds of pounds a day to sit in Madrid sampling room service and appearing on *Newsnight*. Would you admit that the whole thing was nothing to worry about?" [14]

Analysis of incentives is not meant to imply that the IPCC lead authors do not believe what they write in their research, it is just the way that information is presented[15] and what research is undertaken that may be influenced by incentives[16].

---

[13] The EC's Fourth Framework Programme on Research and Technological Development 1994-98 has a total value of 12.3bn ECUs. The Environment and Climate programme is worth 532m ECU over a five-year period. Climate Change is a big part of this. 47% is split between "Climate Change and impact on natural resources and, physics and chemistry of the atmosphere; biosphere processes and their effects. 7.5% goes to "the human dimensions of climate change" and "the purpose of this research is to investigate the interaction between social behaviour, economic behaviour and environmental change". Space studies including Earth Observation gets 20.5% of the budget.

[14] Ridley, M, Sunday Telegraph 10 Dec. 1995.

[15] Commentators have noticed a tendency among impact practitioners to take a negative view of the effects of climate change. Models that predict a region may have more rainfall would be interpreted as more likely to have floods, and a dryer projection would lead to more droughts. (See Tucker, 1994). Criticism of their statements has also come

Scientific Or Political Review?

The way that information is presented is important because most commentators assume that scientific documents are based on science not politics. According to the conventions of the IPCC there is a strict review procedure. However, these procedures have been flouted on many occasions.

For example: At Maastricht in 1994 there was a meeting to discuss the final chapters of Scientific Assessment Working Group I. Before the meeting took place the IPCC released a statement saying that the "scientific consensus established in 1990 still holds". However, at the meeting the text of the report was not complete and the scientists assembled were asked to approve a summary (the implication is that the underlying science would be made to conform to the summary).

The same "process" occurred at the IPCC Second Scientific Assessment meeting in Madrid in November 1995.

Perhaps the most telling comment comes from an IPCC lead author:

"We (the scientists) produce a draft, and then the policymakers go through it line by line and change the way its presented....They don't change the data, but the way its represented. It is peculiar that they have the final say in what goes into a scientists' report"(Dr Keith Shine, Reading University reported in Reuters on 20th December 1995).

The Rome Climate Summit in December 1995 was convened to approve the synthesis report of all the different IPCC Working

---

from other quarters. Professor Richard Lindzen, a well-respected climatologist, at the Massachusetts Institute of Technology was very outspoken. He was quoted as saying: "The IPCC produces waffle statements which don't say anything, which nobody can disagree with". He said science was resorting in a "very unseemly" manner to the language of the advertising industry. Prof. Lindzen maintained, "I think in the long run the IPCC statement will be an embarrassment to the scientific community". By that time, however, he said, the leaders of the IPCC would long since have gone into retirement.

"The IPCC got agreement between its computer models and the actual behaviour of the climate only by including the effect of aerosols in the atmosphere, he said. But the panel had included ' an arbitrary amount of aerosols', and so it was not surprising that it had obtained correlation." (Wilkie, T, The Independent, 1/12/95)

[16] The global-warming panic has spawned a growth industry in peripheral fields, most notably among public health academics who recently have unearthed a connection between warming and worrisome trends in epidemic diseases (see McMichael 1994). Also "related research" has examined the likely effect of climatic change on the frequency of food poisoning.

Groups. It was constantly rewritten under powerful lobbying. There is no doubt that scientific procedure was undermined.

Isn't it time that the entire review process is examined? Especially the pressure put on scientists "to emphasise results supportive of the current scenario and to suppress other results". Richard Lindzen, Professor of Meteorology at MIT (pers. comm.). If, as a lead author of the IPCC states, the Policy Makers' Summary is a "painstakingly negotiated statement of what governments officially accept as a balanced account of the state of knowledge and reasoned judgement based on the chapters", then it shouldn't be presented to the world as a scientific document (Michael Grubb, Nature 379, 108.).

Coalitions

Pressures for the IPCC's consensus come from many quarters and often the least likely. One of the consistent sights of special interest politics is the development of coalitions to force through particular policies. For environmental conventions these coalitions are especially vital as the scientific evidence is often far from conclusive. The most intriguing coalition of the last year in the climate sphere is the linkage between the reinsurance industry and environmental lobby groups, and the former's subsequent conversion to the global warming cause.

This conversion is important because some have claimed it shows that the belief in man-made climate change is becoming increasingly widespread. At the Berlin conference senior underwriters were saying "insurers fear that global warming is accelerating the trend towards costlier natural catastrophes". According to another, "The speed of global warming is a problem" and is causing "the growing number and intensity of storms". The world's largest reinsurers met in Monaco in September 1995 and they concluded that private industry could not be expected to cover losses caused by "natural forces" if they regularly affected the same region. In effect the insurers want governments to provide subsidised payments in, as one of them put it, "Armageddon scenarios".

According to leading reinsurers the insured cost of natural disasters is some 14 times greater now than in the 1960s. But this isn't because climate change is making the world a much more dangerous place[17]. Firstly, the value of property has increased

---

[17] See "Changing Weather? Facts and Fallacies About Climate Change and Weather Extremes", produced by Accu-weather (1995), which challenges the widely held belief that weather is becoming more extreme.

many times. Secondly, much of the world's most valuable property is located in precarious regions. Japan and California have high value property and high earthquake risks. Finally, more property is insured today than ever before as a consequence of greater wealth and the desire to protect that wealth.

The insurance business, like all financial services, was very lucrative in the 1980s boom, encouraging too many imprudent firms to enter the market. Less care was given to assessment of insurance risk in the scramble for business, with lower premiums demanded. There were one or two large claims from winter floods and hurricanes and the losses were significant. It would seem to be a good strategy to blame these disasters on climate change, in the hope that taxpayers would foot the bill.

Environmental NGOs have been quick to support business's view of climate change. After all, the refrain goes, if even business believes global warming is happening then it must be true. Insurers have garnered support from environmental pressure groups and have advanced their green credentials, while raising premiums and reducing cover (all of which may be sensible options as premiums may be too low).

Recent Developments

With the support of a certain vociferous NGO, reinsurers have pushed for governmental insurance: the term referring to the requirement that governments provide insurance against climate change damage on the grounds that the private industry would be unlikely to be able to cope with the losses. Indeed, UNEP's Insurance Sector Initiative on Environment and Sustainable Development already has 14 companies who are committed to incorporating environmental considerations into their risk-management strategies. The insurance industry is now firmly linked to the process. (Obviously bureaucratic interests backed this process as a new sub-organisation, and new employment opportunities and budgets were spawned).

As more industries are shown the benefits of joining the global warming cause, so the pressures on the scientists to produce a dramatic summary will increase.

Economic Measures

Reducing economic activity by limiting energy use will have real adverse consequences, because poverty restricts one's resilience to deal with problems. That is not to say that global warming does not contain potential risks, merely that the safest course is not obvious. Given that the science is still so uncertain, prudent policy dictates following economically sensible policies. But these policies require overcoming entrenched interests.

The IPCC synthesis report approved at the Rome meeting in December 1995 contains many truths about what we can and cannot know about economic life. In section 7.14 (p.29) there is the statement that "the world economy and indeed some individual economies suffer from a number of price distortions which increase greenhouse gas emissions, such as some agricultural and fuel subsidies and distortions in transport pricing."

They then cite several studies that indicate that global emissions reductions of 4 to 18% together with increases in real incomes are possible from phasing out fuel subsidies. Removal of subsidises makes economic sense anyway; the fact that it may benefit the global environment surely makes it imperative. However, it is unlikely that action will be taken on the removal of subsidies until **all** interests are acknowledged and investigated, including the bureaucracies which implement those subsidies and will lose if they are abandoned.

This leads to a further point: the estimated range of 4 to 18% is very broad considering that the energy market is probably the best understood market in the world. This should remind us of the massive uncertainties in our knowledge and hence make us wary of making even the most modest predictions of the very near future.

As Dr Boehmer-Christiansen discusses in her paper, it is those offering interdisciplinary advice that demand scientific consensus. They do this because they need firm foundations on which to make their own predictions. For economists to model the future they have to make fantastic assumptions about growth patterns, discount rates,[18] substitutions between factors of production which are simply guessed, and what changes will take place in the energy sector as fixed capital stock is replaced. Therefore we cannot know what changes will take place. Without the scenarios that these models provide, the IPCC policy options cannot be defended on economic grounds, so they are provided even though they are futile.

---

[18] Choosing 2% rather than 5% means that damages which occur in a century receive twenty times the weight.

Economic forecasts are notoriously inaccurate. All recent forecasts show massive increases in energy use in the next century, but as Grubb and Anderson (1995) point out economists have a 30-year track record in over prediction of energy use in Europe.[19]

Prudent Policy

The planet has so far responded with low sensitivity to a 50% increase in greenhouse gases, which does not suggest that immediate action for significant limitations on energy consumption is urgently required. Energy producers should investigate new technologies and fuel-switching possibilities, but we should be more certain of the science before precipitate action is demanded rather than requested[20].

The Road to Tokyo

Only a handful of countries will comply with their UNFCCC commitments, such as Germany and maybe Belgium and UK. They will do this because of policies that they were following anyway (see Boehmer-Christiansen's chapter and Victor and Salt, 1995), which had nothing to do with global warming. For the rest it will be a fascinating exercise in political dialectic to justify the inevitable abandonment of their implied commitments, whilst arguing for stricter measures in 1997. As one senior scientific commentator put it:

"A precipitate chase for a non-existent solution to the greenhouse problem, based on emotion or on a desire to attain high moral ground internationally, is likely to significantly decrease our ability to produce the disposable wealth required for social improvements and environmental damage-control strategies" (Tucker, 1994, p.8).

CONCLUSIONS

Public choice theory can help us to understand interactions between academics, funding agencies, environmental advocacy groups and politicians. The American political commentator, H.L.

---

[19] Also, CO_2 emissions today in the UK are lower than they were in 1965 and OECD emissions as a whole in 1993 were only 6% higher than in 1973, and have declined in per capita terms.

[20] "The prospect of high damages in itself does not justify substantial emissions reductions today. If the damages are far enough in the future, there would still be time for an economical turnover of existing plants and equipment and for developing the technologies needed for low-cost emissions abatement." (Manne and Richels, 1995, p.35).

Mencken explained that: "the whole aim of practical politics is to keep the populace alarmed – and hence clamorous to be led to safety – by menacing it with endless series of hobgoblins, all of them imaginary". Global warming may not be an imaginary hobgoblin, but catastrophe scenarios probably are.

Science thrives on vigorous debate until evidence is produced which falsifies all but the most robust theories. The fact that there can be irrefutable evidence is what makes science different from politics or economics. The measure of good science is neither the politics of the scientist nor the people with whom the scientist associates. Most scientists working within the IPCC inner circle have been saying what they have for a long time – far longer than the relatively recent increase in their budgets. Similarly, most of the 'sceptical' scientists have maintained their arguments for a long time as well[21].

Only those with other agendas will stifle this interesting debate.

Public choice analysis explains why the representatives of the world's nations have signed a treaty obliging them to meet unattainable carbon dioxide emission targets; why they will make these unattainable targets stricter; and why they will impose poverty-inducing restrictions on their citizens for an issue which can be characterised thus:

- We don't know that the world is definitely warming, given recent satellite data.

- If the world is warming, we don't know what is causing this change – man or nature.

- We don't know whether a warmer world is good or bad.

So far science has played second fiddle to environmentalism in the global warming issue. The papers that follow this foreword are an attempt to start to address this imbalance.

---

[21] Economic theory predicts that there will be considerable resistance to publication of results which might staunch the flow of funds for research. One would therefore expect less peer-reviewed research from global warming sceptics.

REFERENCES

Bolin, B (1994), Next step for climate change analysis, **Nature, vol. 368, 10 March.**

Buchanan, J M and Tullock G (1962) **The Calculus of Consent,** Ann Arbor, MI: Michigan University Press.

Earth Summit Bulletin, (1992) vols. 1-5, Island Press, Rio de Janeiro.

Grubb, M, (Ed) (1993), **The Earth Summit Agreements: A Guide and Assessment,** UK: Earthscan.

Grubb, M and Anderson D (Eds.) (1995) **The Emerging International Regime for Climate Change: Structures and Options After Berlin,** UK: Royal Institute of International Affairs.

Manne A, and Richels R (1995) **The Greenhouse Debate: Economic Efficiency, Burden Sharing and Hedging Strategies,** The Energy Journal, vol. 16, No. 4, pp 1-37.

McMichael, A J (1993) **Planetary Overload: Global Environmental Change and the Health of the Human Species,** Cambridge: CUP.

Mitchell, W C and Simmons R T (1994) **Beyond Politics,** Colorado: Westview Press.

Niskanen, W A (1971) **Bureaucracy and Representative Government,** Chicago: Aldine-Atherton.

Rubin E S, Lave L B and Morgan M G (1991) Keeping climate research relevant, **Issues in Science and Technology, Winter, pp. 47-55.**

Tucker, B (1994) Greenhouse: Facts and Fancies, Environmental Backgrounder, Australia: Institute of Public Affairs.

Victor, D and Salt J (1995) Keeping the climate treaty relevant, **Nature, 373,** pp280-2.

Biography

Roger Bate is Director of the Environment Unit at the Institute of Economic Affairs. He has a BA in Economics, a MPhil in Land Economy and a MSc in Environmental and Resource Economics. He is the author of several papers and articles on global warming published in papers such as the *Wall Street Journal* and the *Sunday Times,* and has appeared regularly on television and radio. He is a fellow of the Royal Society of Arts.

Global Warming:
The Report of the European Science and Environment Forum

Introduction

John Emsley
Committee Member of ESEF
Science Writer in Residence,
Imperial College of Science, Technology and Medicine
Department of Chemistry
London

There are three reasons why the European Science and Environment Forum (ESEF) is publishing this book:

1. To introduce some scientific debate into the issue of the Earth's climate and potential future global warming;

2. To show that carbon dioxide is not the threat that it is purported to be; that to speak of this as a pollutant and as the major greenhouse gas is misleading;

3. To undo the damage which continued alarms about global warming have done to the credibility of scientists and to the public understanding of science.

Many lay people now regard CO_2 as a major pollutant because they have been told that CO_2 is the greenhouse gas which is building up around the planet and trapping the Earth's heat. This will melt the polar caps, causing massive flooding of coastal regions, which are where large sections of the world's population lives. Unless we cut our use of fossil fuels this disaster will happen early in the next century. Pressed to justify these statements, they would no doubt reply that scientists have forecast it will be so, and they should know, and that governments are considering ways to curb the use of fossil fuels to reduce the emissions of CO_2.

Yet many people are puzzled by what they have been told. Despite this message of doom, regularly repeated for the past ten years, why is there no sure evidence of global warming and the coming of the Second Flood? If the world is warming, why then do we still experience record low temperatures, such as -20°C in Scotland in December 1995, and the worst blizzards in the US in living memory in January 1996? Why, if the increasing level of CO_2 is responsible for warming the air, does it not prevent these low temperatures?

Naïve questions maybe, but the kind that members of the general public ask one another. Their obvious conclusion is that the scientists have got it wrong. What concerns me as a science writer is the damage this is doing to the public understanding of science.

Most people are unaware that the predictions of global warming are based mainly on computer simulations, backed up by carefully-selected evidence and special pleading. Behind it all is the Intergovernmental Panel for Climate Change (IPCC), an influential body of science policy makers which presents itself as the consensus of science opinion on the issue. It achieves this consensus by excluding those scientists who question its 'findings'. In this book, the European Science and Environment Forum has offered some of them an alternative platform for their views, in a modest attempt to open up the global warming issue to proper scientific debate.

The IPCC is lavishly funded by the UN, enabling it to hold well-publicised meetings attended by thousands of climatologists, environmentalists, journalists and official observers. It publishes expensive and glossy accounts of its deliberations, and these almost always receive uncritical coverage by the media. Environmental activists, who have in the past helped to set the IPCC agenda, ensure that its forecasts reach the widest possible audience, and they search for interesting back-up stories to link the supposed global warming to any local spell of hot weather, freak flooding or drought. (Naturally, they ignore extremes of cold weather.)

Ten years of crying "Wolf!" has had the expected effect; the public has become inured to the warnings because nothing catastrophic has happened. However, the alarms have achieved one aim: to divert a great deal of government research funding towards the environmental sciences, which are hungry for money to purchase and support their super-computers on which to run ever more elaborate programs. It is now worth asking whether the millions spent this way might not have been better spent solving real environmental problems, by supporting research in biology, ecology and agriculture.

The time has come to bring some hard science into the global warming debate. The early computer predictions, on which the global warming scares of the mid-1980's were based, now look embarrassingly simplistic. Although they were careful not to publicise the fact at the time, the computer simulations of these early forecasters could not even take into account such key factors as oceans, polar ice and clouds. Nevertheless, it did not prevent them from predicting that the temperature would rise by an average of 5.2°C by the end of the next century. Some environmentalists even talked of runaway global warming, turning the Earth into another Venus. Admittedly, from 1992 the IPCC has toned down its alarmist predictions, but they still see a new century of impending disasters. Their supporters still uncritically spread the message of doom.

Hopefully, this era of blinkered science is coming to an end, and with it the attitude that a function of research is to serve the goals of science policy makers. The oft-repeated claim by the IPCC, that it represents a consensus of scientific opinion, is far from the truth – although if you are not part of that consensus, you are often not funded. This demand for consensus stifles scientific debate, undermines the open-mindedness that should be the hallmark of true science, and taints any results that are obtained with the suspicion that they have been influenced by the paymasters.

Carbon dioxide-induced global warming is an issue which deserves to be properly debated, and this is what this book is all about. Here you can read those who question whether there has been any significant man-made climate change; other contributors reveal the politics behind the IPCC and the global warming scare; others question whether increased carbon dioxide can cause global warming; one author even suggests that higher CO_2 levels might be of benefit and lead to a re-greening of the arid regions of our planet; some question the validity of computer modelling and others the data on which the models are based.

Perhaps the next century will see neither the Second Flood nor a new Garden of Eden. It may even be that we are approaching the next Ice Age, which many leading environmentalists were forecasting with certainty only a few years ago. In any case, it is not in the best interests of science to throw untested hypotheses into the public domain if these have not been properly debated, especially so if they are alarmist in tone. The European Science and Environment Forum was set up in 1994 to try and address issues like global warming in a scientific way, free from the influence of pressure groups, and in the hope that we may restore the public's faith in science so that they will appreciate what it really can deliver. We want them to see that their children and grandchildren will reap its benefits in the next millennium, and not to live in fear of what it might produce.

Because so much has been written putting forward the case for global warming, there seemed little point in reviewing these well-known arguments in this book. Those who would like to read the IPCC's side of the debate are well served by its many publications. Most popular books on the greenhouse effect and global warming are by authors who take their material from IPCC sources. Instead, ESEF has concentrated on giving those scientists who have an alternative opinion a platform for their views. Keep an open mind as you read – the last thing we want is to close the debate on the effects of anthropogenic emissions on the Earth's atmosphere. ESEF's primary aim is to stimulate a debate on this key issue.

Papers are already being collected for Volume 2, which will deal with major topics of climate uncertainty that have not been covered in Volume 1, such as clouds, satellite data and the impacts predicted for global warming. A key issue to be addressed will be the value of computer simulations, since it was on the basis of these that the global warming scare of the 1980s was started. Comparisons between those early predictions and experimental observations for the 1990s can now be made.

The aim is to include contributions from as wide a spectrum of scientists as possible. Researchers who would like to be included should send their manuscripts to ESEF. The editors would also welcome letters from readers who wish to take part in the debate, and who have comments, favourable or unfavourable, to make on papers in this first volume.

John Emsley

Dr John Emsley is Science Writer in Residence at Imperial College, London, a position he has held since 1990. He obtained his BSc in chemistry from Manchester University and then went on to do a PhD in inorganic chemistry. Following postgraduate research at Queen Mary Westfield College (London University), he was appointed a lecturer at King's College, and then a reader, in inorganic chemistry. During his academic career Dr Emsley published over 100 research papers and three books, and was awarded a DSc in 1983. His book, "The Elements" (1989) has been reprinted over ten times and appeared in French, German and Russian editions.

THE GLOBAL WARMING DEBATE

During his career as a science writer Dr Emsley published more than 500 articles and features, and has been a regular columnist on *The Independent* newspaper with his "Molecule of the Month", for which he won the Chemistry Industry Association President's Award for science writing in 1994. In 1993 he won a Glaxo Award for the radio script entitled "The Shocking History of Phosphorus", and in 1995 his book, "The Consumer's Good Chemical Guide" won the Rhône Poulenc Science Book Prize. This is currently being translated into several other languages, including French, German and Japanese. Dr Emsley is a frequent broadcaster on BBC and CBC radio, including the BBC World Service.

Section 1

The Role of Carbon Dioxide in the
Global Greenhouse

Plant Responses to Rising Levels of Atmospheric Carbon Dioxide

Sherwood B. Idso
Research Physicist with the US Department of Agriculture at the
US Water Conservation Laboratory in Phoenix, Arizona

Summary

Rising levels of CO_2 in the atmosphere promote plant growth and at the same time reduce their demand for water. These effects should lead to a greening of the Earth and signs are that this has already begun.

Introduction

There is abundant evidence that enriching the air with carbon dioxide helps plants grow better. In a recent review of 342 scientific articles devoted to this subject, it was found that increasing the CO_2 content of the air by 300 ppm (from 350 to 650 ppm) increased the mean growth rate of the 475 varieties of plants studied by more than 50%. (A CO_2 increase of 2250 ppm boosted their productivity by 165%!)

What is the basis for this phenomenal growth response? Very simply, it derives from the fact that carbon dioxide is the primary raw material used by plants to produce food by the process of photosynthesis. The more CO_2 there is in the air, the faster Earth's photosynthetic machinery operates, and the more CO_2 it incorporates into the biomass of the planet's vegetation.

This CO_2-enhanced ability of plants to extract carbon dioxide from the atmosphere and incorporate it into their tissues is a natural consequence of their evolutionary development. As described by Bernard Grodzinski of Canada's University of Guelph,

"plants probably evolved their primary strategy of fixing CO_2 at a time in the earlier history of the Earth when ... CO_2 was far more abundant."

Deep down within their basic genetic makeup, then, plants still carry this ability to adapt to the higher atmospheric CO_2

28

concentrations typical of those earlier times so that when they are exposed to such conditions again, they function much better to what we have come to accept as the norm.

Another way that atmospheric CO_2 enrichment enhances growth is by stimulating plants to reduce the size of the pores in their leaves through which water is evaporated and lost to the atmosphere. Each unit area of leaf surface thereby uses less water as a plant grows. The ratio of these two processes – the amount of organic matter produced divided by the amount of water transpired – is what plant scientists call *water use efficiency*. And since organic matter production is increased by atmospheric CO_2 enrichment while water loss is decreased, plant water use efficiency rises even faster than does plant productivity as the air's CO_2 concentration would likely *double* the water use efficiencies of their individual leaves.

The effect of such an improvement in plant prowess could transform the Earth's vegetation as the CO_2 content of the air continues to rise. Plants that barely subsist on the borders of barren deserts should gradually acquire the ability to grow and reproduce where it is currently too dry for them. As a result, they should be able to expand their ranges to occupy more of the planet's arid areas and make them more productive. Over the coming centuries, then, if atmospheric CO_2 continues to climb, this phenomenon portends a renewed "greening of the Earth"; for it is *water*, more than anything else, that is the chief determinant of whether or not plants will proliferate where temperatures are not too cold for them. And as Earth's vegetation becomes more and more efficient at utilising this essential resource, each drop of water will go further towards fuelling the basic life processes of the biosphere.

In contrast to this positive view of the rising CO_2 content of Earth's atmosphere, some scientists have suggested that natural resource limitations may negate the beneficial effects of atmospheric CO_2 enrichment and leave the growth rates of Earth's vegetation largely unchanged. A careful study of the scientific literature, however, reveals this opinion to be overly pessimistic.

As well as requiring less water, plants in enriched CO_2 air also grow with less light. As the light intensity decreases, rates of net photosynthesis decline for both CO_2-enriched foliage and foliage exposed to ambient air. However, a number of experiments have revealed that as light intensity drops lower and lower, the net photosynthetic rates of plants growing in ambient air often decline to zero well before the net photosynthetic rates of plants growing in CO_2-enriched air do. Hence, the *relative* benefits of atmospheric CO_2 enrichment actually *rise* as light becomes more limiting. And at low light levels where plants begin to experience an overall loss of CO_2 exchange rates, atmospheric CO_2 enrichment can actually mean the difference between life and death over prolonged periods of time. Those plants exposed to elevated levels of CO_2 continue to sequester carbon, and grow, while those exposed to normal air exhaust the reserves upon which they depend for their sustenance, and die.

Decreasing soil moisture has much the same effect. Growth rates drop for both CO_2-enriched plants and plants growing in ambient air as water becomes more limited; but plants in ambient air typically exhaust their soil moisture reserves much quicker, as the pores in their leaves through which water escapes to the atmosphere do not close as effectively as those of CO_2-enriched plants. Again, when water reductions are severe, there can be dramatic differences in plant responses, as plants in ambient air often die before they can produce a harvestable crop, whereas CO_2-enriched plants may succeed in producing a modest yield under such conditions.

CO_2 enrichment of the air has also been shown to protect plants against both extremely hot and cold temperatures. On more than one occasion, for example, my colleagues and I have watched plants – even floating aquatic plants – succumb to the intense summer heat of the Arizona desert, while similar plants exposed to a higher atmospheric CO_2 concentration continued to grow and develop. Indeed, it is now a well-established fact that atmospheric CO_2 enrichment tends to raise the optimum temperature for plant growth. This scientific observation counters the theoretical worry that if global warming occurs as predicted, plants will not be able to migrate fast enough to keep up with the climatic regime to which they are currently accustomed, leading to their ultimate extinction. On the contrary, experimental results suggest that in a higher CO_2 world of the future, plants will actually *prefer* warmer climates; and if temperatures were to rise somewhat, Earth's vegetation would have no need to move poleward at all but would flourish even better than it does now simply by staying where it is.

Plants growing in nutrient-poor soil also benefit from atmospheric CO_2 enrichment, because they typically allocate more of their carbohydrate production to root growth. This strategy enables them to more thoroughly explore the soil for needed nutrients and to acquire those nutrients from a greater depth. In addition, enhanced root growth stimulates nearby soil microbial growth, which triggers a whole series of other nutrient-gathering phenomena.

In a CO_2-enriched world of the future, for example, soil microbes that feed more freely upon the extra root carbohydrates produced by atmospheric CO_2 enrichment would be likely to secrete greater quantities of organic acids that hasten the release of a variety of important minerals. This phenomenon has been demonstrated to increase the mobility of the liberated nutrients and significantly enhance plant growth even further. Many symbiotic fungi living in close associations with plant roots are similarly stimulated. They too assist in the acquisition of nutrients needed by their hosts; and they often protect them from soil-borne disease and root infections.

One group of organisms that deserves special mention in this regard is composed of bacteria that remove gaseous nitrogen fom the atmosphere and make it directly available to plants by a process called *nitrogen fixation*. Atmospheric CO_2 enrichment has been shown to stimulate this process significantly, with several-fold enhancements in the fixation of nitrogen. Consequently, as nitrogen-fixing bacteria are found in nearly all natural ecosystems, atmospheric CO_2 enrichment may be expected to magnify this phenomenon over the entire planet.

As summarised by Australian researcher, R. M. Gifford,

"high CO_2 increases light-use efficiency, water-use efficiency and nitrogen-use efficiency, and ... the 25% increase in atmospheric CO_2 concentration since industrialisation started is likely to be increasing global net primary production relative to what it would be without that atmospheric change."

Much the same conclusion has been reached by several groups of scientists studying the seasonal oscillation of the air's CO_2 content. This yearly-recurring cycle of declining and rising atmospheric CO_2 concentrations begins anew each spring, when vegetation in the Northern Hemisphere awakens from its winter dormancy and starts to grow. So powerful is this hemispheric growth process that it removes enough carbon dioxide from the air to decrease its CO_2 concentration by several parts per million. Then, in the autumn, when growth slows and eventually ceases, decaying organic matter returns an enormous amount of carbon dioxide back to the atmosphere, causing its CO_2 concentration to rise.

The difference between the low and high points of the resulting seasonal oscillation in atmospheric CO_2, which is superimposed upon the steadily rising mean value of the air's CO_2 content, has been growing larger and larger each year; and those who have studied this phenomenon have arrived at essentially the same conclusion: that the Earth's plant life is growing more productive and more extensive each year, as a result of the rising CO_2 content of the atmosphere. The reasoning behind this conclusion is that mankind's continual enrichment of the air with carbon dioxide allows plants to remove ever greater quantities of CO_2 from the atmosphere in the spring and summer of each year, which then leaves ever more CO_2 to be returned to the atmosphere each succeeding autumn and winter. This leads to the increasing size of the yearly fall and rise of the air's CO_2 content that is revealed in long-term measurements. Since 1958 there has been a rise of nearly 30% in the amplitude of the seasonal CO_2 cycle, suggestive of a similar rise in the total productivity of the Earth's vegetation.

Independent evidence for the greening of the Earth is provided by numerous studies that have documented enhanced forest growth rates over the past decades. Studies from as many as 50 different forests scattered across the globe have revealed significant upward trends in productivity since 1960 at least. The long-lived bristlecone pine trees link the initiation of this Biological Revolution with the start of the Industrial Revolution, when humans first began to have a measurable impact on the CO_2 content of the atmosphere. What is more, the phenomenon is spreading in extent, as well as intensifying, and there is evidence from nearly every ice-free continent that woody plants are beginning to extend their ranges and grow in profusion where they have not been able to survive in the past.

With this CO_2-induced increase in the amount and vigour of Earth's plant life comes a benefit to Earth's animal life as well: more habitat and more food, which in the long-term should help to preserve the biodiversity of the planet. Hence, it is clear that the entire biosphere must have already benefited immensely from the rising CO_2 content of the atmosphere; and it should benefit even more in the years to come, as the atmosphere gradually returns to a CO_2 regime more characteristic of its long-term geologic past. This inexpected legacy is due in large measure, if not entirely, to mining and burning of fossil fuels in the prodigious amounts required to sustain industrial civilisation.

REFERENCES

1. Gifford, R. M. Interaction of carbon dioxide with growth-limiting environmental factors in vegetation productivity: Implications for the global carbon cycle. *Advances in Bioclimatology Vol.1* 1992: pp.24-28.

2. Grodzinski, B. Plant nutrition and growth regulation by CO_2 enrichment. *BioScience Vol. 42* 1992: pp.517-525.

3. Idso, S. B. (1995) *CO_2 and the Biosphere: The Incredible Legacy of the Industrial Revolution*. Special publication, Department of Soil, Water and Climate, University of Minnesota, St. Paul, MN. 64p.

Sherwood Idso
Sherwood B. Idso is a research physicist with the US Department of Agriculture at the US Water Conservation Laboratory in Phoenix, Arizona and an adjunct professor in the Departments of Botany and Geography at Arizona State University. He is the author of several hundred scientific articles dealing with the climatic and biological consequences of atmospheric CO_2 enrichment, including the books *Carbon Dioxide: Friend or Foe?* (1982) and *Carbon Dioxide and Global Change: Earth in Transition* (1989).

Carbon Dioxide as a Resource for Industry and Agriculture

John Emsley
Committee Member of ESEF
Science Writer in Residence,
Imperial College of Science, Technology and Medicine
Department of Chemistry
London

Summary

Although it is little appreciated, carbon dioxide is a key industrial resource and one of growing importance. For example, in the USA five million tons of CO_2 are produced commercially each year, making it one of the top 20 bulk chemicals. It is tempting to imagine that this material might eventually be the major source of all organic chemicals, and that one day we might recycle much of the CO_2 which is now wasted. To understand whether this is a viable option for the future, we need to consider the present sources and uses of the gas, and to speculate on the other ways we might develop it.

Exploiting CO2

The major producer of commercial CO_2 is the chemicals industry, which obtains it as a by-product of processes such as the manufacture of ammonia for fertilisers. The second largest producer is the brewing industry, which generates excess CO_2 during the fermentation of grains and grapes in the production of beers and wines. A molecule of CO_2 is released for each molecule of alcohol produced.

Other potential sources of CO_2 are listed in Table 1. Some of these produce vast amounts, such as power stations, cement works and municipal incinerators, but of poor quality because it is diluted with nitrogen gas and contaminated with other products of combustion, such as nitrogen oxides and sulphur dioxide. Nevertheless, there are processes being developed for collecting and purifying the CO_2 from these sources, (See J. T. McMullan in this book). Nature itself has vast reserves of this gas, and these are sometimes drawn upon.[1]

For example the fizz in mineral water is boosted by the addition of CO_2 drawn from natural underground reservoirs of the gas. In South Australia there is an enormous 'lake' of CO_2 beneath the extinct volcano, Mount Gambier, and this too is tapped on a commercial basis. In some places these vast deposits are put to use by transporting them from one part of the Earth's crust to another, as in the USA. There, the gas from wells of CO_2 is pumped hundreds of miles to the Western Texas oilfield, where it is injected in the oil-bearing strata to force out more oil. This is predicted to yield an extra 56 billion barrels of oil.

Table 1: Exploitable Sources of CO_2

	Source	Quality of CO_2*
1.	Chemical industry by-products	10 - 50%
2.	Breweries	50 - 100%
3.	Power stations and incinerators	10 - 15%
4.	Oil and gas wells	10 - 15%
5.	CO_2 gas reservoirs	90 - 100%
6.	Cement works	20 - 50%
7.	Atmosphere	0.035%

* Per cent of CO_2 in gas source.

CO2 as a Chemical Resource

The above uses do not transform CO_2 into new materials. To do so would be the challenge for a future chemicals industry, particularly if it had to use anthropogenic CO_2 and turn this into the products that an advanced society needs: plastics, pharmaceuticals, paints, and packaging, and maybe even into petrol itself. This is the kind of challenge that chemists would relish, and some academic and industrial research is already being focused on this area. Indeed, if chemists and chemical engineers could discover ways of using waste CO_2 economically, then their efforts might well lead to other advances, as has happened with new technologies in the past. In this way, there would be the added bonus of new products and new technologies creating new businesses.

An obvious first step in converting CO_2 to other organic compounds is to follow the natural route of converting it to

---

[1] This CO_2 is not included in the figure of CO_2 produced by industry.

biomass and then extract the desired material, for example, from plants or algae. This is already happening as chemical companies around the world are looking afresh at CO_2. In Japan, Mitsubishi Heavy Industries is using the gas from a power station to boost the growth of algae, which produce a natural form of oil that can be used as biodiesel.

As a starting material for the direct manufacture of other chemicals, CO_2 is somewhat limited. A little CO_2 is reacted with phenol to make aspirin. A lot of CO_2 goes into the manufacture of urea by the reaction of CO_2 with ammonia gas. Urea is a white solid which can be used directly as a fertiliser, as an animal food supplement, or as a chemical itself for the manufacture of plastics. One such is the plastic, melamine, from which light-weight picnic ware and heat-resistant kitchen surfaces are made.

It has been known for a long time that CO_2 will react with hydrogen gas to form methanol – a liquid fuel in its own right. The process is carried out at 250°C and 80 atmospheres pressure and needs a mixed-metal catalyst. The difficulty here is the supply of hydrogen gas, most of which currently comes from natural gas, as we have seen. Other sources of hydrogen could be exploited, such as the hydrolysis of water, but this requires a lot of energy. Currently, most methanol is made from carbon monoxide (CO) and hydrogen gas, but the market is large (10 million tonnes per year) and growing. Methanol can easily be converted to petrol and paraffin by passing it through a zeolite catalyst, and this is done by New Zealanders, turning their abundant supplies of natural gas into fuel for cars.

Perhaps the most attractive use of CO_2 will be in the manufacture of poly(carbonate). This transparent plastic is used to make compact discs, safety spectacles, feeding bottles, unbreakable panes of glass and street signs, but its present manufacture requires the use of chlorinated solvents which are being phased out. Liquid CO_2 is seen as a suitable solvent but the process requires temperatures of 80-100°C and pressures of 135-350 atmospheres.

Superfluid CO2

At atmospheric pressure CO_2 can never be a liquid, and if we cool it we find that at *minus* 78°C it freezes into a solid, so-called dry ice.[2] Its name comes from the fact that on warming, it does not

---

[2] Solid CO_2 was formerly used in long distance transportation of food before refrigerated trucks were developed. It is still used to cool processed food, and a blast of CO_2 snow will ensure the rapid refrigeration of frozen meals.

melt but reverts straight back to a gas, a chemical phenomenon called sublimation.

To get liquid CO_2 we need increased pressures, and the higher the temperature of the liquid, the higher the pressure that has to be applied. For example, liquid CO_2 at 30°C requires a pressure of 70 atmospheres.[3] Industry works with CO_2 up to 100°C, but then it needs 300 atmospheres, and under these conditions, CO_2 is not really a liquid but is a *supercritical fluid* (SCF) which has remarkable solvent properties.

SCF is ideal for processing materials which eventually come into contact with humans, because it is odourless, colourless and tasteless, it does not leave any unwanted residues, unlike many solvents, it is not flammable. Industry finds it attractive because CO_2 is cheap, non-toxic and non-flammable, and SCF has a low viscosity and it will dissolve a wide range of materials such as oils, fats, caffeine, perfume essences and other plant extracts.

When the essential oils of plants, herbs, flowers and spices are extracted using SCF, it gives improved essences, which reflect the natural composition more closely than extracts using traditional solvents. Surface oil on potato snacks can be washed off to produce the 'reduced fat' varieties, with as much as a third less fat. Hops have been extracted in this way since 1977 and such hop extracts have been used in making beers.

SCF is the solvent of choice for decaffeinating coffee. Earlier methods of making this used organochlorine solvents such as chloroform, but these left behind minute residues of solvent which still worried people. The best-selling decaffeinated coffees, such as Café Hag in Europe, are made using SCF. The process involves extracting the caffeine from the beans with superheated water, and then subtracting the caffeine from the water with SCF. The result is to reduce the amount of caffeine in a cup of instant coffee from 60 mg to only 3 mg.

Another suggestion for using liquid CO_2 is as a solvent for dyeing. The effluent from textile dye works is particularly difficult to clean up and, although the amount of chemical waste may be relatively small, a little goes a long way in making a river appear heavily polluted. Some dyes are very soluble in SCF and this turns out to be an ideal dyeing medium, according to Wolfgang Dierk Knittel and Eckhard Schollmayer of the Deutches Textilforschungszentrum of Krefeld, Germany. There is no water involved and the results are often much brighter shades of colour.

---

[3] Tankers transport liquid CO_2 at high pressure.

This is another example whereby in investing in new chemical technology we may produce a new generation of colours and clean up our rivers at the same time.

The most recent use of SCF is in the production of superfine powders, of the kind required by pharmaceutical companies for medical inhalers. Peter York and Mozen Hanna of the School of Pharmacy at the University of Bradford in Yorkshire, England, have patented a process by which a jet of SCF is directed at a jet of the drug dissolved in ethanol. The SCF disperses the ethanol jet, causing the drug it contains to precipitate as micron-sized (millionth of a metre) crystals, which are easily separated and the whole system is closed, so there are no emissions. The process might well be developed for making other materials where fine particles are an advantage, such as in the agrochemicals, photographic and explosives industries. Catalyst manufacturers are also possible users of the new technology.

Stimulating Plant Growth with CO_2

Nature uses atmospheric CO_2 as the primary source of carbon for all living things, despite the low concentration of this gas in the atmosphere. If this concentration increases then so does its conversion into living matter, and we can make use of this fact and help Nature along. Farmers can boost glasshouse crops by pumping in CO_2 to double the amount of this gas in the air from the natural level of 350 ppm to 700 ppm. In the Netherlands, the use of CO_2 in glasshouses began about five years ago, and is now used by all growers. Crops respond to a doubling of the amount of CO_2 in the air and generally the yield of produce goes up by 25%, making the process highly economical. Some growers even find that tripling the amount to 1000 ppm of CO_2 will increase crop yields by 40 per cent. Another beneficial effect of increased CO_2 is that crops need less water.

Plants grow bigger where there is more CO_2 and this is also true in the wild. Research by Professor James Teeri of the University of Michigan, has demonstrated that if the amount of CO_2 in the air were to double, then tree growth would go up by 20 per cent. Researcher R. A. Sedjo of Resources for the Future Inc., of Washington DC, thinks that as much as 2 billion tonnes of the anthropogenic CO_2 may be ending up this way each year, as yet undetected.

A realistic appraisal

Even if we could supply all the needs of the chemicals industry from CO_2 as the starting material, we are still only talking about recycling a mere one per cent of the gases emitted by fossil fuel burning. That would be enough to supply all the carbon needed. To struggle to do this would be fruitless, except as an intellectual exercise, but it is worth moving in that direction. The gains to be made are not in a trivial reduction in emissions of this gas, but in better and safer ways of making the things we need. And, along the way, chemists will undoubtedly discover new processes and unexpected materials which we might exploit. Meanwhile, the chief beneficiary of the CO_2 which enters the atmosphere, from cars, power stations, cement works and incinerators, is the plant life of our planet, which is beginning to grow more abundantly. Some of it is already making a contribution to our food supply and our crops of renewable resources. This will always be the best way of recycling CO_2.

REFERENCES

1. Emsley, J., 'The good side of carbon dioxide', in *The Consumer's Good Chemical Guide*, Chapter 9, pp.257-261. W. H. Freeman, Oxford 1995.

2. Magrini, K. A., and D. Boron, 'Carbon dioxide: global problem and global resource', in *Chemistry and Industry*, pp.997-1000, 19 December 1994.

3. Saus. W., D. Knittel and E. Schollmeyer, 'Dyeing of textiles in supercritical carbon dioxide', *Textile Research Journal, vol. 63*, pp.135-141 1993.

4. York, P. and M. Hanna, Producing perfect powders, reported in *Chemistry in Britain,* p15, January 1996

The Distribution of CO_2 between Atmosphere, Hydrosphere, and Lithosphere; Minimal Influence from Anthropogenic CO_2 on the Global Greenhouse Effect

Tom V. Segalstad
Mineralogical-Geological Museum
University of Oslo
Norway

Summary

The global climate is primarily governed by the enormous heat energy stored in the oceans and the latent heat of the ice caps, not by the small amount of heat that can be absorbed in atmospheric CO_2. Human contribution to atmospheric CO_2 from the burning of fossil fuels is small (4% at most), according to carbon isotope mass balance calculations. The effect of this contribution to global warming is small and well within natural climatic variability. The amount of fossil fuel carbon is small compared to the total amount of carbon in the atmosphere, hydrosphere, and lithosphere. The lifetime of atmospheric CO_2 is about 5 years. The ocean will be able to absorb the larger part of the CO_2 that humans can produce through burning of fossil fuels. The IPCC CO_2 global warming model is not supported by the scientific data. Based on geochemical knowledge there should be no reason to fear a climatic catastrophe because of human release of the CO_2 gas.

Introduction

The IPCC claims that an apparent increase in atmospheric CO_2 concentration is caused by anthropogenic burning of fossil carbon in petroleum, coal, and natural gas. The extra atmospheric CO_2 has been claimed to cause global climatic change with a significant atmospheric temperature rise, of 1.5 to 4.5°C in the next decennium

(Houghton et al., 1990). This postulate is here discussed and rejected on energetic and geochemical grounds.

Heat energy and temperatures

The average temperature on the surface of the Earth, is 14 to 15°C, caused by heat-absorbing gases in the atmosphere, mainly H_2O vapour. Without the Earth's atmosphere the surface temperature would be approximately -18°C.

Although they go back 150 years or more, atmospheric temperature measurements cover too short a time-span to be useful for climate prediction, or to be used as evidence for anthropogenic heating (or cooling). The global mean temperature has risen and fallen several times over the last 400 years, with no proof of anthropogenic causes, although strong explosive volcanic eruptions have caused periodically colder climates (Jaworowski et al., 1992 a).

The Earth receives about 1368 W/m^2 of radiative heat from the Sun. The total amount of this retained in the Earth's lower atmosphere is approximately 11%, and has traditionally been named the Earth's 'Greenhouse Effect'. For a cloudless atmosphere this effect is on average about 146 W/m^2 for the Earth, with an uncertainty of ± 5 to 10 W/m^2 due to analytic uncertainties and natural climatic variations. Human activities have been claimed to contribute about 1.3% of this (approx. 2 W/m^2), while a hypothetical doubling of the atmospheric CO_2 concentration would contribute about 2.6% (approx. 4 W/m^2) (Raval & Ramanathan, 1989; Ramanathan et al., 1989).

It should also be noted that clouds can reflect up to approx. 50 W/m^2 and can absorb up to approximately 30 W/m^2 of the solar radiation (Ramanathan et al., 1989), making the Earth's average 'Greenhouse Effect' vary naturally within approximately 96 and 176 W/m^2. The contribution of anthropogenic atmospheric CO_2 heat absorption is much smaller than the natural variation of the Earth's 'Greenhouse Effect' (Segalstad & Jaworowski, 1991).

The oceans act as a huge heat energy buffer and the global climate is primarily governed by the enormous amount of heat stored in the oceans (total mass approx. 1.4×10^{24} g), rather than the minute amount of heat held in the heat-absorbing part of the atmosphere (total mass approx. 1.4×10^{18} g), a mass difference of one million times (Peixoto & Oort, 1992). Most of the atmospheric heat absorption occurs in water vapour (total mass approx. 1.3×10^{18} g), with a residence time of about 9 days (Peixoto & Oort, 1992).

The total internal energy of the whole ocean is more than 1.6×10^{27} joule, about 1700 times larger than the total internal energy of the whole atmosphere 9.4×10^{23} joule. Note that this energy is defined with respect to 0 Kelvin (Peixoto & Oort, 1992).

Furthermore the cryosphere (ice sheets, sea ice, permafrost, and glaciers; total mass of the continental ice is approx. 3.3×10^{22} g) plays a central role in the Earth's climate as an effective heat sink for the atmosphere and oceans, with a large latent heat of melting on the order of 9.3×10^{24} joule, a hypothetical energy equivalent to cooling the entire oceans by about 2°C (5.8×10^{24} J/°C). For comparison, the energy needed to warm the entire atmosphere by 1°C is only 5.1×10^{21} joule (Oerlemans & van der Veen, 1984). It will be impossible to melt the Earth's ice caps and thereby increase the sea level just by increasing the heat energy of the atmosphere a few percent, due to the added heat absorption of anthropogenic CO_2 in the lower atmosphere.

CO_2 measurements in atmosphere and ice cores

Houghton et al. (1990) make three claims in support of the theory that the contemporary atmospheric CO_2 increase is anthropogenic: *First,* CO_2 measurements from ice cores show a 21% rise from 280 to 353 ppmv (parts per million by volume) since pre-industrial times; *second,* the atmospheric CO_2 increase parallels the accumulated emission trends from fossil fuel combustion and from land use changes, although the annual increase has been smaller each year than the fossil CO_2 input (by as much as 50%, e.g. Kerr, 1992); *third,* the isotopic trends of ^{13}C and ^{14}C agree qualitatively with those expected for CO_2 emissions from fossil fuels and the biosphere.

Jaworowski et al. (1992 a, 1992 b) reviewed published CO_2 measurements from ice cores, and emphasised that the pre-industrial atmospheric CO_2 concentration, according to early accurate analyses, was many times larger (measurements up to 2450 ppmv) than the present atmospheric value. They also pointed out that CO_2 variations in ice are mainly the product of a large number of natural physical-chemical processes in ice and the recovered ice cores. These effects dominate the traces of anthropogenic CO_2. Criticism of the methodology of collecting and analysing CO_2 in ice cores has also independently been presented by Heyke (1992 a, 1992 b, 1992 c).

Jaworowski et al. (1992 a) have presented a number of criticisms regarding the methodology of atmospheric CO_2 measurements, including spectroscopic instrumental peak overlap errors (from N_2O, CH_4, and CFCs in the air). They also pointed out that the CO_2 measurements at current CO_2 observatories use a procedure involving a subjective editing (Keeling et al., 1976) of measured

43

data, only representative of a few tens of percent of the total data. There are also fundamental problems connected with the use of stable carbon isotopes ($^{13}C/^{12}C$) in tree rings for model calculations of earlier atmospheres' CO_2 concentration, a method which now seems to have been abandoned (Jaworowski et al., 1992 a).

The third evidence, based on carbon isotopes, will be discussed below.

Chemical laws for distribution of CO_2 in nature

Statistically it has been found that the atmospheric CO_2 concentration rises after the temperature rises (Kuo et al., 1990), and it has been suggested that the reason is that warmer water dissolves less CO_2 (e.g. Segalstad, 1990). Hence, if the water temperature increases, the water cannot keep as much CO_2 in solution, resulting in CO_2 degassing from the water to the atmosphere. According to Takahashi (1961) heating sea water by 1°C will increase the partial pressure of atmospheric CO_2 by 12.5 ppmv during upwelling of deep water. For example 12°C warming of the Benguela Current should increase the atmospheric CO_2 concentration by 150 ppmv.

Volk & Liu (1988) modelled the CO_2 flux between atmosphere and oceans, and concluded that approximately 70% of the flux was governed by this "thermal solubility pump", while approximately 30% was governed by the organic nutrient "biological pump". Faure (1990) estimated that ca. 4000 GT (Gigatonnes = billion metric tonnes) of CO_2 is transferred from the ocean via the atmosphere to the continental biosphere following the end of an Ice Age.

From a geochemical consideration of sedimentary rocks deposited throughout the Earth's history, and the chemical composition of the ocean and atmosphere, Holland (1984) showed that degassing the Earth's interior has given us chloride in the ocean; and nitrogen, CO_2, and noble gases in the atmosphere. Mineral equilibria have established concentrations of major cations in the ocean, and the CO_2 concentration in the atmosphere, through different chemical buffer reactions. Biological reactions have given us sulphate in the ocean and oxygen in the atmosphere.

Carbon dioxide is an equally important requisite for life on Earth as oxygen. Plants need CO_2 to grow, and humans and animals breath out CO_2 from their respiration. In addition to this biogeochemical balance, there is also an important geochemical balance. CO_2 in the atmosphere is in equilibrium with carbonic acid dissolved in the ocean, which in turn is close to $CaCO_3$ saturation and in equilibrium with carbonate shells of organisms and lime (calcium carbonate; limestone) in the ocean.

In addition there are a number of different aqueous metal complexes of lesser concentrations.

A buffer can be defined as a reaction system which modifies or controls the value of a thermodynamic variable (pressure, temperature, concentration, pH, etc.). The ocean's carbonate system will act as a pH buffer, by the presence of a weak acid (H_2CO_3) and a salt of the acid ($CaCO_3$). The concentration of CO_2 and of Ca^{2+} will in the equilibrium Earth system also be buffered by the presence of $CaCO_3$, at a given temperature. If the partial pressure of CO_2 is increased, the net reaction will go towards $CaCO_3$ because of the Law of Mass Action. If the temperature changes, the chemical equilibrium constant will change and the partial pressure of CO_2 will increase or decrease. The equilibrium will mainly be governed by Henry's Law: the partial pressure of CO_2 in the air will be proportional to the concentration of CO_2 dissolved in water. The proportional constant is the Henry's Law Constant, which is strongly temperature dependent, and dependent to a lesser extent on total pressure and salinity (Drummond, 1981).

Questions have been raised about how strong this buffer is. It has been postulated (Bolin & Keeling, 1963) that an increase in atmospheric CO_2 will be balanced when only approximately one tenth of this is dissolved in the ocean. This postulate fails for a number of reasons. An increase in atmospheric CO_2 will namely increase the buffer capacity of ocean water, and thereby strengthen the ocean's capacity to moderate an increase of atmospheric CO_2; maximum buffer capacity for the system CO_2 - H_2O is reached at 2.5 to 6 times the present atmospheric partial pressure of CO_2, depending on temperature and alkalinity (Butler, 1982). According to Maier-Reimer & Hasselmann (1987) the borate in the seas also increases the ocean storage capacity for CO_2 by more than 20% over an ocean with the carbonate-system alone.

Furthermore, this carbonate buffer is not the only global buffer. The Earth has a set of other buffering mineral reactions. The geochemical equilibrium system anorthite $CaAl_2Si_2O_8$ - kaolinite $Al_2Si_2O_5(OH)_4$ has, at the pH of ocean water, a buffer capacity which is a thousand times larger than a 0.001 M carbonate solution (Stumm & Morgan, 1970). In addition we have clay mineral buffers, and a calcium silicate + CO_2 $\approx$ calcium carbonate + SiO_2 buffer (MacIntyre, 1970; Krauskopf, 1979). These buffers all act as a "security net" underlying the most important buffer: CO_2 (g) $\approx$ HCO_3^- (aq) $\approx$ $CaCO_3$ (s). All together these buffers, in principle, add up to an almost **infinite buffer capacity** (Stumm & Morgan, 1970).

Stable carbon isotopes ($^{13}C/^{12}C$) show that CO_2 in the atmosphere is in chemical equilibrium with ocean bicarbonate and lithospheric

45

carbonate (Ohmoto, 1986). The chemical equilibrium constants for the chemical reactions in the sea provide us with a partition coefficient for CO_2 between the atmosphere and the ocean of approximately 1 : 50 (approx. 0.02) at the global mean temperature (Revelle & Suess, 1957; Skirrow, 1975). This means that for an atmospheric doubling of CO_2, there will have to be supplied 50 times more CO_2 to the ocean to obtain chemical equilibrium. This is more than the known reserves of fossil carbon. It is possible to exploit approximately 7000 GT of fossil carbon, which means that, if all this is burned, the atmospheric CO_2 would be increased by 20% at the most once geochemical equilibrium has been re-established with the oceans, although this may take some time.

[14]C isotopes show that the circulation time for carbon in the upper part of the ocean is some few decades (Druffel & Williams, 1990). This is sufficient time for the ocean to absorb an increase in atmospheric CO_2 from burning of fossil fuel at the present projected rate (Jaworowski et al., 1992 a).

Carbon isotopes in atmospheric CO2

Houghton et al. (1990) assumed for the IPCC model 21% of our present-day atmospheric CO_2 has been contributed from burning of fossil fuel. This has been made possible by the assumption that CO_2 has a lifetime of 50 - 200 years in the atmosphere. It is possible to test this by inspecting the stable $^{13}C/^{12}C$ isotope ratio (expressed as $\sigma^{13}C_{PDB}$)[1] of atmospheric CO_2. It is important to note that this value is the net value of mixing all different CO_2 components, and would show the results of all natural and non-natural (i.e. anthropogenic) processes involving CO_2.

The natural atmospheric CO_2 reservoir has $\sigma^{13}C \approx -7\%o$ when in isotopic equilibrium with marine HCO_3^- and $CaCO_3$ (Ohmoto, 1986). CO_2 from burning of fossil-fuel and biogenic materials has $\sigma^{13}C \approx -26\%o$ (Hoefs, 1980). Mixing these two CO_2 components with the ratio 21% CO_2 from fossil fuel burning 79% "natural" CO_2 should give a $\sigma^{13}C$ for the present atmospheric CO_2 of approximately -11‰.

Keeling et al. (1989) have recorded $\sigma^{13}C$ of atmospheric CO_2 over many years. $\sigma^{13}C$ -7.489‰ in December 1978, decreasing to -7.807‰ in December 1988, values close to that of the natural atmospheric CO_2 reservoir, far from the $\sigma^{13}C$ value of -11‰ expected from the IPCC model. Hence the IPCC model is not supported by $^{13}C/^{12}C$ evidence.

---

[1] $\sigma^{13}C = (^{13}C/^{12}C)_{sample} - (^{13}C/^{12}C)_{sample}/(^{13}C/^{12}C)_{sample} \bullet 1000\%o$

Segalstad (1992, 1993) has used isotope mass balance considerations to calculate the atmospheric CO_2 lifetime and the amount of fossil fuel CO_2 in the atmosphere. The December 1988 atmospheric CO_2 composition was computed for its 748 GT C total mass and $d^{13}C = -7.807‰$ for 3 components: *(1)* natural fraction remaining from the pre-industrial atmosphere; *(2)* cumulative fraction remaining from all annual fossil-fuel CO_2 emissions (from production data); *(3)* carbon isotope mass-balanced natural fraction. The masses of the components were computed for different atmospheric lifetimes of CO_2.

The calculations show how the IPCC's (Houghton et al., 1990) atmospheric CO_2 lifetime of 50-200 years only accounts for half the mass of atmospheric CO_2. However, the results fit an atmospheric CO_2 lifetime of around 5 years, in agreement with numerous ^{14}C studies compiled by Sundquist (1985) and chemical kinetics data (Stumm & Morgan, 1970). The mass of all past fossil-fuel and biogenic emissions remaining in the current atmosphere was in December 1988 calculated to be around 30 GT C, which at most is around 4% of the total, corresponding to an atmospheric CO_2 concentration of around 14 ppmv.

This small amount of anthropogenic atmospheric CO_2 probably contributes less than 0.5 Watt/m^2 of the 146 W/m^2 "Greenhouse Effect" of a cloudless atmosphere, contributing to less than half a degree C of radiative heating of the lower atmosphere.

The implication of the 5-year lifetime of CO_2 in the atmosphere is that 135 GT C (18%) of the atmospheric CO_2 pool is exchanged each year. This is far more than the 6 GT of carbon in fossil fuel CO_2 now contributed annually to the atmosphere.

The isotopic mass balance calculations show that at least 96% of the current atmospheric CO_2 is isotopically indistinguishable from non-fossil-fuel sources, i.e. natural marine sources from the Earth's interior. Hence, for the atmospheric CO_2 budget, marine equilibration and degassing, and degassing from e.g. volcanic sources, must be much more important, and burning of fossil-fuel and biogenic materials must be much less important, than assumed in IPCC model (Houghton et al., 1990).

Acknowledgements: Technological Oriented Studies, University of Oslo, for financial support; Dr. Zbigniew Jaworowski for scientific discussions and contributions.

REFERENCES

Bolin, B. & Keeling, C.D. (1963): Large-scale atmospheric mixing as deduced from the seasonal and meridional variations of carbon dioxide. Journal of Geophysical Research Vol. 68 (13), pp.3899-3927.

Butler, J. N. (1982): Carbon dioxide equilibria and their applications. Addison-Wesley Publishing Company, 259 pp.

Druffel, E. R. M. & Williams, P.M. (1990): Identification of a deep marine source of particulate organic carbon using bomb 14C. Nature 347, pp.172-174.

Drummond, S. E., Jr. (1981): Boiling and mixing of hydrothermal fluids: chemical effects on mineral precipitation. Ph.D. thesis, The Pennsylvania State University, 381 pp.

Faure, H. (1990): Changes in the global continental reservoir of carbon. Paleontology, Paleogeography, Paleoecology (Global Planetary Change Section) Vol. 82, pp.47-52.

Hoefs, J. (1980): Stable isotope geochemistry, 2nd ed. Minerals and Rocks, 9. Springer-Verlag, 208 pp.

Heyke, H.-E. (1992 a): Zu den CO2-Klimakurven aus Eisbohrkernen. Erdöl und Kohle, Erdgas, Petrochemie vereinigt mit Brennstoff-Chemie Vol. 45 (5), pp.208-214.

Heyke, H.-E. (1992 b): Zu den CO2-Klimakurven aus Eisbohrkernen - Diskussion. Erdöl und Kohle, Erdgas, Petrochemie vereinigt mit Brennstoff-Chemie Vol. 45 (9), pp.360-362.

Heyke, H.-E. (1992 c): Gasblasen im Eis sind brüchiges Fundament für die CO2-Steuer. Fusion 13 (3), pp.32-39.

Holland, H. D. (1984): The chemical evolution of the atmosphere and oceans. Princeton University Press, 582 pp.

Houghton, J. T., Jenkins, G. J. & Ephraums, J. J. (Eds.) (1990): Climate Change. The IPCC Scientific Assessment. Intergovernmental Panel on Climate Change. Cambridge University Press, Cambridge, 365 pp.

Jaworowski, Z., Segalstad, T. V. & Hisdal, V. (1992 a): Atmospheric CO2 and global warming: a critical review; 2nd revised edition. Norsk Polarinstitutt, Meddelelser [Norwegian Polar Institute, Memoirs] 119, 76 pp.

Jaworowski, Z., Segalstad, T. V. & Ono, N. (1992 b): Do glaciers tell a true atmospheric CO_2 story? Science of the Total Environment 114, pp.227-284.

Keeling, C.D., Bacastow, R. B., Bainbridge, A. E., Ekdahl, C.A. Jr., Guenther, P. R., Waterman, L. S. & Chin, J. F. S. (1976): Atmospheric carbon dioxide variations at Mauna Loa Observatory, Hawaii. Tellus Vol. 28 (6), 538-551.

Keeling, C.D., Bacastow, R. B., Carter, S C., Whorf, T. P., Heimann, M., Mook, W. G. & Roeloffzen, H. (1989): A three-dimensional model of atmospheric CO_2 transport based on observed winds: 1. Analysis of observational data. In Peterson, D. H. (Ed.): Aspects of climate variability in the Pacific and the Western Americas. American Geophysical Union, Geophysical Monograph Vol. 55, pp.165-236.

Kerr, R. A. (1992): Fugitive carbon dioxide: it's not hiding in the ocean. Science 256, 35.

Kuo, C., Lindberg, C. & Thomson, D. J. (1990): Coherence established between atmospheric carbon dioxide and global temperature. Nature 343, pp.709-714.

MacIntyre, R. (1970): Why the sea is salt. Scientific American 223 (5), pp.104-115.

Krauskopf, K. B. (1979): Introduction to geochemistry; 2nd edition. McGraw-Hill, Inc., 617 pp.

Maier-Reiner, E. & Hasselmann, K. (1987): Transport and storage of CO2 in the ocean – an inorganic ocean-circulation carbon cycle model. Climate Dynamics Vol. 2, pp.63-90.

Oerlemans, J. & van der Veen, C. J. (1984): Ice sheets and climate. D. Reidel Publishing Company, 217 pp.

Ohmoto, H. (1986): Stable isotope geochemistry of ore deposits. Reviews in Mineralogy Vol. 16, pp.491-559.

Peixoto, J. P. & Oort, A. H. (1992): Physics of climate. American Institute of Physics, 520 pp.

Ramanathan, V., Barkstrom, B. R. & Harrison, E. F. (1989): Climate and the Earth's radiation budget. Physics Today Vol. 42 (5), pp.22-32.

Raval, A. & Ramanathan, V. (1989): Observational determination of the greenhouse effect. Nature 342, pp.758-761.

Revelle, R. & Suess, H. E. (1957): Carbon dioxide exchange between atmosphere and ocean and the question of an increase of atmospheric CO_2 during the past decades. Tellus Vol. 9, pp.18-27.

Segalstad, T. V. (1990): Temperatur og CO2. Teknisk Ukeblad 137 (17; yellow part), pp.4-5.

Segalstad, T. V. (1992): The amount of non-fossil-fuel CO_2 in the atmosphere. American Geophysical Union, Chapman Conference on Climate, Volcanism, and Global Change, March 23-27, 1992, Hilo, Hawaii. Abstracts, 25.

Segalstad, T. V. (1993): Stable isotope geochemistry applied to paleoclimatological and greenhouse gas problems. 1st International Symposium on Applied Isotope Geochemistry (AIG-1), Aug. 29 - Sept. 3, 1993, Geiranger, Norway. Program and Abstracts, Institute for Energy Research IFE/KR/E-93/007, pp.95-96.

Segalstad, T. V. & Jaworowski, Z. (1991): CO2 og globalt klima. Kjemi 51 (10), pp.13-15.

Skirrow, G. (1975): The dissolved gases - carbon dioxide. In Riley, J. P. & Skirrow, G. (Eds.): Chemical oceanography, Vol. 2; 2nd edition. Academic Press, pp.1-192.

Stumm, W. & Morgan, J. J. (1970): Aquatic chemistry. An introduction emphasising chemical equilibria in natural waters. John Wiley & Sons, 583 pp.

Sundquist, E. T. (1985): Geological perspectives on carbon dioxide and the carbon cycle. In Sundquist, E. T. & Broecker, W. S. (Eds.): The carbon cycle and atmospheric CO2: natural variations Archean to present. American Geophysical Union, Geophysical Monograph Vol. 32, pp.5-59.

Takahashi, T. (1961): Carbon dioxide in the atmosphere and in Atlantic ocean water. Journal of Geophysical Research Vol. 66 (2), pp.477-494.

Volk, T. & Liu, Z. (1988): Controls of CO2 sources and sinks in the Earth scale surface ocean: temperature and nutrients. Global Biogeochemical Cycles Vol. 2, pp.73-89.

Biography of Tom Victor Segalstad

Born in Norway in 1949. University degrees (natural sciences with geology) from The University of Oslo. Has conducted university research, publishing, and teaching in geochemistry, mineralogy, petrology, volcanology, structural geology, ore geology, and geophysics at The University of Oslo, Norway, and The Pennsylvania State University, USA. At present keeping professional positions as Associate Professor of Geochemistry at The University of Oslo; Head of The Mineralogical-Geological Museum at The University of Oslo; and Director of The Natural History Museums and Botanical Garden of The University of Oslo. Member of different international and national professional working groups and committees.

Carbon Dioxide Collection And Disposal

Professor J.T. McMullan
Energy Research Centre, University of Ulster
Cromore Road,
Coleraine, UK

Summary

Technologies already exist for the separation and collection of carbon dioxide from large scale combustion plant, and for its subsequent disposal. There are some environmental concerns about some of the disposal technologies, but these do not appear to be insurmountable. Equally, while the costs are not prohibitive, they are significant and will be a determining factor regarding the implementation of carbon dioxide removal technologies.

Introduction

Given the aspirations of the developing countries and the fact that their industrial revolution, like that of Europe, will be based on coal, it is unlikely that improvements in efficiency or measures to reduce energy demand in industrialised countries will have a significant long-term effect on global emissions of carbon dioxide. Thus, attention must be given to ways of removing carbon dioxide during or after the combustion process and sending it to long-term storage which is both dependable and safe. This would allow CO_2 to be slowly released to the atmosphere at a rate which is consistent with natural processes taking place in the environment which absorbs it.

Thus, leaving aside the intractable problems of emissions from vehicles and from small-scale and domestic combustion, for which no obvious solutions are apparent, one must ask first if suitable, safe, long-term storage routes can be identified, and second if CO_2 can be separated from the combustion air in large-scale combustion processes and collected for subsequent disposal. The intermediate stage of transporting the collected CO_2 to the storage facility poses no significant problems as pipeline technology is well developed and well understood.

51

Assuming that the technology can be developed and is environmentally acceptable, the other important factor will be cost. The choice of technology will depend on its comparative costs, and ultimately, cost will determine whether CO_2 disposal will take place at all. Such costs might be borne in developed societies, but developing societies are unlikely to be willing to bear the cost.

CO_2 Disposal

Six basic routes have been identified for achieving the long-term disposal or storage of carbon dioxide (Ormerod, et al. 1993):

- *Ocean disposal* CO_2 is liquified or solidified and then sunk in deep water where it will go into solution.

- *Terrestrial disposal* CO_2 is stored on land in large insulated containers.

- *Aquifer disposal* CO_2 is dissolved in deep subterranean aquifers.

- *Disposal in exhausted oil and gas wells* In this proposal, the CO_2 is injected into the wells at the original reservoir pressure, the assumption being that this will be environmentally satisfactory since the wells were originally gas tight before their exploitation was begun.

- *Enhanced oil recovery* CO_2 injection is currently used to enhance the oil recovery from depleting wells, and it is proposed that this practice could be increased as a mechanism for storing CO_2.

- *Biological fixation* Tree and crop planting is undertaken to absorb CO_2 through photosynthesis.

The estimated CO_2 storage capacity of each of these technologies is listed in Table 1 (Ormerod, et al. 1993), which shows that ocean disposal is extremely attractive in capacity terms, followed by biological fixation and terrestrial storage.

In energy cost terms, at about \$75 per tonne of carbon stored, terrestrial disposal (Seifritz, 1992) can be taken as the reference case because it involves no transport costs; the CO_2 is stored on-site at the point of production. There are some safety and maintenance issues but this problem is common to all of the other proposals.

Table 1: Estimated CO_2 storage potentials (in gigatonnes of carbon)

DISPOSAL METHOD	ESTIMATED CO_2 STORAGE CAPACITY (Gt Carbon)*
Ocean Disposal	20,000,000
Terrestrial Disposal	High
Aquifers	100 - 3000
Exhausted Oil and Gas Wells	125
Enhanced Oil Recovery	4
Biological Fixation	50 - 100

* 1 Gt = 10^9 tonnes

Terrestrial disposal involves the construction of large thermally insulated spheres of CO_2, with a diameter of 400 m and an insulation thickness of 2 m. With these dimensions, the stored CO_2 would take about 4000 years to sublime completely, which would imply the same damping effect on peak CO_2 concentration as ocean disposal. Typically, a 500 MW coal-fired power station with a life of 50 years would require the construction of three or four spheres on the power station site.

As shown in Table 1, ocean dumping is extremely attractive in capacity terms. The deep ocean has a very large capacity for dissolving CO_2, and at depths of 3000m the retention time has been calculated at over 1000 years (Stegan, et al. 1993). At depths greater than 3000m, the density of carbon dioxide is greater than that of water which means that the CO_2 would sink even further. The technical problems of injecting CO_2 at 3000m are large, but alternative proposals have been advanced which would allow injection at depths less than 1000m, relying on natural currents to carry the carbon dioxide downwards (Marchetti, 1977; Drange, et al., 1992). Ocean dumping is technically feasible. The limitations are financial. It is now believed that injection at 500m would have high biological impact, and injection depths greater than 1000m would be more acceptable (International Energy Agency, 1994).

Aquifer storage is another attractive option because of the widespread distribution of deep aquifers. The figures in Table 1 show the range of estimates from the somewhat conservative (100) to the highly optimistic (3000). IEA (1994) reports an extensive study of the Western Canada Sedimentary Basin as a possible site for aquifer disposal, and indicates that, on a conservative estimate, the 25,000 km^3 basin could accept about 1 Gt C of CO_2, with a retention period of about one million years. Additionally, because of the long residence time, there is a strong possibility that the retention might become permanent because of chemical reactions between the acidic CO_2 solution and the host rock, particularly if it contains calcium and magnesium silicates (Gunter et al., 1993). The environmental risks are believed to be low, and the cost is reasonable at approximately $50 per tonne of carbon stored.

Storage in exhausted oil and gas reservoirs depends on the nature of the reservoir. Closed, under-pressurised reservoirs that have not been invaded by water would be ideal, and the CO_2 would be used to re-pressurise the reservoir back to its original level. If water has invaded the reservoir, then it becomes analogous to an aquifer. Oil reservoirs are more difficult than gas reservoirs because the drive mechanism is more complicated and the pressure may not drop as the reservoir is depleted. Additionally, as the primary recovery of oil from a reservoir is typically less than 30%, there is great attraction in associating the initial stages of CO_2 injection with an enhanced oil recovery (EOR) scheme. EOR using CO_2 is an existing oil-industry practice in which the injection of CO_2 is used to pressurise the well and increase the amount of oil recovered from the reservoir (Bondor, 1992). The environmental risks associated with disposal based on oil and gas reservoirs are quite well documented because of experience with enhanced oil recovery. These include leakage of CO_2 from pipes and surface installations, leakage from the reservoir to the surface and into neighbouring geological formations, pollution of ground water and subsidence or absidence of the earth surface (Van der Meer, 1993). These should be kept in perspective, however, and natural CO_2 fields have retained their contents for over 60 million years and are not regarded as a hazard. The costs would appear to be less than $10 per tonne of carbon stored.

Biological fixation is based on the concept of planting crops to remove CO_2 from the atmosphere by photosynthetic processes. In this way, each tonne of CO_2 sequestered compensates, at the very low cost of $3.5 per tonne C, for its equivalent emission from a combustion plant (Winjum, et al. 1992). Unfortunately, this is only partly true as trees typically live for about 50 years before dying and returning their sequestered carbon dioxide to the atmosphere. Nonetheless, trees and other plants will act as a buffer store for CO_2 and will extend the period over which the concentration increases. Another negative factor is the land use which is associated with sequestering using trees; a 500 MW power plant would require 1700 km^2 of forestry to offset its emissions. Considerable effort is presently being expended into enhancing the photosynthetic effect using algae (Watanabe et al., 1992).

CO_2 Collection From Large Combustion Plant

As a precursor to any of the disposal techniques outlined above, the CO_2 must first be captured and separated from the air. This is straightforward in principle, and can be achieved in a number of ways. It is important to remember, however, the sheer size of large combustion plant and the implications that this has for the technology. A 1200 MW coal-fired power station burns approximately 10,000 tonnes of coal per day. Each tonne of coal burnt produces approximately 3.5 tonnes of CO_2. Thus, the CO_2 output of such a power station is about 35,000 tonnes per day. To complicate matters even further, the carbon dioxide is diluted by the nitrogen which was originally present in the combustion air, so that the total amount of flue gas that has to be treated is about 185,000 tonnes per day.

Two techniques are commonly proposed to separate CO_2 on this scale. The first is to use solvents such as MonoEthanolAmine (MEA) in a scrubbing system to remove the CO_2 from the gas stream with an effectiveness of about 90% (IEA, 1993). Subsequently, the CO_2 is regenerated from the solvent, which is then returned to the scrubber. The CO_2 can then be cleaned and compressed to liquid form for storage and transport to the disposal site. The other approach is to use a membrane material which preferentially allows the CO_2 to pass through, so separating it from the rest of the flue gas (IEA, 1993).

Both of these approaches will remove 85 - 90% of the CO_2, but both require sulphur and other contaminants to be removed from the flue gas in order to prevent degradation of the solvent or the membrane.

A third approach is shown in the figure (McMullan et al., 1995). An air separator is used to separate the oxygen in the air from the nitrogen. The boiler is then fired using oxygen instead of air, which means that the flue gas is almost entirely composed of CO_2. A second advantage is that the flue gas volume is reduced by about 80% because of the nitrogen removal. In order to maintain conditions in the boiler and keep temperatures at acceptable levels, part of the CO_2 flue gas is recycled back to the inlet. This means that the actual combustion atmosphere is a mixture of oxygen and carbon dioxide rather than oxygen and nitrogen. The flue gas (consisting of CO_2 with contaminants such as SO_2) is cooled, compressed and sent for disposal. The advantage of this approach is that there is no need to remove sulphur or NOx as these components will liquefy with the carbon dioxide and can be disposed of at the same time.

These separation technologies carry no environmental implications as these are associated with the disposal process. Large pilot-scale tests have been carried out over recent years which show all three techniques to be viable (IEA, 1993, JOULE II, 1994), though membrane-based removal is limited by the size of existing membrane separators. Cost, once again, remains the issue.

Table 2 shows the results of one study (McMullan et al., 1995) for a conventional pulverised fuel coal fired system. The reference case is based on a 500 MW conventional plant with flue gas desulphurisation (FGD). This can be regarded as the standard for conventional technology. The two CO_2 removal technologies are MEA scrubber (which requires the FGD stage) and oxygen-firing with CO_2-recycle, which does not require an FGD stage. The recovered CO_2 is delivered as a liquid at a pressure of 60 bar.

The implications are quite clear. Significant reductions can be made in the amounts of carbon dioxide directly released to the atmosphere from large scale combustion plant by using either a scrubbing system or the advanced oxygen-firing approach. The cost penalty in either case is about 80%, to which must be added the consequent cost of disposal.

Table 2: Comparison of CO_2 Separation and Concentration

TECHNOLOGY	Efficiency (*LHV%*)	CO_2 Emission (kg/kWh)	Specific Investment (£/kWh)	Break-Even Electricity Selling Price (£/kWh)
Pulverised Fuel + Flue Gas Desulphurisation	38.3	0.887	673	0.033
PF + FGD + MEA scrubbing	27.7	0.123	1114	0.052
PF + O_2 firing + CO_2-recycle	26.4	0	1149	0.052

REFERENCES

Bondor, P.L. (1992). *Applications of carbon dioxide in enhanced oil recovery*. Energy Conversion and Management, **33**, pp 579-586.

Drange, H. and Haugan, P.M. (1992). *Sequestration of CO_2 in the deep ocean by shallow injection*. Nature, **357**, pp 318 - 320.

Gunter, W.D., Perkins, E.H. and McCann, T.J. (1993). *Aquifer disposal of CO_2-rich gases: reactor design for added capacity*. Energy Conversion and Management, **34**, pp 941-948.

IEA (1993). *The capture of carbon dioxide from fossil fuel fired power stations*. Pierce Riemer (Ed.) IEA Greenhouse Gas R&D Programme, Cheltenham.

IEA (1994) *The disposal of carbon dioxide from fossil fuel fired power stations*. Bill Ormerod (Ed.) IEA Greenhouse Gas R&D Programme, Cheltenham.

JOULE II (1994). Clean Coal Technology Second Annual Meeting, Veldhoven, Netherlands, September, 1994, K. Matthews, (Ed.), European Commission, Brussels.

McMullan, J.T., Williams, B.C., Campbell, P., McIlveen-Wright and Bemtgen, J-M (1995). *Techno-economic assessment studies of fossil fuel and fuel wood power generation technologies*. European Commission DGXII, Brussels.

Marchetti, C. (1977). *On geoengineering and the CO_2 problem*. Climate Change, **1**, pp 59-68.

Ormerod, W.G., Webster, I.C., Audus, H. and Riemer, P.W.F. (1993). An Overview of Large Scale CO_2 Disposal Options, *Proc. Int. Energy Agency Carbon Dioxide Disposal Symposium*, Oxford, 29-31 March 1993 Riemer, P.W.F. (Ed.). Pergamon Press, Oxford, pp 833-840.

Seifritz, W. (1992). The terrestrial storage of CO_2 - ice as a means to mitigate the greenhouse effect. *Hydrogen Energy Progress IX* (Potter, C.D.J. and Veziroglu, T.N., Eds.), pp 59-68.

Stegan, G.R, Cole, K.H. and Bacastow, R. (1993). *The influence of discharge depth and location on the sequestration of carbon dioxide*. Energy Conversion and Management, **34**, pp 857-864.

Van der Meer, (1992). *Investigations regarding the storage of carbon dioxide in aquifers in the Netherlands.* Energy Conversion and Management, **33**, pp 611-618.

Watanabe, Y., Ohmura, N. and Saiki, H. (1992). *Isolation and determination of cultural characteristics of microalgae which function under CO_2-enriched* atmosphere. Energy Conversion and Management, **33**, pp 545-552.

Winjum, J.K., Dixon, R.K. and Schroeder, P.E. (1992). *Estimating the global potential of forest and agroforest management practices to sequester carbon.* Water, Air and Soil Pollution, **64**, pp 213-227.

John McMullan Bsc, MA, PhD, Dsc, C.Eng. C.Phys, F.Inst, F.Inst.P

John McMullan is Professor of Physics and Director of the Energy Research Centre of the University of Ulster, Coleraine, Northern Ireland, UK.

He is Editor of the International Journal of Energy Research and is a member of the Editorial Board of Progress in Photovoltaics, both published by John Wiley and Sons Ltd.

He has published over 190 books and papers. His primary research interests lie in the techno-economic assessment and optimisation of advanced power generation systems and on reducing their emission, on CFC replacement in refrigeration and air-conditioning equipment, and on energy systems analysis and energy policy.

He has acted as the co-ordinator of several multi-national research projects in these areas and the results of his research are used to provide baseline data for the formulation of European Energy R&D Strategy.

Do CO_2 emissions pose a global threat?

Jack Barrett
Imperial College of Science, Technology and Medicine
Department of Chemistry
London

Summary

Measurements of the earth's temperature made by instruments carried by a network of satellites since 1978 show that random variations of as much as ±0.5°C occur, some changes occurring over periods of only two weeks. It would seem inadvisable to attribute variations of the same magnitude over the course of a century to an enhancement of the greenhouse effect.

Any effects of the 25% increase in atmospheric carbon dioxide on the Earth's average surface temperature cannot be distinguished from the background of natural variability. All the energy that can be absorbed by the atmosphere is being absorbed by the lower atmosphere (water, aerosols and CO_2) under present conditions.

Introduction

Although many factors, some still not fully understood, affect the temperature of the Earth and its atmosphere, the *Intergovernmental Panel on Climate Change* (IPCC) [1] attempts to explain long-term temperature variations almost entirely in terms of changes in man-made emissions of carbon dioxide. Climatologists regard the role of additional carbon dioxide as one of increasing the trapping of solar radiation which heats the Earth's surface, leading to a warming of the lower atmosphere (i.e., the first 16 km) and to significant changes in climate.

This paper is devoted to an examination of the evidence for this alleged role. Most of the data referred to are those for the 20th century, mainly because they are considered to be the most reliable. Doubts are expressed concerning the quality and interpretation of the data and of the application of fundamental radiation theory to the predictive aspects of the IPCC's work.

Discussion

Temperature and carbon dioxide (CO_2) changes
The combined data for changes in air and sea temperatures [2] and in carbon dioxide concentrations [3] for this century are shown in Fig. 1. The scales of the vertical axes have been chosen to allow an easy visual comparison of the two sets of data.

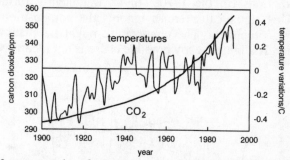

Fig. 1: Mean sea and surface temperature changes and atmospheric dioxide concentrations (parts per million) for the years 1900-1992. The zero for the temperature changes is the mean value from 1950.

Predictions from the IPCC model [4], based on a doubling of man-made CO_2 emissions, are shown in Fig. 2 together with the previous 92 years of mean temperature deviations from the 1950-1980 average.

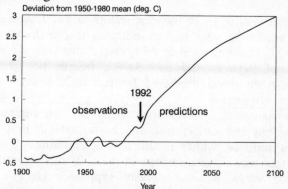

Fig. 2: The temperature record since 1900 and future predictions by the IPCC (based on a doubling of the present carbon dioxide concentration by 2100). The reference zero for the temperature changes is the mean of the values from 1950-1980.

THE GLOBAL WARMING DEBATE

The results of statistical analysis of the temperature data are shown in Fig. 3 superimposed upon the observed temperature variations. All four lines are significant at the 95% confidence level, which perhaps suggests that the variations are too small to be really significant. The predictions of the four trend-lines for the temperature variation from the 1950-1980 mean in the year 2100 are given in Table 1. The results for the first, third and fourth periods are not significantly different from the predictions of the IPCC model. The trend-line based upon the 1942-1977 data caused some predictions (in the 1970s) of an imminently forthcoming ice-age. This statistical exercise ignores the composition of the atmosphere completely. The temperature might be changing, but the variation is slight and any possible cause is not identified.

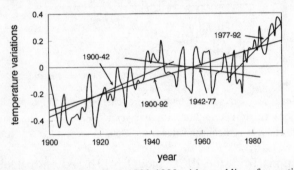

Fig. 3: The temperature record from 1900-1992 with trend lines for particular periods. The reference zero for the temperature changes is the mean of the values from 1950-1980.

Correlation analysis of the temperature and carbon dioxide data for the whole 92 year period indicates that a doubling of the current CO_2 concentration could be associated with a temperature increase of between 2.5 and 3.9°C, figures not significantly different from those predicted by the IPCC's very expensive computer programme.

The statistical correlation between atmospheric CO_2 concentration and temperature may be accidental. If it is real, it does not indicate which is the leading variable. A change in temperature can cause a change in the CO_2 concentration, rather than vice versa, as is popularly supposed; Henry's law [5] indicates that gases are less soluble in water at higher temperatures. Studies of past CO_2 temperature records [6] indicate that increases in CO_2 occurred about five months after corresponding rises in temperature. The Vostok core results [7] indicate that an increase in CO_2 level from 190 to 290 ppm was associated with a rise of 8°C in Antarctic temperature.

Time span	2100 AD prediction/°C*
1900-1942	1.3
1942-1977	-0.41
1977-1992	2.44
1900-1992	0.81

* Variation from the mean temperature from 1950-1980.

Table 1: Predictions of the Earth's temperature in the year 2100 based on earlier temperature trends.

Possible correlation between temperature of the oceans and the level of atmospheric CO_2 needs to be studied seriously. The oceans presently contain 52 times as much CO_2 as does the atmosphere [8]. The equilibrium between gas and aqueous phase is established fairly rapidly (8-11 years). Even with present emissions of man-made CO_2 occurring at a rate of 20,000 million tonnes per annum (0.7% of the atmospheric contents), it is impossible for the equilibrium concentration to double unless there is a rise in temperature of about 10°C. It is likely that the CO_2 concentration in the atmosphere will level out and possibly decrease in the near future unless there is a dramatic temperature rise produced by factors unconnected with the composition of the atmosphere. The extra CO_2 which dissolves in the oceans will eventually be observed as extra limestone production because the aqueous phase is practically saturated with respect to calcium and carbonate ions. The cause of the 25% increase in atmospheric CO_2 which has occurred over this century is not obvious. A possible cause is that pollution of the oceans in the supertanker age (with its associated accidents) has produced a surface layer which has reduced the rate of dissolution of CO_2.

Warming and cooling of the Earth's surface

The predictions [1] of the IPCC are not based upon statistical analysis of past records, but are based upon the theoretical principles assumed to govern the behaviour of the Earth's atmosphere. The applied theory apparently justifies the claims that an increase in the carbon dioxide concentration leads to an increase in the Earth's surface temperature and modification of the climate.

THE GLOBAL WARMING DEBATE

The energy 'budget' of the Earth and its atmosphere is in a quasi-equilibrium state, the solar energy received by the Earth being balanced by the emission of the same amount of energy into space. The Sun emits broad spectrum radiation (so-called cavity or black-body type) typical of a source with a temperature of around 6000 K. The majority of the output is in the visible region. If the Earth did not benefit from the 'greenhouse effect' of the atmosphere, exposure to solar radiation would cause the average temperature of the surface to be 255 K (-18°C). The average temperature of the Earth's surface is 288 K (15°C), so the presence of the atmosphere causes a warming of 33 K (33°C).

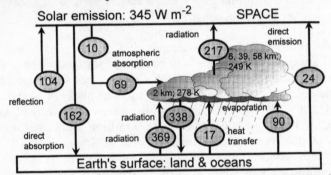

Fig. 4: The Earth's Energy Budget; the distributions os solar radiation and of energy loss from the Earth, with concomitant warming and cooling of the atmosphere. The energy flow units are Watts per square metre.

The main features of the distribution of solar radiation [9] and the energy flows (i.e. energy fluxes, with units of Watts per square metre, Wm^{-2}) to and from the Earth's surface and its atmosphere are summarized in Fig. 4. The quantities are global long-time averages over the twenty-four hours of each day at all points on the Earth's surface and are subject to uncertainties of up to ±5%.

The incident solar radiation has an average intensity of 345 Wm^{-2} of which 3% (10 Wm^{-2}) is absorbed by the stratosphere where it replenishes the protective ozone layer and another 20% (69 Wm^{-2}) is absorbed by the constituents of the lower atmosphere, including water molecules, carbon dioxide, clouds and other aerosols (these are smaller aggregations of water molecules which may also contain dissolved substances, e.g. sulfur dioxide and sulfuric acid). About 30% (104 Wm^{-2}) of the incoming radiation is reflected by clouds, other particulate matter and the Earth's surface, so the surface has a resultant absorption of 47% (162 Wm^{-2}).

The atmosphere is warmed by the 23% (79 Wm^{-2}) of solar energy which it absorbs and extra energy received from the heated

64

Earth. The surface emits radiation at a rate of 393 Wm^{-2} as expected for a cavity radiator at 288 K. A small fraction (6% or 24 Wm^{-2}) of this radiation escapes directly into space through the spectroscopic 'window'; the band of frequencies where none of the atmospheric constituents absorbs much energy. The remainder of the radiation is absorbed completely by the water and CO_2 in the lower part of the atmosphere [10]. Although CO_2 absorbs strongly in the infra-red region, water molecules (particularly in their condensed phases, liquid and solid) absorb much more strongly and over a much broader frequency range. The overlap of the absorption spectra of the two substances means that the CO_2 absorption is relatively unimportant.

Absorption of infra-red radiation causes molecules to be vibrationally and rotationally energized. The energized molecules lose their excesses of energy mainly by colliding with the bulk constituent molecules of the atmosphere, i.e. nitrogen and oxygen. In this way a thin layer of the lower atmosphere becomes warmer. The infra-red radiation emanating from the warmed Earth that is absorbed by the 'greenhouse' gases is converted, via vibrational-rotational excitation of water and CO_2, to the energy of motion of the remainder of the atmosphere. Because thermal motion is the basis of temperature (the faster molecules are moving the higher is the temperature of the gas) there is general warming of the lower atmosphere.

Additional warming of the atmosphere arises from evaporated water and from heat transfer processes. Water vapour is produced from the warmed oceans and is distributed by convection and winds and contributes to the general warming of the lower atmosphere as clouds are formed and precipitation occurs. The extent of the warming is about 90 Wm^{-2}.

The very lowest portion of the atmosphere is warmed as its constituent molecules collide with the surface, the consequent heat transfer from the warmed Earth to the atmosphere causing an increase in temperature of the surface layer. Heat transfer accounts for atmospheric warming of 17 Wm^{-2}.

The atmosphere is warmed by the 79 Wm^{-2} (10 + 69) from solar energy and by 476 Wm^{-2} (369 + 90 + 17) from the radiative, evaporative and heat transfer processes of the Earth's cooling mechanism. The total received flux of 555 Wm^{-2} allows the atmosphere to act approximately as a cavity radiator (i.e. it contains water and other constituents in condensed phases which can radiate broad range radiation typical of their temperatures, rather than their chemical nature).

The total inward flux to the Earth from solar radiation is $162 + 79 = 241$ Wm^{-2} which must be balanced by an identical outward flux to space consisting of radiation through the 'window' (24 Wm^{-2}) and other radiation from the atmosphere. The radiative flux from the atmosphere is estimated to be $241 - 24 = 217$ Wm^{-2} which would be that emitted by a cavity radiator with an average temperature of 249 K, such a temperature occurring at altitudes of about 6, 39, and 58 km. The emission spectrum of the outward flux can be understood in terms of absorptions by water, CO_2 and ozone in an otherwise broad cavity-type emission from a range of relatively high altitudes.

If the outward flux from the atmosphere is 217 Wm^{-2}, the remainder of the heating flux ($555 - 217$ Wm^{-2}) must return towards the Earth's surface resulting in a downward flux of 338 Wm^{-2}, typical of cavity radiation from a region with an average temperature of 278 K which occurs in the atmosphere at an altitude of around 2 km.

The relative distribution of the evaporative (90 Wm^{-2}), radiative ($369 - 338 = 31$ Wm^{-2}), and heat transfer (17 Wm^{-2}) warming mechanisms of the lower atmosphere is estimated to be 65.2%, 22.5% and 12.3% respectively, from the above figures, reasonably consistent with those of London and Sasamori [11] who give values of 47.5%, 27.5% and 25% respectively. The differences between the two sets of figures demonstrates the uncertainties which occur in such estimations.

Based on the more recent estimations, of the energy emanating from the Earth's surface, only 22.5% is effectively emitted as radiation which warms the lower atmosphere. The global warming provided by the Earth's atmosphere by this radiation is therefore 22.5% of 33°C, which is only 7.4°C. The other 25.6°C (77.5%) of heating are transferred primarily to the atmosphere by non-radiative processes, i.e. collisions of evaporated water molecules with other constituents of the atmosphere or collisions of molecules of the surface layer with the warmed surface. The 7.4°C of radiative warming, caused by absorption of energy by water and CO_2 may be divided between the two compounds in the ratio of their absorptions of the Earth's radiation. Detailed calculations using the HITRAN simulation programme indicate that the warming of the lower atmosphere by water and CO_2 are 7.0°C and 0.4°C respectively. In the upper atmosphere where the contribution of water is relatively smaller, the CO_2 absorption is significant and restricts the emission of radiation to space. An increase in the CO_2 level might be expected to cause an increase in the temperature of the upper atmosphere, but the altitude would be much higher than those where the weather occurs (0 - 15 km).

Possible alterations to the quasi-equilibrium

The current controversies concerning the enhancement of global warming by man-made emissions of CO_2 are intimately connected with the mechanism of the heating and cooling of the lower atmosphere. Clouds and other aerosols, like most condensed phases (i.e., liquids and/or solids) act as cavity radiators, absorbing and emitting infra-red frequencies typical of their temperature and which are independent of their individual molecular characteristics. Individual gaseous molecules (e.g. H_2O and CO_2) cannot act as cavity radiators, their energy levels are discretely quantized so they have specific selected regions of the spectrum where absorption and emission are possible.

The alleged mechanism [12] for atmospheric cooling includes the re-emission of excitation energy by water and CO_2 molecules at all altitudes. The fraction that is emitted towards the Earth's surface is re-absorbed and contributes to an enhancement of surface warming. The fraction which is emitted away from the Earth is re-absorbed by the next layer. Some of that energy is re-emitted upwards and is re-absorbed. This reverse cascade of emission of absorbed radiation and re-absorption continues to the 'top' of the atmosphere and eventually allows further escape of energy into space with consequent cooling of the atmosphere. An increase in the CO_2 concentration is supposed to hinder the process of reverse cascade and therefore to allow an enhancement of global warming. This is the reason for the enhancement of global warming according to currently accepted theory. Essentially, the effect of an increase in CO_2 concentration reduces the radiative fluxes operating between the Earth and its atmosphere. This reduces the eventual output of radiation into space and upsets the energy equilibrium. In order to restore the equilibrium, the atmosphere warms up so that the flux of radiation leaving the atmosphere increases to balance the incoming flux.

This is the area of major disagreement with the IPCC. It has been shown [13] that the emission of radiation from the excited carbon dioxide molecules is insignificant in the cooling process in the lower atmosphere, only 1-3% of the molecules being in their excited states under the prevailing conditions. In the upper atmosphere the pressure is low enough to make the time between collisions long enough to allow fluorescence to be the more probable means of energy loss. The IPCC theory includes emission occurring at higher levels of the lower atmosphere [14] (6-10 km altitude), but such emission is of the cavity type expected from condensed phases, rather than from discrete molecules. At such altitudes the pressure is too high to allow vibrational fluorescence to occur. The conclusion from this is that CO_2 cannot contribute significantly to the cooling of the lower atmosphere and that an increase in atmospheric carbon dioxide concentration cannot lead to a higher retention of heat by the lower atmosphere by such a mechanism.

The IPCC calculations for a 'clear skies' model [15] (i.e. ignoring clouds and aerosols) indicate that a hypothetical doubling of the CO_2 level will cause a warming of the atmosphere associated with a reduction in outward flux of only 4.3 (±0.7 or ±15%) l Wm^{-2} leaving the atmosphere. This amount is within the limits of error by which the quantities in Fig. 4 can be estimated (all the fluxes except that of the entering solar energy have at least a ±5% error in their estimations). The calculations are based upon a large extrapolation of spectroscopic behaviour from observations in a small path-length of gas in a controlled laboratory instrument and the behaviour in a path-length of 30 km with very variable temperatures and pressures. The calculated value, although it would be expected to be positive, is subject to considerable error and any predictions based upon it must be viewed with some caution, particularly in comparison to the larger quantities contributing to the energy budget. The Mount Pinatubo volcanic eruption in 1991 threw large quantities of dust and sulfur into the atmosphere and is reputed [16] to have caused the Earth's surface temperature to decrease by 0.4°C in the ensuing year, the associated calculated value of reduction of inward flux being 2-4 Wm^{-2} . The IPCC claim that changes of the same magnitude (4 Wm^{-2}) caused by the hypothetical doubling of CO_2 will lead to changes in the surface temperature, but which might not be realised for some decades since '*the oceans take time to heat up*' (Houghton et al., 1994)

None of the ten main factors that influence the energy budget, shown in Fig. 4, is understood fully and changes in any of them could be responsible to greater or lesser degrees for any alterations to the quasi-equilibrium. Some of the factors are interdependent, e.g. the rate of evaporation of water from the oceans is dependent upon the temperature, but the temperature is affected by the extent of cloud formation. This interdependence is notable, for instance, in the relatively cool tropical ocean climate as compared to that of deserts which are almost cloud-free. A greater cloud cover would also increase the fraction of solar energy reflected and would be a cooling influence. The IPCC figure of 4.3 Wm^{-2} for the increased

68

warming associated with a doubling of the CO_2 concentration is only 2.1% of the flux leaving the atmosphere by indirect routes. As such this represents a warming of only 0.2°C.

Conclusions

Satellite measurements of the Earth's temperature [17] since 1978 show that random variations of as much as ±0.5°C occur, some changes of as much as 0.5°C occurring over periods of only two weeks. It would seem inadvisable to attribute variations of the same magnitude over the course of a century to an enhancement of the greenhouse effect.

Any effects of the 25% increase in atmospheric carbon dioxide on the Earth's average surface temperature cannot be distinguished from the background of natural variability. All the energy that can be absorbed by the atmosphere is being absorbed by the lower atmosphere (water, aerosols and CO_2 under present conditions. The only possibility for enhancement of global warming which might be connected with the spectroscopic properties of CO_2 is its action in the higher atmosphere where it, together with water and ozone, can restrict the rate of escape of radiation into space. The absorption leads to a warming of the upper atmosphere which has possibly negligible effects upon the temperature of the lower atmosphere and the weather.

The evidence from past climates indicates that, although there is a correlation between mean temperature and CO_2 levels, the temperature change is the determining factor since it occurs prior to the change in CO_2 level. Other factors may be changing the temperature of the Earth with subsequent adjustment of the CO_2 level so that it is in equilibrium with that dissolved in the oceans. The basic problem that is considered by the IPCC, the prediction of the effects of doubling the CO_2 level in the atmosphere, is hypothetical. The doubling is not a practical possibility unless there is considerable warming of the oceans. Any emissions of CO_2 by any other sources would be balanced by the production of more limestone as a precipitate in the oceans and by extra usage in photosynthetic vegetation growth. The increase in the concentration of atmospheric CO_2 observed this century might have been caused by a decrease in the rate of dissolution of the gas in the oceans because of surface pollution.

To conclude that CO_2 emissions are a threat to the environment is doubtful and premature. All the factors which are responsible for influencing the Earth's surface temperature need to be more firmly established and understood, together with their interdependencies, before any meaningful predictions can be made.

References

[1] Houghton, J.T., Meira Filho, L.G., Bruce, J., Hoesung Lee, Callander, B.A., Haites, E., Harris, N., & Maskell, K., (eds), *Climate Change 1994*, Cambridge University Press, p. 15, (1994).

[2] Houghton, J.T., *Global Warming*, Lion Publishing plc, p. 47, (1995).

[3] *Handbook of Chemistry and Physics*, 73rd edn, CRC Press, (1992-3).

[4] Barrett, J., *Chemistry in Your Environment*, Albion Publishing Ltd, p. 78, (1994).

[5] Atkins, P.W., *Physical Chemistry*, 5th edn, Oxford University Press, p. 218, (1994).

[6] Kuo, C., Lindberg, C., & Thomson, D.J., *Nature*, **343**, 709, (1991).

[7] ref 1, p. 45.

[8] ref 1, p. 41.

[9] Boeker, E., & van Grondelle, R., *Environmental Physics*, John Wiley & Sons, p. 32, (1995).

[10] Kunde, V.G., Conrath, B.J., Hanel, R.A., Maguire, W.C., Prabhakara, C., & Salomonson, V.V., *J.Geophys.Res.*, **79**, 777, (1974).

[11] London, J., & Sasamori, T., *Space Research*, **XI**, 639, (1971).

[12] McIlveen, R., *Fundamentals of Weather and Climate*, Chapman & Hall, p. 251, (1992).

[13] Barrett, J., *Spectrochimica Acta*, **51A**, 415, (1995).

[14] ref. 2, p. 21.

[15] ref. 1, p. 170.

[16] ref. 1, p. 188.

[17] Wayne, R.P., *Chemistries of Atmospheres*, 2nd edn, Oxford University Press, p. 413, (1991).

Jack Barrett
Dr Barrett spent most of his academic career at King's College, London, where he lectured in inorganic chemistry. He is now affiliated to Imperial College, London, and a frequent contributor to radio and television. He has published books and papers on inorganic chemistry, most recently, *Chemistry in Your Environment* (1995).

Does CO_2 respond to global temperature changes rather than cause them? - Counter evidence to greenhouse assumptions from ice core data and volcanoes

Piers Corbyn, FRAS,
Weather Action and South Bank University.
London

Summary

Observational evidence from ice cores, recent temperature and CO_2 measurements and volcanic activity show that the fundamental assumptions of greenhouse theory of the importance of CO_2 in controlling temperatures are exaggerated; and that the true temperature changes over the last 140 years, taking into account volcanic corrections, make the greenhouse case, as currently stated, untenable.

Introduction

The fundamental assumptions and assertions of global warming by human emissions of greenhouse gases are challenged by evidence from ice core studies and volcanic activity. Detailed study of ice core data covering hundreds of thousands of years and also analysis of weather and climate records covering this century both show that changes in temperature generally precede changes in CO_2 levels, rather than the other way around. The evidence for this powerful refutation of CO_2 fluctuations as the basic driver of temperature change either on long time scales (thousands of years) or short time scales (years) are reviewed. The possibility that volcanic dust in recent years may have hidden recent global warming trends is shown to be irrelevant to global warming over the last 100 years or so because the cooling effect of the larger volcanoes in the late 19th century was significantly more than that of recent activity.

THE GLOBAL WARMING DEBATE

1. Long time scales -Vostok Ice Core

Analysis of air trapped in Antarctic ice cores shows that CO_2 and CH_4 concentrations and local temperatures were closely correlated over the last 220,000 years (See Fig. 1). Although this information is commonly used by some Greenhouse protagonists as implying support for the idea that Greenhouse gases are the prime arbiters of temperature, detailed analysis shows the opposite to be true.

Results from the Vostok Ice Core (Ref. 2) reveal phase differences between CO_2 and temperature and show for example, that "at the end of the penultimate interglacial the CO_2 decrease lagged behind the Antarctic cooling leading to glacial conditions". Furthermore it appears that in general (See Ref. 2a) CO_2 changes lag behind temperature changes, or sometimes they are in phase, to within the time resolution of the ice core data - which is at least some hundreds of years. There is no evidence cited in the detailed Vostok ice core studies that CO_2 changes precede temperature changes.

1.1. Orbital and other forcing functions

Analysis of the time scales of variation of the ice core temperature data (Ref. 2 and Ref. 3) show significant variations of periods concerned with changes in the obliquity (tilt) of the Earth's axis (period about 41,000 years) and the orientation of the Earth's spin axis, i.e. the precession of the equinoxes (periods about 23,000 years and 19,000 years), with the precessional signals being particularly strong (Ref. 3a).

This points to temperature changes on long time scales being essentially orbitally driven in some way by changes in the way the Earth receives solar radiation in various orbits and/or spin orientations (Ref. 3a). No-one seriously suggests that the CO_2 and CH_4 levels on earth respond directly to changes in the Earth's orbit or spin axis; so clearly along with the evidence of phase lag of CO_2 and CH_4 behind temperature changes we are led to the conclusion that for these slow time scales it is primarily external factors such as orbital changes (and we believe other factors such as solar activity which also operate on much shorter time scales) which cause world temperature changes which in turn cause changes in CO_2 and CH_4 levels.

Of course there will be feedback processes particularly when the oceans and land warm up, whereby the dynamic absorption and emission process involving CO_2 and CH_4 exchange with the atmosphere, lead to more CO_2 and CH4 coming out of the sea as the oceans, land and tundra warms and ocean circulation patterns change causing different CO_2 and CH_4 emission possibilities from the sea or resulting changed land environment. These will lead to phase shifts so that CO_2 and CH_4 lag behind temperature changes. (See Fig. 2).

Extra greenhouse gases, (including water vapour) resulting from these processes will undoubtedly cause further warming by the normal greenhouse mechanisms but we must be clear this is entirely a secondary process and does not result in 'greenhouse runaway'.

1.2. Correlation Studies

The central role of temperatures in determining CO_2 and CH_4 levels interestingly appears to be expressed in correlation studies of CO_2, CH_4 and temperature data in the Vostok ice core. The "combined greenhouse" (CO_2 and CH_4 together) correlates better with temperature than either CO_2 or CH_4 alone with temperature (Ref. 3b). This suggests that there is essentially a noisy connection whereby temperature changes cause CO_2 changes plus "noise" and also CH_4 changes plus other "noise". This would mean that when the CO_2 and CH_4 responses which are essentially in phase (both being temperature driven) are added together some of the (random) noise in each response will cancel out so the combined CO_2 and CH_4 response will be less noisy in fractional terms and hence give better correlation with the temperature causing the changes.

2. Short Time Scales - The Last 30 Years

Many studies of CO_2 levels over the last 30 years and estimates of global temperatures appear to show that both have increased. However, it has frequently been pointed out (e.g. Ref. 4) that this does not *prove* they are causally connected and certainly does not prove CO_2 levels are a dominant or major force in changing temperatures, despite the frequent implied claims of the greenhouse protagonists.

Detailed studies of short term variations, designed to look for close relationships over the last 30 years of data (with annual signals removed), do appear to show close connections, but typically changes in CO_2 levels lag those in temperature by about 5 months (Ref. 4).

Although some workers try to explain away these observations they seem to suggest a number of possibilities such as sea surface temperatures increases do cause CO_2 levels to rise typically about 5 months later, or CO_2 levels and sea surface or air temperature changes have some sort of common cause but CO_2 changes are delayed perhaps by various interactions.

3. Making sense of time scales

The lag of CO_2 level variations behind changes in temperature both for slow changes over many centuries (where the observed lag is at least in centuries), and for rapid changes over a few years (where the observed lag is typically 5 months) are probably *not* of the same origin since they clearly act at different frequencies. The geological time scale lags are probably concerned with physical changes in vast areas of vegetation, sea water, changes in oceanic circulation, ice melt etc. The observed lag in the rapid response mechanisms, which involves much smaller changes, is probably due to dynamic quasi-equilibrium effects such as CO_2 absorption and emission at the sea surface.

Given the observed primacy of temperature in determining CO_2 and CH_4 levels we can only conclude that the importance of any secondary effect of man made additions of CO_2 into the atmosphere have been exaggerated. Essentially extra CO2 above its "natural dynamic level" added into the atmosphere by humans will quickly start to be re-absorbed by the oceans and biosphere.

The main error of the greenhouse lobby is to grossly underestimate the primacy of temperature in determining CO_2 and CH_4 levels, and correspondingly overestimate the effective lifetime of any man-made CO_2 in the atmosphere. This has led to unsubstantiated assumptions that all or most of the supposed increase in temperatures over the last 50 or 100 years is due to some corresponding increase in CO_2, whereas in reality it seems far more likely that temperature was increasing anyway due to natural forces and causing natural CO_2 levels to rise. Interestingly the warmest - or near warmest - decade in the last 300 years of Central England data is 1729 to 1738 - before the industrial revolution. (Ref. 5).

An analogy to the greenhouse lobby confusion would be to consider a lake whereby the water level (analoguous to CO_2 levels in the atmosphere) is governed by inflow and the height of a dam or weir. Pouring a few buckets of water into the lake (analoguous to man's addition of CO_2 to the atmosphere which is small compared with the total CO_2 flux) will of course result in some increase in lake level, but it will be tiny, the extra water flows away, the level being primarily determined by the inflow and the weir. However, were the buckets of water to be added, as the level of the weir was also being raised, one could easily get the illusion that the buckets of water were the main cause of the rise when they were not.

The natural carbon cycle is a hugely complex natural quasi equilibrium dynamic process which is decisively influenced by temperature. Small extra additions of CO_2 of course will cause *some* enhanced greenhouse effect but the question is, how much?

The whole process is clearly not as responsive to human influence as greenhouse protagonists claim; but is much more robust. Greenhouse modellers of course admit they do not understand all the processes involved but say their models 'fit' the last 150 years. This may indeed be the case in one sense, but their models are largely empirical curve fits with the incorrect assumption that all or most of the observed warming is caused by man-made CO_2.

It appears now that the natural (we suggest solar powered) warming processes are coming to an end, hence the greenhouse predictions should run into increasingly dramatic failure.

4. Volcanic Dust

The eruption of Pinatubo and the resulting dust-veil cooling effect has been cited as the reason for supposed greenhouse warming not reaching predicted levels. The deficit has been cited as about 0.5°C (Ref. 1 & 10) in 1992-1993, one year after the event. Most greenhouse literature refers to the last 135 years or so (e.g. Ref. 1) and starts with the mid/late 19th century when there had been much volcanic activity (e.g. Coseguina Nicaragua 1835, Armagora S. Pacific 1846, Makjan Moluccas 1861, Ghaie Bismark Archipelago 1878, Krakatau 1883).

Various measures of cumulative dust-veil indexes (DVI) reached maximum cooling effects around 1840 and again around 1890 whereas the cumulative DVI from 1920 to 1950 has been relatively very small (Ref. 6). Whatever the DVI correction applied to recent temperatures due to Pinatubo, a larger correction should be applied to temperatures in the second half of the 19th century. This could probably easily be about three times the Pinatubo correction, and totalling 1.5°C.

Consequently, raising the present world temperature level by about 0.5°C and the suggested values in the second half of the 19th Century by 1.5°C changes the picture significantly and may almost eliminate the supposed global warming.

Whatever the precise figures, and they are not easy to quantify, the upshot of this is that volcanic activity, if honestly allowed for, dramatically reduces the supposed current greenhouse warming. (Fig. 3).

Various marine and ice studies (Refs 7, 8 & 9) show a number of strong cycles in ocean deposits of volcanic dust and temperatures on time scales of thousands of years, or less, which may be expressions of forcing functions and drive CO_2

fluctuations on those time scales.

Acknowledgments
Thanks for useful discussions and information are due to Des McLernon of the University of Leeds; Kourosh Bamsi-Yazdi of South Bank University and Manoucher Golipour of South Bank University.

References

1. Global Climate Change, The Department of Environment (in association with the Met Office) 3rd Edition 1994.

2. Extending the Vostok Ice Core record of paleoclimate to the penultimate glacial period. J. Jouzel et al Nature *364*, 407-412 (1993) For 2a see page 410 & 411.

3. The Ice Core record: Climate sensitivity and future greenhouse warming. C Lorius et al Nature *347*, 139-144 (1990). For 3a see page 141. For 3b see page 143.

4. Coherence established between atmospheric carbon dioxide and global temperature. Cynthia Kuo et al Nature, *343*, 709-713 (1990).

5. Central England Temperatures 1659-1973. Manley G. 1974.

6. Climate Past, Present and Future, Hubert Lamb Methuen 1972 (and   subsequent editions).

7. Gabrielle Walker, New Scientist, 6th Jan 1996 p.15.

8. Richard Behl et al, Nature *379* p.243 (1996).

9. Kourosh Bamsi-Yazdi, South Bank University, PhD thesis (1996).

10. James F. Luhr, Nature, *354*,14th November 1991.

Piers Corbyn
Piers Corbyn is the originator of the Solar Weather Technique for long-range forecasting and founder of the independent company Weather Action. He had articles published about weather and other scientific matters while still at school, and as an undergraduate, in the Journals of the Royal Meteorological Society, British Astronomical , and Royal Geographical Societies. Piers is a Fellow of the Royal Astronomical Society. His publications and contributions to international conferences include: Mean Matter Density of the Universe; Cosmic Microwave Background & Neutrino Mass; String-Loop Theory of Galaxy Formation.

Measurement Problems

What is Global Temperature? The Inadequacy of Estimation Methods

Piers Corbyn & Manoucher Golipour
Weather Action and South Bank University
London

Summary

Although the world temperature series have been carefully prepared the problems relating to station homogeneity, spatial coverage and time coverage still remain to be resolved.

The underlying assumptions used to create long data sets describing "World Temperature" and "Hemispheric Temperatures" are examined and the shortcomings of global temperature estimates as used by the IPCC are considered to be unacceptable. Inferences drawn from limited measurements, various spatial biases and non-climatic effects such as urbanisation need to be considered.

Introduction

Attempts have been made by many workers to combine station surface temperature data into a global average value. This review aims to present the underlying assumptions and specifically consider methods used to determine the so-called Northern Hemisphere Surface Air Temperature Variations: 1851-1984 (See Ref. 1), and then to consider the corresponding time series for the Southern hemisphere. Broadly speaking there are three major uncertainties to overcome in order to define an average value for a hemisphere and/or global surface air temperature, namely (1) Station Homogeneity; (2) Spatial Coverage; (3) Time Coverage.

Station Homogeneity

Homogeneity here refers to the consistency and purity of the data, recorded at a particular station, unaffected by non-climatic effects such as changes in:-

a) Instrumentation, exposure and measurement techniques.
b) Station altitude and position.
c) Observation, and the methods used to calculate monthly means.
d) The environment of the station, particularly with respect to urbanisation.

As an example of (c), it is found that some stations may take the minimum and maximum daily temperature values and calculate the mean as (Max+Min)/2, while others may read a few daily values on equal intervals and calculate the mean by adding all values and dividing the result by the number of readings. In general there will be small differences between these approaches for the provision of mean values.

According to Jones et al., there are two possible approaches to ensuring data accuracy. Either all records must be checked using station history information (subject to availability), or inconsistencies between neighbouring stations are used as a guide to the major inhomogeneities in the data set. The second method has been applied by Jones et al., their choice being based on concerns over errors that are large enough to affect studies of large scale climate changes. The principal assumption in applying this method is that within small areas the effect of changes in climate will be similar. However the size of the area within which the data are compared depends on data availability and the latitude at which they were recorded.

Records of four to five neighbouring stations were compared on a time scale of the order of 20 years. The procedure was as follows:

1. Each station's record was first converted to a data set of deviations from the monthly mean based on the entire record length.

2. For all stations within a region each annual temperature deviation was compared with all other records, by plotting the differences between series. By comparing a number of station pairs an "erroneous station" can be identified by an abrupt change or discontinuity.

3. In such cases the errant data was adjusted. Correction is made by differencing the mean temperature before and after the change at the errant station and comparing it with a similar difference at the neighbouring stations deemed to be correct. It should be noted this is not an wholly objective process.

National Meteorological Services have been known to reject real confirmed observations because they were "too abnormal".

Records of 2666 stations (not all having equal data length), in the northern hemisphere, were analysed by the authors using this method. Out of these 56% were classified as correct after a specified year, 9.5% were "homogenised". 24% had records that were too short or there were not enough neighbouring stations for comparison, 9% were flagged as incorrect, and 1.5% were identified as having non-climatic trends. Mean hemispheric temperature deviations are compared with a reference period, taken as 1951-1970 in this study. Out of the 2666 stations only 1584 had sufficient data in that reference period, and out of these only 509 stations had their records starting in the mid-nineteenth century, and they were mainly based on middle-latitude Europe.

Spatial Coverage

There have been various methods of defining temperature deviations at grid regions (e.g. rectangles of 5° latitude by 10° longitude) employed by many authors, such as Vinnikiv, Jones and Hansen, to overcome the irregular distribution of stations, although "degree rectangles" give a large overweight to temperate and polar records. In Jones et al. (1986) the authors used an improved method of interpolating the data into a regular grid with the same geographical dimension. In their previous analysis, Jones et al. used 1946-1960 mean data as the reference period, whereas in the 1986 paper it was changed to 1951-1970, because they claim this is the best period of data coverage.

To obtain so-called degree gridded data points, each station is first associated with its nearest grid point, then for each grid point (on each latitude and longitude grid rectangle) all the available station deviation values are averaged using 'Inverse Distance Weighting', whereby each station anomaly is weighted according to the inverse of the distance to the grid point. This weighted average is called the grid anomaly. To convert from 'degree grid anomalies' to 'geographic grid anomalies' a cosine of latitude weighting is applied to each degree rectangle grid point and a new 'geographic grid average' calculated.

Points to note in this procedure are: (1) For a station to be included in the analysis at least 15 years of data were required between 1951-70, (2) The number of stations making up a grid point anomaly varies through time at each grid point.

The Effect of Incomplete Time Coverage During the Early Years

To assess the effect of the very incomplete data during the earlier decades, (e.g. prior to 1900), the authors compare results, using a series of 'frozen grids'. Frozen grids estimate the hemispheric average for all years using only those grid points that are operating 80% of time during a particular decade. For example the first frozen grid is based on the 1851-1860 period and a hemispheric average is calculated using only these grid points.

It is important to note that the maximum area coverage (including the ocean area) of the Northern Hemisphere for each decade from 1851 up to 1985 varies significantly, having a minimum value of the order of less than 10% up to 1870, to a maximum value of about 50% in 1985.

Southern Hemisphere Surface Air Temperature Variations: 1851-1984

Similar procedures and methods to those described have been applied to the Southern Hemisphere. The average area covered (including Antarctic data after 1957) is about 32% and this figure is much reduced going back in time, covering from 2.5 degrees to 62.5 degrees South (See Ref. 3). The total number of stations used was 610, of which 38.9% are considered as correct after a specified year, 10.7% were homogenised, 45.9% were not examined (due to inadequate data or neighbouring stations), 4.1% were regarded as incorrect, and 0.5 % had non-climatic trends. The total number of stations with sufficient data in the reference period, 1951-70, was 293, and of these 8% were incorrect and 22% were homogenised.

Huge regions and periods have no data for example, the number of station(s) entering in this analysis in the whole of Africa, , was 0 prior to 1860 and only 1 from 1860 to 1900. Even by 1920 there were still only 19. For marine data there is a large gap between 45 degrees and 65 degrees South.

Jones (1991) and later Jones and Briffa (1992) combined the land data with marine data (5 degree square grid-box) to produce 5 degree square box values for as much of the world as possible. The marine reference period 1950-1979 was taken for global evaluation.

Updates

With an increase in the availability of data over the last few years (1985-1993), various research groups have reanalysed the previous studies from time to time (e.g.. The Climatic Research Group,

Jones, 1994). In the paper titled 'Hemispheric Surface Air Temperature Variations', 1993 (See Ref. 4) a number of changes were introduced, as follows:

i)   The reference period was changed to 1961-90.
ii) The total number of stations used (before adjustments, using the methods mentioned earlier) is 2961.
iii) The grid-box size was changed to 5 degree squares (from 5 degree latitude X 10 degree longitude).
iv) For a station to enter the analysis it must have at least 21 years of data out of 30 years.

A comparison between the previous and the new analysis shows:

Analysis	Stations Used	Boxes	Land Area of Globe
Previous	1873	680	31%
New	2961	779	35%

The 99 extra boxes were scattered over parts of the former Soviet Union, Mongolia, Australia, South America and a few over the Middle East. There has been no improvement in Antarctica. The new results showed a cooling trend between 1991-2, particularly in the summer and autumn seasons, and a less pronounced cooling in the same seasons in 1993.

Because of the similarities of the results for varying spatial coverage and data length, the authors argue that a limited number of stations, on each hemisphere (e.g. 109 stations in the Northern Hemisphere) will be enough to produce the same result for very large scale estimates. However, they acknowledge that the estimated errors are much larger for regions.

Observations on Validity of World Temperature Time Series

The fact that satellite measurements of world temperatures since 1979 show no significant temperature increase, leads to doubts about the validity of published 'world temperature' data. (Ref 5). Greenhouse protagonists point out that the satellites are measuring "different things". This is true, but which data should best be used?

The various constructed data sets used by the IPCC are often blithely quoted as 'World Temperatures' but despite the care taken to construct them, their assumptions must call their validity into question. Specific points of concern include:

1. The sparsity of data in the second half of the 19th century, when, for example, only one station was available for the whole of Africa.

2. The observation that different, but large parts of single continents show different variations in temperature over the same periods. This implies that it is not safe to assume the missing regions follow the rest of the world.

3. Urbanisation effects, e.g. urban heating are considerable, but have not been adequately dealt with because the "homogeneity procedure" used is too subjective, especially when 'nearby' compared stations used for purposes of comparison happen also to be in towns or airports.

References

1. P. D. Jones, S. C. B. Raper, R. S. Bradley, H. F. Diaz, P.M. Kelly and T. M. L. Wigley; "Northern Hemisphere Surface Air Temperature Variations: 1851-1984"; "Journal of Climate and Applied Meteorology", Vol. 25, Feb. 1986.

2. Vinnikov 1980; Hansen 1981; Jones 1982.

3. P. D. Jones, S. C. B. Rapers and T. M. L. Wigley; "Southern Hemisphere Surface Air Temperature Variations: 1851-1984"; "Journal of Climate and Applied Meteorology", 1986.

4. P. D. Jones; "Hemispheric Surface Air Temperature Variations"; "Journal of Climate", Vol. 7, Nov 1994.

5. See, e.g., Patrick J Michaels paper to Institute of Economic Affairs, 20 October 1995.

Manoucher Golipour
Mano Golipour is undertaking PhD research into the physics of the upper atmosphere, magnetosphere-ionosphere coupling and upper and lower atmospheric interaction. He is researching under the supervision of Piers Corbyn.

The Past is the Key to the Future

Harry N. A. Priem
Natura Artis Magistra
Amsterdam/Utrecht
The Netherlands

Summary

The geological record, from both the near and the remote past, does not provide evidence to support the dominant role that is nowadays attributed to the atmospheric CO_2 pressure in global climate regulation. When empirically tested against past global climate changes, the 'predictions' of the climate models are not borne out. The modellers pay little or no attention to the opportunities that are provided by the geological record to try out and test retrospectively the predictions of future climatic change. In spite of all uncertainties, and thanks in part to lavish media coverage, the CO_2 issue has been inflated to the single biggest concern about the future. This may be a blessing for politicians, who can profile themselves as 'green' in doing something grand about planet-sized catastrophes of the future, without the need to take forceful action against more local environmental damage.

Introduction

Since the 1980s the environment issue of the day has been the alleged global warming due to the rising level of atmospheric carbon dioxide (CO_2). The causal connection between the two phenomena is widely regarded as both real and a major threat to mankind. However, as a geologist, I am somewhat sceptical about the frightening greenhouse warming scenarios being popularly advocated. The forecasts of future climate rest on reductionistic computer models that attempt to represent mathematically the highly complex 'chaotic' planetary system that shaped the Earth's climate – a system in which the whole of the atmosphere, the hydrosphere, the biosphere, the Earth's surface, the interior Earth (through volcanism and plate tectonics) and all their interactions are involved. Of the numerous controlling mechanisms, many are still not, or only incompletely, understood. They operate at varying scales of time and space and are extremely complicated, even when they function independently. When they act together, or are coupled, the complications multiply greatly. Any climate models built on this limited knowledge must necessarily be far from perfect, to say the least. (*Not* 33°C as usually put forward by the greenhouse advocacy[3,4] which figure represents the warming by *all* physical processes in the atmosphere, not only the greenhouse effect.[1,5])

The basis for concern about global warming rests on three undisputed facts. The first is that the natural greenhouse effect of water vapour, CO_2 and some other trace gases in the atmosphere. This (fortunately) keeps the surface air temperatures higher than it would otherwise be, although CO_2 contributes no more than around $1°C^2$ to the total greenhouse warming of 6-7°C[1]. The second is the observed increase in the amount of CO_2 and other greenhouse gases in the atmosphere over the past century and a half (from 280 to 353 ppmv CO_2), and the predicted further increase in the near future. The third is the observed rise by about 0.5°C of the mean global temperature since 1920, although the rise has been far from steady: there was, for example, a period of cooling between 1940 and 1965.

Unlike the short-term numerical weather predictions, which can be developed and corrected by trial and error, the climate computer simulations are actually one-time experiments which cannot be tuned any faster than the evolution of climate itself. The predictions of future climate catastrophes on the basis of the climate models are thus at variance with Karl Popper's basic rule that only those theories are scientifically valid that can be experimentally tested and falsified. A theory that makes predictions beyond our ability to test is of little scientific value.

However, nature provides means to test to some extent how well the current models of future climate can simulate conditions different from the present day, notably as far as the role of CO_2 is concerned. These tests are contained in the *geological record*, which provides several 'case studies' of global change in the past. They reveal the actual air temperatures at the surface that prevailed under different CO_2 pressures. Simulations of these past climates serve as a good check on the overall validity of the climate models for the long-term effects of the ongoing greenhouse-gas increase.

Case Studies

For the last 250,000 years (covering the two most recent ice ages and the last interglacial) the fluctuations in the atmospheric composition and local temperature have been determined from bubbles of air trapped in ice cores drilled in glaciers on Antarctica and Greenland. Whether these bubbles really reflect the original atmospheric composition has recently been challenged,[1, 6] because the CO_2 molecules, contrary to the N_2 and O_2 molecules, should penetrate into the surrounding ice to form clathrates. If so, the CO_2 concentration would thus decrease with time. Recently, doubt has also been cast on the ice core analyses suggesting that during the last interglacial, after millennia-long periods of relatively steady climate, unstable climate conditions prevailed for some time. Temperatures would have jumped with alarming abruptness from warm to cold, and vice versa. However, as the lower part of the cores is shown to have been distorted by ice flow, these observed rapid fluctuations could be deceptive.[7]

If we accept that the trapped air does approximate to the original atmosphere, the bubbles do reveal that the CO_2 concentration tracks the temperature changes to a remarkable degree, but generally *lags behind* the temperature fluctuations. This behaviour can be explained by releasing of CO_2 from ocean water during warming and redissolving during cooling. A changing CO_2 level was thus not the *cause* of the change in temperature, but it may have amplified the climate change in a positive feedback. Also, recent climatic events like the Little Ice Age (about AD 1400 to 1900) and the Medieval Warm Period (about AD 900 to 1200) are not reflected in significant changes in the atmospheric CO_2 level, which has remained rather steady at 280 ppmv during the last millennium prior to the industrial era.

Further back in time, the chemistry of fossil subaerial weathering profiles in sedentary soils shows that the atmospheric CO_2 level has been an order of magnitude higher than today in the Early Paleozoic and about 4-6 times higher in the Middle Mesozoic.[8,-12] In the Late Ordovician period (440 million years ago), the partial pressure of CO_2 was about 16 times higher than today.[13] This was, however, not accompanied by unusually warm temperatures in the tropics, while there was widespread continental glaciation at higher latitudes on Gondwanaland.[14,15] The average global temperature at that time did thus not differ greatly from today's.

For the mid-Cretaceous period, about 100-120 million years ago, geochemical observations indicate that the atmospheric CO_2 level was 4 to 8 times the present-day value.[16] On the basis of an early synthesis of climate observations of Cretaceous sediments, and also the application of the current climate models to an atmosphere with the composition of that time,[17] it was generally assumed that this period was far warmer than today, with mean annual temperature above freezing at the poles and a higher temperature in the tropics. However, recent studies[18,19] show that the global mean temperature was much cooler: the equatorial temperatures were similar to, or possibly lower than, the present values, and the polar temperatures were close to 0°C. The latitudinal temperature gradient was thus flatter than today, but the global mean temperature did not much differ from today's.

Most climate models predict that a doubling of the amount of CO_2 in the atmosphere, which is expected (but not uncontested) to have been realised by the end of the 21st century, should lead to a rise in the global mean air temperature at the surface of about 2° to 5°C.[3,4] However, application of the same models to an atmosphere with the CO_2 pressure of the mid-Cretaceous should 'predict' a global mean temperature about 6° to 12°C warmer than today.[19] For the late Ordovician it should have been even warmer. Clearly, in both cases the actual prevailing temperatures did not obey the models: they were much lower.

Of course, there are many environmental differences between the past and the present, which makes it unlikely that any past climate can be a true analogue for future climate change. Nevertheless, the 'case stories' cited above should require climate modellers to ask themselves how they can predict future climatic change if they are unable to 'predict' recorded past climates. The atmospheric CO_2 level cannot be the only, and not even the main climate forcing factor. Other factors must have counteracted the enhanced greenhouse warming by higher atmospheric CO_2 levels.

Earth's Thermostat
According to the standard model of stellar evolution, the Sun in its infancy was faint and only two-thirds of the current amount of solar heat reached the Earth. Since then, the solar luminosity has gradually increased by some 30%. Every 1% increase in solar output should increase the Earth's mean surface temperature approximately 2°C. Nevertheless, the oldest preserved sedimentary rocks (in Usua, Godthåbsfjord, West Greenland) show that they were deposited 3.8 billion years ago by the same geological processes that are in operation today, implying the presence of oceans filled with water, not ice. Notwithstanding the ever-brightening Sun, water-lain sediments are known from the whole 3.8 billion years recorded in sedimentary rocks. Also, over all that time Earth was teeming with life.

The global mean air temperature at the surface thus always remained within a narrow range: above the freezing point (at least at lower latitudes) and never rising near the 50°C or 60°C that the Sun's warming would imply. This has become known as the 'faint young Sun paradox'.[20]

The maintenance of a moderate surface temperature despite the increase in solar luminosity requires the operation of a global self-regulating climate control system. Several models have been proposed that could account for the operation of such a system. The most popular is that the increase in solar flux was offset by a decrease in atmospheric CO_2 pressure, for example, caused by negative feedbacks in geochemical processes at the surface.[21] However, there is no geological evidence that a CO_2 pressure some 1000 times higher than today has prevailed on the young Earth.

Rather, the system that has maintained a fairly constant surface temperature over at least 3.8 billion years, and is still regulating Earth's temperature, is shaped by a great many factors, some long-term, some short-term. Next to the greenhouse effect of CO_2 and other gases in the atmosphere, other factors include variations in the solar radiation and input of solar heat; weathering rates, governed by the extent and relief of the land surface, along with the rate of precipitation; volcanic activity, which oscillated about a long-term decreasing trend as the planet cooled; the extent, height and position of mountain ranges which, along with the distribution of land and oceans, determine the circulation patterns in the atmosphere and oceans; thermodynamical properties of the oceans; rate of evaporation, air humidity and soil moisture content; insulation and reflection by clouds; spatial distribution of ice, snow cover and other factors influencing the albedo of the Earth; forests, plankton and the whole of the biosphere; and all their interactions. In a way, *Earth's thermostat* can be compared to the physiology of an organism whose body temperature is maintained at a constant level by all sorts of complicated and interrelated internal control systems.

Carbon Dioxide

CO_2 is continuously added to the atmosphere by degassing of the Earth, partly via volcanoes, partly via hydrothermal systems. The gas cycles rapidly through the biosphere and spends a good deal of time in the oceans, largely as a constituent of HCO^3. The residence time of CO_2 in the atmosphere-biosphere-ocean system is approximately 100,000 years. It is finally removed from the system partly as constituent of $CaCO_3$ through weathering processes and biological precipitation, and partly as a constituent of organic matter buried in sediments by geological processes (for a small part in the long run giving rise to oil, gas, peat, (brown) coal, etc.)

The total amount of CO_2 stored in this way in sedimentary rocks comes to about 200,000 times the amount now present in the atmosphere. When the climate warms, both the biological productivity and the rate of chemical weathering increase, extracting more CO_2 from the atmosphere. The atmospheric level of the gas and hence the greenhouse warning will then decrease. This counteracts the rise in temperature. At a climatic cooling the process is reversed, slowing down the cooling.

The atmospheric CO_2 pressure is thus regulated by a complex global biological-geological system that is also a factor in the regulation of Earth's surface temperature. However, the 'case studies' quoted above, in the geological past show that CO_2 cannot be the main controlling factor. At present, the input rate of the gas through degassing of the Earth is approximately 4.10^{14}g/year, but for most of the geological past it has been higher, at some periods even much higher – for example in the mid-Cretaceous, which was a period of gigantic volcanic activity (a 'superplume') in the Pacific region.[22] The present CO_2 emissions in the industrial era amount to approximately 10^{18}g CO_2[23] , but the increase in the atmospheric CO_2 pressure in this period can account for only about half of it. The other half has already been removed by natural processes, probably mostly by oceans and vegetation. The biological-geological control system is thus able to respond quickly in counteracting a rise in atmospheric CO_2 pressure.

It is also doubtful whether the whole increase in CO_2 pressure in the 150 years has to be attributed to anthropogenic emission. From the end of the last ice age, 10,000 years ago, up to the beginning of the industrial era, atmospheric CO_2 content rose, from 190 ppmv to 280 ppmv, (although with oscillations) without any significant anthropogenic emission. The increase since then to the present 353 ppmv, although again with a few oscillations (for example, the spectacular decline since the June 1991 eruption of Mount Pinatubo in the Philippines[24,25]) probably represents in part a continuation of the natural overall rising trend that set in 10,000 years ago.

References

1. J. F. Böttcher (1992) 'Science and fiction of the greenhouse effect and carbon dioxide'. The Global Institute for the Study of Natural Resources, The Hague.

2. Emsley (1994). New Scientist **1 4 4,** No. 1946: 19.

3. T. Houghton, G. J. Jenkins, J. J. Ephraums *editors* (1990) 'Climate Change - the IPCC Scientific Assessment'. Cambridge University Press.

4. Houghton, B. A. Callender, S. K. Varney *editors* (1992) 'Climate Change 1992: the Supplementary Report to the IPCC Scientific Assessment'. Cambridge University Press.

5. S. Lindzen (1992). Bull. Amer. Soc. 7 **1:** 288.

6. Jaworowski, T. V. Segalstad, V. Hisdal (1992) 'Atmospheric CO_2 and global warming: a critical review'. Norsk Polarinstitutt, Oslo.

7. Appenzeller (1993). Science **2 6 2:** 1818.

8. A. Berner (1990). Science **2 4 9:** 1382.

9. A. Berner (1991). Am. J. Sci. **2 9 1:** 339.

10. E. Cerling (1991). Am. J. Sci. **2 9 1:** 377.

11. J. Yapp (1987). Chem. Geol. **64:** 259.

12. J. Yapp, H. Poths (1986). Geochim. Cosmochim. Acta **5 0:** 1213.

13. J. Yapp, H. Poths (1992). Nature **235:** 342.

14. V. Caputo, J. C. Crowell (1985). Geol. Soc. Am. Bull. **9 6:** 1020.

15. B. van Houten (1990). Paleogeogr. Paleoclimatol. **8 0:** 245.

16. A. Berner (1992). Nature **3 5 8:** 114.

17. J. Barron (1983). Earth Sci. Rev. **1 8:** 305.

18. J. Barron (1994). Nature **3 7 0:** 415.

19. W. Sellwood, G. D. Price, P. J. Valdes (1994). Nature **3 7 0:** 453. (1972). Science **1 7 7:** 52.

20. Sagan, G. Mullen (1972). Science **1 7 7:** 52.

21. F. Kasting (1989). Paleogeogr. Paleoclimatol. Paleocol. (Global and Planetary Section) **7 5:** 83.

22. L. Larson (1995). Sci. Amer. **2 7 2,** No. 2: 66.

23. T. Watson, H. Rodhe, H. Oeaschger, U. Siegenthaler (1992), in: J. T. Houghton, B. A. Callendar, S. K. Varney, *editors*, 'Climate Change 1992: the Supplementary Report to the IPCC Scientific Assessment', Cambridge University Press: 1.

24. Leutwyler (1994). Sci. Amer. **2 7 0,** No. 2: 12.

25. L. Sarmiento (1993). Nature **3 6 5:** 697.

Harry N. A. Priem
Harry Priem is professor of planetary geology and isotope geology at Utrecht University, curator of the Artis Geological Museum, Amsterdam, and science coordinator at the Global Institute for the Study of Natural Resources, The Hague. He is former President of the Royal Geological and Mining Society of The Netherlands.

Reliability of Ice Core Records for Climatic Projections

Zbigniew Jaworowski
Central Laboratory for Radiological Protection,
Warsaw
Poland

Summary

Ice core records are widely used for projections of climatic change, yet there has been no quantitative evaluation of migration of gases in firn, and of chemical and physical processes which cause fractionation of gases in air inclusions. There is a need for experimental studies which would provide basic information for understanding these processes. High contamination of inner parts of ice cores by drilling procedures demonstrates that the cores do not fulfill the absolutely essential closed-system criterion. The low pre-industrial level of greenhouse gases accepted from glacier studies results from invalid assumptions, processes in the ice sheets, artifacts in the ice cores, and arbitrary selection of data.

1. Introduction

Projections of anthropogenic climate warming are based on the premise that the present concentration of CO_2 in the atmosphere of about 350 ppm is 26 percent higher than in the pre-industrial period (IPCC 1990). This premise is based on the CO_2 analyses of the gas recovered from "air bubbles" in glacier ice.

Because of uncertainties in the 19th century air measurements, the results of CO_2 analysis in the cores of polar ice are now regarded as the most reliable estimates of CO_2 and of other greenhouse gases (methane and nitrous oxide) in the pre-industrial atmosphere (Raynaud et al. 1993), and as "the only possible validation of models that were set up to describe future climatic changes caused by anthropogenic emissions" (ICSI 1992). However, no experimental study has yet demonstrated that the content of greenhouse gases in old ice, or even in the interstitial air from recent snow, represents the atmospheric composition. It is surprising that the glacier ice data were so credulously accepted as the very cornerstone of global warming predictions (IPCC 1990),

95

especially as no attempt has been made to verify experimentally their validity. In this paper I discuss some of these assumptions and interpretations, and question whether the quality of ice cores permits a reconstruction of the past atmospheric composition.

2. Assumptions

For climatic interpretation of the ice core data the following three assumptions are used:

1. The entrapment of air in the ice is essentially a mechanical process which occurs with no fractionation of the gas components (Oeschger et al. 1985).

2. The original chemical composition of air trapped in the ice is permanently preserved in the polar ice sheets and in the collected ice cores. This assumes that the ice, with its included air bubbles, has remained a closed system during tens or hundreds of thousands of years in the ice sheets, and that it is not disturbed during the core drilling, the transporting to the laboratory and its storage.

3. The age of gas inclusions is 80 to 2800 years younger than the age of the ice in which they are entrapped (e.g., Schwander and Stauffer 1984). This assumption was needed to accommodate the data from the shallow ice cores which showed that air entrapped in 19th century ice, or earlier, exhibits levels of CO_2, CH_2 and N_2O similar to present atmospheric concentrations.

It has recently been pointed out that these three assumptions are unsubstantiated (Jaworowski et al. 1992b; Heyke 1992; Jaworowski 1994), and that the data from the shallow and deep ice cores do not show temporal variations in atmospheric chemistry, but rather represent the gas fractionation in the ice. As pointed out (Jaworowski et al. 1992b) there are about 20 physical and chemical processes in the ice sheets and in the ice cores which make gas samples recovered from them unrepresentative of the original composition of the ancient atmosphere. No convincing arguments have been offered to counter this criticism (Raynaud et al. 1993).

3. Gas fractionation

The main argument in support of the first two assumptions is another assumption that no liquid water occurs in the polar ice at a mean annual temperature of -24°C or less (Raynaud and Barnola 1985; Friedli et al. 1986). With this assumption, diffusion effects, mass transport, and differential solubility of gases in the fluid phase were ignored, and it was generally accepted that the cold polar ice can preserve unchanged the original composition of entrapped gas for long periods of time. However, numerous studies reviewed in Jaworowski et al. (1992b) have provided abundant evidence that liquid water is present in ice even at the lowest Antarctic temperatures, down to the eutectic temperature of -73°C.

Fractionation of gases starts with the formation of snowflakes in the atmosphere, and continues in the near-surface snow, in the deep firn and ice, and in the ice cores. The fractionation is caused by: differences in solubility of air components in cold liquid water and brine; chemical reactions; formation of solid gas hydrates; and gravitational and thermal effects.

The solubility of greenhouse gases (CO_2, CH_4, N_2O) in water at 0°C is 2.8 to 73 times higher than of nitrogen and oxygen. Fractionation due to differential dissolution of gases occurs; firstly, in micro-bubbles present in the snowflakes, which are covered with droplets and films of liquid water; secondly, in firn during its metamorphosis caused by absorption of solar radiation below the snow surface, where increased subsurface temperature causes melting and evaporation of ice crystals. This happens even at inland Antarctic sites with an average annual temperature of -55.8°C (Watanabe 1977). Thirdly, it occurs during equilibration of gases between the air bubbles and liquid in ice.

The solubility of gases in water increases with depth and pressure in the ice sheet. For example, between the surface (pressure of 1 bar) and about 180 m depth (15 bars) solubility of CO_2 at 0°C increases by a factor of about 14, and solubility of CH_4 by a factor of 16.5. At a depth of about 2200m (200 bars) solubility of CO_2 is 120 times higher than at the surface, and solubility of CH_4 100 times higher (Duan et al., 1992). The solubility of gases depends also on concentration of salts in liquid water and on its volume in the intercrystalline capillary network, which change dramatically with depth in the ice sheet (Jaworowski et al., 1992 b). Thus, the interplay of load pressure, changing salinity and volume of liquid water is responsible for varying vertical distribution of greenhouse gases in gas inclusions entrapped in the ice sheets.

In the deep parts of the ice sheets, below 900-1200 metres, the air bubbles disappear due to increased pressure at which nitrogen enters the solid crystal phase, in the form of hydrates (120 bars at -20°C). But hydrates of trace gases N_2O, CO_2, and CH_4 start to form already at 4, 5 and 13.5 bars, respectively, i.e. at a depth between about 60 and 170 meters, and thus these gases are depleted from the gas mixture in air bubbles. After the cores are recovered from deep bubble-free ice, the load pressure is relaxed, and secondary gas cavities are formed due to differential dissociation of hydrates. As discussed in Jaworowski (1994) fractionation of gases occurs both during differential formation and dissociation of clathrates.

Differentiation of entrapped air during the melting of ice crystals, evaporation of water, transport of vapor in the firn pores along the thermal gradient, condensation of vapor, recrystallization, and formation of ice layers and of depth hoar are of random character. Therefore, one should expect an uneven distribution of fractionated gases in ice. This is reflected in changes of CO_2 concentrations of up to 50 ppm over distances of only 5 cm in the ice cores (Neftel 1991). In the near surface snow in Antarctica and Greenland the air was depleted in CO_2 by about 20 to 50 percent (Lorius et al. 1968; Raynaud and Delmas 1977). The results of many studies compiled in Jaworowski et al. (1992a) and Jaworowski et al. (1992b) showed that the composition of major components of air recovered from polar ice cores differ from that in the atmosphere, and that the concentration of CO_2 in air bubbles and gas cavities ranged in pre-industrial ice from 160 to 2450 ppm.

4. Selection of data

Such a wide range of CO_2 concentrations is hardly compatible with variations which one might expect in the atmosphere, and it is rather an effect of depletion and enrichment of this trace gas in the air bubbles. To fit the ice core results to the global warming theory, a selection of CO_2 and other greenhouse gas data was needed. Various criteria were used for such selection, and it was concluded that in old ice: *"the lowest CO_2 values best represent the CO_2 concentrations in the originally trapped ice"* (Neftel et al. 1982). In this paper Neftel et al. reported in 1982 rather high CO_2 concentrations in the pre-industrial ice core from Byrd, Antarctica of 325 and 417 ppm. However, a few years later Neftel et al. (1988) omitted these high readings in the same core, and the highest concentration reported was about 290 ppm, in agreement with the global warming theory. A striking feature of CO_2 records from air bubbles in pre-industrial ice is that the high concentrations, often much higher than in the present atmosphere, were reported until 1985, but not since then.

Leuenberger and Siegenthaler (1992) stated that their data from a Greenland ice core demonstrate that the present level of N_2O in the atmosphere of 310 ppb (IPCC 1990) is an effect of a recent 19 percent increase caused by industrial activity. This conclusion was reached after rejecting 27 percent of the samples with N_2O concentrations deemed to be "too high" for ice deposited between 1712 and 1822. After this "correction", the average pre-industrial atmospheric concentration of N_2O was calculated as 260 ppb.

Etheridge et al. (1988) stated that their ice core results show a pre-industrial N_2O concentration of 285 ppb. This value was calculated after rejection of 44 percent of their measurements. From the remaining analyses the high readings from 16th and 17th century ice (328.3 and 329.8 ppb), which were higher than in the 20th century samples (285.7 - 322.9), were again eliminated without explanation.

Zardini et al. (1989) rejected a low N_2O reading of 240 ppb in the youngest part of an Antarctic core from 1919 AD. From the several thousand years old part of the core they did not reject an even lower value of 217 ppb, but they eliminated the high values of 310, 354, 359 and 362 ppb. After these "improvements" they concluded that the pre-industrial N_2O level in the atmosphere was 270 ppb, and that in the present atmosphere had increased "due to fossil fuel burning".

Similar data selection was carried out in CH_4 studies (see e.g. Pearman et al. 1986). These carefully doctored results were taken as a basis for estimation of changes in greenhouse gases by the IPCC (IPCC 1990).

5. Contaminated ice cores

The drilling process for gathering ice core samples precludes the reliability of these as sealed systems for gas inclusions. Drilling is a brutal and dirty procedure subjecting the ice to mechanical and thermal stress, drastic decompression, and pollution. These factors cause micro- and macro-cracking of the ice, opening the air bubbles, and causing internal contamination of cores.

Due to the sheeting phenomenon in ice, caused by elastic relaxation of load pressure and stress-releases, the cores in which the pressure relaxation is more than about 8 bars (i.e. from depths below 110 meters) develop typical horizontal fractures (Jaworowski, 1994). The cracks are soon healed by regelation, and their remnants are visible as horizontal stratification of the cores (see, for example, the photographs in Narita, 1978; Schneider, 1989; and Jaworowski et al., 1992 b). Drilling fluid (diesel oil, jet fuel, etc.) enters the cracks even penetrating into the central parts of the cores. The gases released by decomposition of hydrates can escape into the drilling fluid before the cracks are healed at the surface of the ice sheet. As suggested by Craig et al. (1988), molecular and isotopic fractionation of gases may occur during this process.

Numerous studies on radial distribution of metals in the cores revealed a drastic contamination of internal parts of cores by the metals present in the drilling fluid. For example, the concentration of zinc in a core from 499 m depth in Vostok, Antarctica was systematically decreasing along a 5.5 cm long radius from the near surface value of 100,000 to 50 pg per g of ice at the center. In the same core corresponding values for lead were 20,000 pg/g and 60 pg/g: At the center of the cores the concentrations of these metals were still higher than in the snow at the surface of the ice sheet (Boutron et al. 1990). This demonstrated that the ice cores are not a closed system, and suggests that heavy metals from drilling fluid penetrated into the cores *via* micro- and macro-cracks during the drilling and the bringing of the core to the surface. During this process ice cores may be regarded as porous, open to both inflow and outflow of gases and liquids. This phenomenon, fundamental for interpretation of analytical results, was never discussed in papers reporting greenhouse data from polar ice cores.

6. Age of air in ice

Of crucial importance in using the greenhouse gas records for climatic projection is an assumption that the air inclusions are much younger than the ice in which they are entrapped. This *ad hoc* assumption was posed independently by Berner et al. (1980) and Craig and Chou (1982) at a time when the concentrations of greenhouse gases in air bubbles from ice deposited in the 18th and 19th century were found to be similar as in the present atmosphere. In this assumption the whole column of firn is supposed to be devoid of layers impermeable to atmospheric air, which can freely penetrate into the ice sheet down to about 100 m depth. The consequence of this assumption is evident in Figure 1 b, which is widely used as a proof of a large anthropogenic increase of atmospheric CO_2 (e.g. in Neftel et al., 1985; Friedli et al., 1986; IPCC 1990).

In this figure, data from the 19th century ice collected at Siple Station, Antarctica, were made to overlay exactly the present atmospheric CO_2 concentrations measured at Mauna Loa, Hawaii, by assuming that the occluded air is 83 years younger than the ice. Without this "air age correction" and using the real age of ice, the Siple and Mauna Loa curves do not overlay each other, and indicate that CO_2 atmospheric concentration was the same in the latter part of 19th century as in the 1970s. One can also note that the CO_2 concentration in the air bubbles decreases with depth, along the increasing pressure gradient, probably due to hydrate formation and the solubility of CO_2 increasing with depth.

As discussed in Jaworowski (1994), no convincing experimental evidence was offered in support of the air-age-speculation, and a multi-layer structure of ice crusts exists across the cold polar ice sheets. These strata of high density ice may be unbroken for several kilometers, have a frequency of 1 to 15 per meter, and separate firn into horizontal pockets. This structure acts as a barrier to the free penetration of air into firn.

Craig and Chou (1982) presenting a CH_4 curve analogous to that in Figure 1B, argued that the air-age-speculation must be correct because the ice core CH_4 data "corrected" by 90 years "lead rather precisely into the recent atmospheric measurements". The same circular logic was used by others (Neftel et al. 1985; Raynaud et al. 1993).

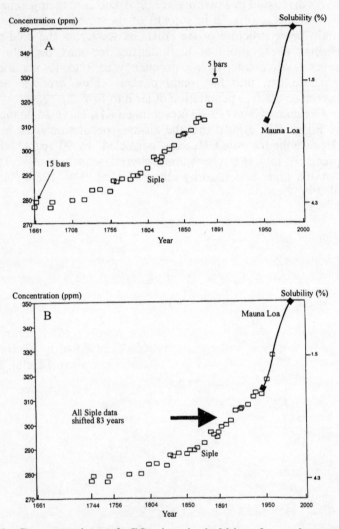

Figure 1   Concentration of CO_2 in air bubbles from the pre-industrial ice from Siple, Antarctica (open squares), and in the 1958-1986 atmosphere at Mauna Loa, Hawaii (solid line): (A) original Siple data without assuming a 83 year younger age of air than the age of the enclosing ice, and (B) the same data after arbitrary "correction" of age of air (Neftel et al., 1985; Friedli et al., 1986; and IPCC, 1990).

References

Berner, W., H. Oeschger and B. Stauffer. (1980). "Information on the CO_2 cycle from ice core studies." Radiocarbon **22**(2): 227-235.

Boutron, C. F., C. C. Patterson and N. J. Barkov. (1990). "The occurrence of zinc in Antarctic ancient ice and recent snow." Earth Planet. Sci. Lett. **101**: 248-259.

Craig, H. and C. C. Chou. (1982). "Methane: the record in polar ice cores." Geophys. Res. Lett. **9**(11): 1221-1224.

Craig, H., C. C. Chou, J. A. Welhan, C. M. Stevens and A. Engelkemeir. (1988). "The isotopic composition of methane in polar ice cores." Science **242**: 1535-1539.

Duan, Z., N. Møller, J. Greenberg and J.H. Weare. (1992). "The prediction of methane solubility in natural waters to high ionic strength from 0 to 250°C and from 0 to 1600 bar." Geochim. Cosmochim. Acta **56**: 1451-1460.

Etheridge, D. M., G. I. Pearman and F. de Silva. (1988). "Atmospheric trace-gas variations as revealed by air trapped in an ice core from Low Dome, Antarctica." Ann. Glaciol. **10**: 1-6.

Friedli, H., H. Lotscher, H. Oeschger, U. Siegenthaler and B. Stauffer. (1986). "Ice core record of the $^{13}C/^{12}C$ ratio of atmospheric CO_2 in the past two centuries." Nature **324**: 237-238.

Heyke, H. E. (1992). "Zu den CO_2-klimakurven aus Eisbohrkernen." Erdöl und Kohle-Erdgas-Petrochemie vereignigt mit Brennstoff-Chemie **45**(5): 208-214.

IPCC. (1990). First Assessment, Cambridge University Press, p. 364.

ICSI. (1992). Workshop organized by the Working Group on Snow-Atmosphere Chemical Exchange of the International Commission on Snow and Ice, p. 1-17.

Jaworowski, Z. (1994). "Ancient atmosphere - validity of ice records." Environ. Sci. & Pollut. Res. **1**(3): 161-171.

Jaworowski, Z., T. V. Segalstad and V. Hisdal. (1992a). p. 76.

Jaworowski, Z., T. V. Segalstad and N. Ono. (1992b). "Do glaciers tell the atmospheric CO_2 story?" The Sci. Tot. Environ. **114**: 227-284.

Leuenberger, M. and U. Siegenthaler. (1992). "Ice-age atmospheric concentration of nitrous oxide from an Antarctic ice core." Nature **360**: 449-451.

Lorius, C., D. Raynaud and L. Dolle. (1968). "Densite de la glace et etude des gaz en profondeur dans un glacier antarctique." Tellus **20**(3): 449-459.

Narita, H. (1978). Petrographic data from cores drilled at Mizuho Station. Mem. Natl. Inst. Polar Res., Spec. Issue, **10**: 159-164.

Neftel, A. (1991). Use of snow and firn analysis to reconstruct past atmospheric composition. . Berlin, Springer-Verlag, 386-415.

Neftel, A., E. Moor, H. Oeschger and B. Stauffer. (1985). "Evidence from polar ice cores for the increase in atmospheric CO_2 in the past two centuries." Nature **315**: 45-47.

Neftel, A., H. Oeschger, J. Schwander, B. Stauffer and R. Zumbrunn. (1982). "Ice core sample measurements give atmospheric CO_2 content during the past 40,000 years." Nature **295**: 220-223.

Neftel, A., H. Oeschger, T. Staffelbach and B. Stauffer. (1988). "CO_2 record in the Byrd ice core 50,000-5,000 years BP." Nature **331**: 609-611.

Oeschger, H., B. Stauffer, R. Finkel and C. C. Langway Jr. (1985). Variations of the CO_2 concentration of occluded air and of anions and dust in polar ice cores. Washington, D.C., American Geophysical Union, 132-142.

Pearman, G. I., D. Etheridge, F. de Silva and P. J. Fraser. (1986). "Evidence of changing concentrations of atmospheric CO_2, N_2O and CH_4 from air bubbles in antarctic ice." Nature **320**: 248-250.

Raynaud, D. and J. M. Barnola. (1985). "An Antarctic ice core reveals atmospheric CO_2 variations over the past few centuries." Nature **315**: 309-311.

Raynaud, D. and R. Delmas. (1977). Composition des gas contenus dans la glace polaire. IAHS, 377-381.

Raynaud, D., J. Jouzel, J. M. Barnola, J. Chappellaz, R. J. Delmas and C. Lorius. (1993). "The ice record of greenhouse gases." Science **259**: 926-934.

Schneider, S.H. (1989). The changing climate. Sci. Am. **261**(4): 38-47.

Schwander, J. and B. Stauffer. (1984). "Age difference between polar ice and the air trapped in its bubbles." Nature **311**: 45-47.

Watanabe, O. (1977). Stratigraphic observations of surface snow cover. Tokyo, National Institute of Polar Research. JARE Data Rep., **36**: 61-125.

Zardini, D., D. Raynaud, D. Schaffer and W. Seiler. (1989). "N$_2$O measurements of air extracted from antarctic ice cores: implication on atmospheric N$_2$O back to the last glacial-interglacial transition." J. Atmos. Chem. **8**: 189-201.

Zbigniew Jaworowski
Zbigniew Jaworowski, MD, PhD, DSc, is a multi-disciplinary scientist and professor emeritus from the Central Laboratory for Radiological Protection in Warsaw. He has recently been a guest scientist at the Institute for Energy in Kjeller, Norway. He has studied pollution with radionuclides and heavy metals and served as a chairman of the United Nations Scientific Committee on the effects of atomic radiation.

Do Sulphates Cool the Greenhouse Debate?

Robert C. Balling, Jr.
Office of Climatology
Arizona State University
USA

Summary

It has been postulated that sulphate aerosols over industrialised regions are responsible for a certain amount of global cooling, and that this cancels, to a significant extent, the global warming predicted for increased levels of CO_2 in the atmosphere. A closer look at the sulphates issue finds that there is little evidence in support of this explanation. Nevertheless, the role of sulphates and aerosols adds yet another degree of complexity and uncertainty to the attempts at predicting future climate from computer simulations.

1. Introduction

Over the past decade, interest in climate change has increased due to the perceived threat of global warming. According to the highly popular viewpoint, greenhouse gases are increasing in atmospheric concentration due largely to our use of fossil fuels, and these gases will trap additional heat energy that would otherwise escape into space. The planet will warm significantly, sea level will rise, ice caps will melt, storms will become more frequent and intense, and droughts will become more severe. However, many scientists have argued that such changes should already be occurring in the climate system if we are heading down such an apocalyptic pathway, and in general, these changes have not been identified in the climate record. Recognising the mismatch between expected and observed changes, many climate scientists have suggested that other anthropogenerated gases may have a cooling effect that is masking the expected greenhouse signal.

The role of sulphates in moderating the rise in planetary temperature has received the greatest attention in recent years. Although the cooling effects of sulphate aerosols have been discussed for several decades, recent landmark articles by

Charlson et. al. (1987, 1990, 1992) have brought considerable attention to the role of sulphates in altering regional and global climates. But just as tension exists between the modellers and the empiricists in discussing the role of greenhouse gases in governing planetary temperature, so too a spectrum of opinions has developed regarding the role of sulphates in controlling our climate. Many of the theoretical predictions from the world's most sophisticated numerical climate models are challenged seriously by the patterns observed in the climate system.

2. Proposed Role of Sulphates

Just as burning fossil fuel emits carbon dioxide into the atmosphere, the same combustion emits sulphur dioxide as well. Although the estimates vary in the literature, it is likely that humans are now emitting over 75 million tonnes of sulphur directly into the atmosphere each year, largely through our use of fossil fuels. This sulphur appears in the free atmosphere as sulphur dioxide which can be converted into sulphate aerosols (small particles with diameters between 0.001 and $10\mu m$). While the world as a whole has shown an increase in the anthropogenic emission of sulphur, Western Europe and eastern North America have actually shown declining emissions in recent decades. Quite unlike carbon dioxide emissions, the sulphate aerosols last only a few days in the atmosphere and remain relatively close to emission sources. Today, sulphate aerosols are highly concentrated in the Northern Hemisphere with greatest concentrations found in the eastern United States, central and eastern Europe, and central China.

There are three processes that should yield a cooling in areas with relatively high atmospheric concentrations of sulphate aerosols. First, the aerosols reflect incoming sunlight thereby reducing solar energy arriving at the surface. Second, the aerosols brighten existing clouds and further increase the solar radiation reflected away from the Earth. Finally, the introduction of sulphate aerosols into a cloud environment should have the net effect of making clouds last longer in the atmosphere, again increasing the reflectivity of the atmosphere. While the estimates vary, scientists have reported that sulphates could generate a total loss of near 2 W m^{-2} for the globe as a whole with much higher values found in areas of highest sulphate concentrations (Jones et al.). For comparative purposes, the forcing associated with the build-up of greenhouse gases since the beginning of the Industrial Revolution is thought to be near 2.5 W m^{-2}, while the solar constant is 1,367 W m^{-2}.

Given these estimates of climate thermal forcing from greenhouse gases and sulphate aerosols, scientists have run numerical models of climate capable of predicting the climate outcome. Taylor and Penner reported that the global temperature should have increased by 2.1°C over the past few centuries due to the build-up of greenhouse gases, but has cooled by 1.0°C from the effects of sulphates. The effects are not purely additive, and as a result, Taylor and Penner simulated a net 0.8°C rise in planetary temperature from these two effects. Others have found similar results in attempting to simulate the effects of both greenhouse gases and sulphate aerosols (e.g., Balling).

3. Finding the Sulphate Signal

Many climate scientists have recognised that theoretical predictions associated with the build-up of sulphate aerosols, and have analysed the historical records of climate in hopes of identifying the sulphate signal. The results to date have been mixed – inadequate climate records, competing forcing of climate (e.g. impact of volcanic eruptions, El Niño patterns, solar variability), as well as the natural variability of climate on regional and global scales, make the task of finding a sulphate signal quite difficult.

Based on Taylor and Penner and others, we should have seen a global warming approaching 0.8°C over the past century. Best estimates place the observed warming near 0.5°C (Jones). At this gross level, there is reasonable agreement between model predictions and the observational record. Moving to the hemispheric scale, Schwartz suggested that the Northern Hemisphere should be cooling with respect to the Southern Hemisphere due to the differences in sulphate loads between the hemispheres. Indeed, Idso and Balling and Idso (1991b) found such a signal in their analyses of hemispheric temperature patterns over the past half century. On a regional scale, Balling and Idso (1991a) were able to show relative cooling in areas of high sulphate loadings and relative warming in areas with low sulphate concentrations. Many others have found that areas of high concentrations of sulphate aerosols have shown an increase in cloud cover and a decrease in the diurnal temperature range (see Karl et al.).

Not all the evidence is in agreement with the sulphate hypothesis. Michaels et al. show that (1) sulphates should have their greatest impact during the summer season and least impact in the winter season of the Southern Hemisphere, (2) sulphates should have a much larger impact in the Northern Hemisphere than the Southern Hemisphere, and (3) sulphates should have the least impact in the winter season in the Arctic. Based on model outputs and empirical data, Michaels et al. show that none of these statements could be verified. Furthermore, Michaels et al. showed that model simulations in which the level of CO_2 in the atmosphere is doubled, should fail most often in regions where high sulphate concentrations have compounded the climate response to the build-up of greenhouse gases. They found, to the contrary, that the model simulation with doubled CO_2 performed as well, or even better, in areas of high sulphate concentrations. Their findings imply that the lack of agreement between such model simulations and the long-term climate record cannot be attributed to the sulphate cooling effect.

Scientists fully recognise that the numerical models of climate are still in the primitive stage of development. The models struggle with simulations, even at the global scale, that deal with the climate impact of rather evenly mixed greenhouse gases. The sulphate issue demands regional representation of the sulphate concentrations, and regional computations of their climatic impact. Given the high variability of the sulphate concentrations and expected climate response, the present-day numerical models are strained to the limit in their calculations and to the confidence that should be placed on the results. Similarly, finding a sulphate signal in highly variable climate records is equally difficult.

Ultimately, the sulphate issue represents yet another uncertainty in forecasting the climate of the future. Over the past decade, the craze in climatology has been the search for the climate response to a doubling of the greenhouse gases. While that exercise may be quite valuable in an academic sense, it may tell us little about the climate patterns to expect in the future. As we have seen, the build-up of greenhouse gases has been accompanied by the build-up of anti-greenhouse gases and aerosols. Simulating the climate of the future will clearly involve the effects of all changes to the composition of the atmosphere, and not just the build-up of carbon dioxide. Despite all the models and all the climate records, we still know very little about the climate changes that will occur in the next century.

Selected Bibliography

Balling, R. C., Jr., 1994: Greenhouse gas and sulphate aerosol experiments using a simple global-energy-balance model. *Physical Geography,* **15**, 299-309.

Balling, R. C., Jr., and S. B. Idso, 1991a: Decreasing diurnal temperature range: CO_2 greenhouse effect or SO_2 energy balance effect? *Atmospheric Research,* **26**, 455-459.

Balling, R. C., Jr., and S. B. Idso, 1991b: Sulphate aerosols of the stratosphere and troposphere: Combined effects on surface air temperature. *Theoretical and Applied Climatology,* **44**, 239-241.

Charlson, R. J., J. Langner, and H. Rodhe, 1990: Sulphate aerosol and climate. *Nature,* **348**, 22.

Charlson, R. J., J. E. Lovelock, M. O. Andreae, and S. G. Warren, 1987: Oceanic phytoplankton, atmospheric sulphur, cloud albedo and climate. *Nature,* **326**, 655-661.

Charlson, R. J., S. E. Schwartz, J. M. Hales, R. D. Cess, J. A. Coakley Jr., J. E. Hansen, and D. J. Hofmann. Climate forcing by anthropogenic aerosols. *Science,* **255**, 432-430.

Idso, S. B., 1990: Evidence in support of Gaian climate control: Hemispheric temperature trends of the past century. *Theoretical and Applied Climatology,* **42**, 135-137.

Jones, A., D. L. Roberts, and A. Slingo, 1994: A climate model study of indirect, radiative forcing by anthropogenic sulphate aerosols. *Nature,* **370**, 450-453.

Jones, P. D., 1994: Hemispheric surface air temperature variations: A reanalysis and an update to 1993. *J. Climate.* **7**, 1974-1802.

Karl, T. R., P. D. Jones, R. W. Knight, G. Kukla, N. Plummer, V. Razuvayev, K. P. Gallo, J. Lindseay, R. J. Charlson, and T. C. Peterson, 1993: Asymmetric trends of daily maximum and minimum temperature. *Bulletin of the American Meteorological Society,* **74**, 1007-1023.

Kiehl, J. T., and B. P. Briegleb, 1993: The relative roles of sulphate aerosols and greenhouse gases in climate forcing. *Science,* **260**, 311-314.

Langner, J., H. Rodhe, P. J. Crutzen, and P. Zimmerman, 1992: Anthropogenic influence on the distribution of tropospheric sulphate aerosol. *Nature*, **359,** 712-716.

Legrand, M. R., R. J. Delmas, and R. J. Charlson, 1988: Climate forcing implications from the Vostock ice-core sulphate data. *Nature,* **334,** 418-420.

Mayewski, P.A., W. B. Lyons, M. J. Spencer, M. S. Twickler, C.F. Buck, and S. Whitlow, 1990: An ice-core record of atmospheric response to anthropogenic sulphate and nitrate. *Nature*, **346,** 554-556.

Michaels, P. J., P. C. Knappenberger, and D. A. Gay, 1994: General circulation models: Testing the forecast. *Technology,* **331A,** 123-133.

Moller, D., 1984: Estimation of the global man-made sulphur emission. *Atmospheric Environment,* **18,** 19-27.

Monserud, R. A., N. M. Tchebakova, and R. Leemans, 1993: Global vegetation predicted by the modified Budyko model. *Climatic Change,* **25,** 59-83.

Penner, J. E., R. E. Dickinson, and C. A. O'Neill, 1992: Effect of aerosol from biomass burning on the global radiation budget. *Science,* **256,** pp1432-1434.

Schwartz, S. E., 1988: Are global cloud cover and climate controlled by marine phytoplankton? *Nature,* **336,** 441-445.

Spiro, P. A., D. J. Jacob, and J. A. Logan, 1992: Global inventory of sulphur emissions with 1° x 1° resolution. *Journal of Geophysical Research,* **97,** 6023-6036.

Taylor, K. E., and J. E. Penner, 1994: Response of the climate system to atmospheric aerosols and greenhouse gases. *Nature,* **369,** 734-737.

Weber, G. R., 1994: On seasonal variation of local relationships between temperature, temperature range, sunshine and clouds. *Theoretical and Applied Climatology,* **50,** 15-22.

Wigley, T. M. L., 1991: Could reducing fossil-fuel emissions cause global warming? *Nature,* **349,** 503-506.

Wigley, T. M. L., and S. C. B. Raper, 1992: Implications for climate and sea level of revised IPCC emission scenarios. *Nature,* **357,** 503-506.

Biography

Dr Robert C Balling, Jr. is currently the Director of the Office of Climatology at Arizona State University. Over the last five years, Dr Balling has been heavily involved in the greenhouse debate. He has published over 70 articles in the professional scientific literature, received over $1,000,000 in research grants, presented lectures throughout the United States and more than a dozen foreign countries, and appeared in a number of scientific documentaries and news features. He is presently serving as a climate consultant to the United Nations, the World Meteorological Organisation, and the Intergovernmental Panel on Climate Change. Dr Balling's recent book on his research is entitled *The Heated Debate: Greenhouse Predictions Versus Climate Reality.*

European Temperature Variations Since 1525

Gerd-Rainer Weber
Department of Environmental Protection
German Hardcoal Mining Association
Essen
Germany

Summary

Long-term European temperature records have been analysed from 1525 to the present. These show that the warmest period occurred around the middle of this century, whereas the coldest period occurred around the middle of the last century. Urban warming may have occurred in the 19th century relative to rural areas and smaller towns. The magnitude of natural climatic variability has been determined and trends calculated for various time intervals. There was cooling between the late 18th century and late last century and warming between late last century and the present. In some longer-term records, there was cooling between the 16th and late 19th century. The largest warming occurred in the 1900s and in the 1930s. There has been a pronounced seasonal variation in trends of the last 200 years, with warming being centred in late fall to early spring, whereas the summer half of the year either did not warm or cooled. European temperatures in the last decade are significantly above longer-term averages. However, they are well below estimates of modelled greenhouse warming. When considering the magnitude of historic climate fluctuations, the comparison of observed with modelled temperatures suggests that the true greenhouse warming should have been much smaller than the modelled warming. Since the differences between the observed and the modelled warming cannot be explained by natural climatic fluctuations, they may be due to over-prediction by the climate models.

THE GLOBAL WARMING DEBATE

1. Introduction

The analysis of historic temperature data is one of the central issues of a number of studies dealing with "greenhouse-induced" warming, which have been devoted to whether there has been a definite trend in the temperature record since the middle of the 19th century. Most conclude that there has and this has been quantified at 0.45°C.

Prior to 1850, there was insufficient direct instrumental observation to allow reconstruction of a global or even hemispheric temperature record. There have been some attempts to derive estimates of global temperatures based on longer-term regional temperature records and on the basis of proxy data. By this means, Groveman and Landsberg (1979) have derived a northern hemispheric temperature record back to the year 1579 and Lamb (1988) extended this for the British Isles back to c.1000 AD.

Regional temperature records are in some cases available after the invention of the thermometer. The most famous of these is the Central England record, which begins in 1659. Regional temperature records which begin prior to 1850 have furthermore been derived by – among others – Hansen and Lebedeff (1987) for Central Europe and the Eastern US.

The purpose of this study is the identification and analysis of longer-term European temperature records and the construction of a European temperature record from the late Middle Ages to the present.

2. Data

The major data source is an analysis of monthly temperature data provided by Schönwiese et al. (1990), who combined a large number of individual station records based on "World Weather Records", "Monthly Climatic Data of the World", a numerical compilation for the National Center for Atmospheric Research (NCAR) plus additional information drawn from von Rudloff, (1967) and Lauscher (1981). Schönwiese et al. (1990) identified a number of problems and pointed out that a thorough check of the history of individual stations, instrument changes, etc. would amount to a monumental task. (Some information on station history has been compiled by von Rudloff (1967).)

Table 1 gives a comprehensive overview of the station records used in terms of annual and seasonal averages, including length of the data set. A station was classified as "rural, small town" if the

Tab. 1: LIST OF STATIONS USED IN ANALYSIS AND GENERAL INFORMATION

STATION	LENGTH OF RECORD	TYPE OF DATA*	POPULATION (1950)
BASEL	1755 - 1989	M	107,000
BERGEN	1816 - 1988	M	110,000
BERLIN	1769 - 1993	M	3,336,000
BRESLAU	1791 - 1990	Y	629,000
BUDAPEST	1780 - 1992	M	1,000,000
CENTRAL ENGLAND	1659 - 1991	M	RURAL
COPENHAGEN	1798 - 1992	M	1,000,000
DE BILT	1706 - 1992	M	246,000 [Utrecht]
EDINBURGH	1764 - 1988	M	446,000
GRAND St. BERNARD	1818 - 1980	M	RURAL
HOHENPEISSENBERG	1781 - 1993	Y	RURAL
INNSBRUCK	1777 - 1989	M	102,000
JENA	1820 - 1980	M	82,000
KLAGENFURT	1813 - 1989	Y	63,000
KREMSMÜNSTER	1814 - 1989	Y	RURAL
MILAN	1763 - 1980	M	1,272,000
PARIS	1757 - 1992	Y	2,775,000[†]
PRAGUE	1780 - 1992	M	922,000
ROME	1811 - 1988	M	1,750,000
SWISS RECORD	1525 - 1989	S	RURAL
STOCKHOLM	1756 - 1992	M	777,000
STPETERSBURG	1752 - 1992	M	3,191,000
STRASSBOURG	1806 - 1992	M	200,000
TRONDHEIM	1761 - 1988	M	57,000
UPPSALA	1774 - 1992	M	62,000
WARSAW	1779 - 1992	M	1,000,000
VIENNA	1775 - 1992	M	1,617,000

population in 1950 was less than about 100,000 and as "urban" if it was significantly above 100,000. Some of the data are used on a basis of annual averages only as indicated in Table 1. Data newer than 1988 are available on a basis of annual averages only. The geographic distribution of these stations is shown in Fig. 1.

Data on global and hemispheric temperatures since 1850 were taken from Jones and Wigley (1991) as published by Boden et al. (1991).

3. Methods of Analysis

i) **Consistency between records**. In a first step, all records considered here were subjected to a correlational analysis in order to identify those stations which show an anomalously low correlation to neighbouring stations. Low correlations to neighbouring stations may indicate site-specific problems and low regional representativeness of that station.

ii) **Estimation of urban warming in the 19th century**. Averages were computed for 20-year periods ending at the turn of a century, e.g. 1781 - 1800, 1801 - 1820 etc. Changes from one 20-year period to the next between pairs of "urban" and "rural" stations was computed between 1780 - 1900, or, if a record was shorter, for the respective period ending in 1900.

iii) **Warm and cold periods.** Moving 20-year averages of the annual mean temperatures were computed to identify the warmest and coldest 20-year period at every station. Averages of the last 20 years of a record were compared to (a) the average 1841 - 1860 and (b) to the average 1881 - 1900 and (c) to the long-term average. The object was to decide whether the middle of the 19th century may be considered representative of longer-term climatic conditions in Europe and if the temperature of the last 20 years is significantly different from either one of those averages.

iv) **Trends in various sub-periods**. Trends have been computed for the following periods: 1780 to 1880, 1881 to 1980, 1781 to 1980. Where available, trends for individual seasons were computed, to identify seasonal differences in the temperature trends.

4. Results

Consistencies between Records

Of the stations listed in Table 1, Prague showed an anomalously low correlation, and Rome a relatively low correlation, to neighbouring stations. In the case of Prague, substantial cooling of about 2°C occurred in the 1980s, which must be due to site-specific causes, because none of the surrounding stations shows a similar pattern. Rome's low correlation may be explained by its geographically isolated position.

Regional averages were computed for Western, Northern, Southern and Eastern Europe. Additional data sub-sets were calculated for urban sites only, small town sites only, and a combined record of rural and small town stations.

The correlation matrix of annual average temperature of the stations shown in Table 1 generally yields correlations in the range between 0.8 to 0.9 to neighbouring stations with a tendency to decline as the distance to the neighbouring station increases, a behaviour which can be expected from the analysis of Schönwiese et al. (1990), for example.

Over a one-year period, European records do not correlate particularly well with global and Northern Hemispheric temperatures, explaining at best around 25 per cent of the variance in most cases. Re-calculating on the basis of 10-year moving averages dramatically improves those correlations. This may be interpreted in such a way that on smaller time scales, climate variations occur are localised in Europe, which are unrelated to global variations, whereas on longer time scales, global climate variations are also reflected in European climate variations during 1850 - 1980. The highest of those correlations with global temperatures emerged from Copenhagen, Paris, Jena and the grouped record of smaller European cities. The highest correlations between the Northern Hemispheric record and European stations are with Paris and the grouped record of smaller European cities.

It can therefore be concluded that, on climatically relevant time scales, European temperature variations between 1850 and the 1980s were closely related to global and Northern Hemispheric temperature variations. This would indicate that – on those time scales – the underlying causes of climatic variation were of a global nature.

Estimation of the Urban Heat Island Warming Prior to 1900

A study by Dronia (1967) identified the urban heat island effect as a significant contributor to the warming observed between 1880 and 1950. The urban heat island effect is not expected to be of importance in the temperature records beginning in the second half of the 19th century as given in Houghton et al. (1990) or in Hansen and Lebedeff (1987). The issue seems not entirely resolved though since urban warming effects can also be expected in smaller towns.

However, no such analysis on the magnitude of the urban warming effect seems to have been carried out for the 19th century apart from Dronia (1967), who compared one rural-urban station pair and found a significant warming of the urban site with respect to the rural site. Most of the longer-term European records which begin around or prior to the year 1800 must be considered urban records (see Table 1). Most of the European conurbations experienced dramatic population growth in the 19th century. For instance, Berlin grew from 147,000 in 1786 to 2,100,000 in 1900. Paris grew from 1,000,000 to 1,800,000 between 1846 and 1861 alone. Therefore, urban warming effects can be expected to influence longer-term temperature trends even prior to the year 1900.

The magnitude of the urban warming effect has been estimated by applying Dronia's method to a number of stations pairs which are shown in Table 2. Further, this method was applied to grouped averages of urban and rural stations. Two separate groups of rural/small towns were formed, one beginning in 1781 in order to achieve a 200-year record, and another beginning in 1820 to include rural/small town data which was not available earlier. The following stations were used. **Small towns**: Central England; De Bilt; Hohenpeißenberg; Innsbruck; Trondheim; Uppsala. **Rural**: Bergen; Central England; De Bilt; Grand St. Bernard; Hohenpeißenberg; Innsbruck; Jena; Klagenfurt; Kremsmünster; Trondheim; Uppsala. **Urban**: Berlin; Budapest; Edinburgh; Milan; Paris; St. Petersburg; Stockholm; Warsaw; Vienna.

On the basis of the grouped averages of "rural, small town" and "urban" stations, the cumulative warming of the urban vs. the rural stations amounted to about 0.3°C between 1780 and 1900.

It may be concluded that urban warming effects led to a noticeable non-climatic warming of long-term European temperature trends prior to the year 1900. Since most longer-term records available from Europe must be considered urban records, a

Tab. 2: CUMULATIVE TEMPERATURE DIFFERENCES (URBAN MINUS RURAL) OF STATION PAIRS (IN °C)

	1780 - 1900		1800 - 1900			1820 - 1900		
UPPSALA	vs Stockholm:	0.59	Kremsmünster	vs Vienna:	0.10	Jena	vs Berlin:	0.55
	vs Trondheim:	0.25		vs Budapest:	0.16		vs Warsaw:	0.84
	vs St. Petersburg:	1.13		vs Innsbruck:	0.74		vs Strassbourg:	0.07
	vs Bergen:	0.32		vs Milan:	1.05	Grand St. Bernhard	vs Basel:	+ 0.23
CENTRAL ENGLAND	vs Edinburgh:	0.07					vs Milan:	0.88
	vs Paris:	0.18					vs Vienna:	0.14
		- 0.05					vs Strassbourg:	0.01
DE BILT	vs Edinburgh:	- 0.14						
HOHENPIESSENBERG	vs Basel:	0.70						
	vs Innsbruck:	0.62						
	vs Vienna:	0.22						
	vs Paris:	1.20						
	vs Berlin:	1.05						
	vs Strassbourg:	0.20						

Tab.:3: COLDEST AND WARMEST 20 YEAR PERIODS IN EUROPEAN TEMPERATURE RECORDS (DEPARTURES FROM LONG-TERM AVERAGE) THE YEAR DENOTES CENTRAL POINT OF 20 YEAR PERIOD.

STATION	COLDEST	WARMEST
BERGEN	-0.41 (1846) -0.41 (1879)	0.50 (1940) 0.30 (1825)
BERLIN	-0.80 (1809) -0.42 (1847)	0.53 (1921) 0.36 (1875) 0.27 (1788)
BRESLAU	-0.99 (1835) -0.90 (1823)	0.73 (1907) 0.39 (1944)
BUDAPEST	-0.63 (1887) -0.36 (1847)	0.43 (1798) 0.43 (1981) 0.37 (1944)
CENTRAL ENGLAND	-0.70 (1692) -0.29 (1887) [-0.25 (1808)] -0.22 (1846)	0.50 (1952) 0.42 (1729) 0.41 (1981)
COPENHAGEN	-0.96 (1847)	0.08 (1827) 0.86 (1983)
DE BILT	-0.58 (1808) -0.34 (1719) -0.28 (1729)	0.49 (1981) 0.36 (1944) 0.25 (1729)
EDINBURGH	-0.38 (1815) -0.32 (1775) -0.21 (1870)	0.33 (1940) 0.26 (1979)
EURAL	-0.48 (1885) -0.35 (1845)	0.49 (1950) 0.34 (1965) [0.24 (1825)] at year 8
EURSMT	-0.42 (1885) -0.32 (1846) -0.29 (1809)	0.53 (1944) 0.36 (1967) 0.20 (1827)
GRAND ST. BERNHARD	-0.46 (1851) -0.31 (1887)	0.58 (1952) 0.28 (1825)
HOHENPEISSENBERG	-0.90 (1887) -0.35 (1846)	0.74 (1802) 0.50 (1983)
INNSBRUCK	-0.51 (1885) -0.46 (1846) -0.36 (1809)	0.55 (1952) 0.31 (1930) 0.20 (1800)
JENA	-0.58 (1888) -0.55 (1846)	0.65 (1967) 0.59 (1944) 0.19 (1825)
KLAGENFURT	-0.55 (1884) -0.41 (1847)	0.50 (1976) 0.44 (1958) 0.30 (1827)
KREMSMÜNSTER	-0.62 (1888) -0.36 (1847)	0.48 (1980) 0.44 (1952) 0.32 (1805)
MILAN	-0.74 (1839) -0.72 (1762)	1.05 (1953) 0.79 (1967)
PARIS	-0.56 (1792) -0.49 (1888) -0.47 (1846)	0.92 (1953) 0.08 (1827)
PRAGUE	-0.70 (1856) -0.42 (1897)	0.82 (1807) 0.50 (1953)
ROME	-0.47 (1857 -0.22 (1883) -0.21 (1906)	0.54 (1934) 0.18 (1825) 0.13 (1979)
STOCKHOLM	-0.71 (1872) -0.61 (1809) -0.59 (1835)	0.90 (1944) 0.78 (1953) 0.72 (1981)
STRASSBURG	-0.48 (1888) -0.39 (1847)	0.58 (1968) 0.37 (1944) 0.08 (1867)
ST. PETERSBURG	-0.95 (1808) -0.75 (1791) -0.57 (1838)	1.07 (1981) 0.89 (1930)
SWISS REC	-0.67 (1815) -0.65 (1889) -0.62 (1852) -0.60 (1696)	0.74 (1949) 0.65 (1982) 0.44 (1539)
TRONDHEIM	-0.53 (1809) -0.46 (1872) -0.33 (1846)	0.78 (1940) 0.20 (1825) 0.18 (1975)
UPPSALA	-0.78 (1872) -0.45 (1847) -033 (1808)	0.71 (1942) 0.41 (1975) 0.38 (1827)
VIENNA	-0.66 (1847) -0.45 (1888)	0.52 (1980) 0.46 (1798) 0.36 (1953)
WARSAW	-0.71 (1813) -0.57 (1838) -0.32 (1880)	0.75 (1944) 0.51 (1919)

re-appraisal of those prior to the year 1900 is needed for analysing longer-term climate variations.

Warm and Cold Periods

For each of the records used here, the three coldest and the three warmest 20-year periods were determined and sequential 20-year averages were computed in order to determine if certain time intervals were particularly cold or warm. This would be of interest when addressing the question of whether the time intervals around 1880 and 1850, namely those periods when global temperature coverage began and from which global temperature trends were calculated, were unusually cold or warm. Hansen and Lebedeff (1987) concluded that neither period was unusual and that therefore, trends beginning at these times reflect a true departure from long-term average conditions.

The distribution in time of the three warmest and three coldest 20-year periods of each station record is shown in Table 3. The following pattern emerges:

The three coldest periods generally occur in the 19th century with clustering points in the 1810s, the 1840s and the 1880s. This is the case for almost every continental European station. It may be noticed that most of the rural/small town stations experienced the coldest 20-year period in the 1880s, whereas the urban stations had the lowest 20-year average either in the 1840s, the 1810s or earlier. Of the very long-term records, i.e. those that extend beyond 1750, the Central England record shows the 20-year period centred at 1693 as the coldest 20-year period, followed by ones in the 19th century. De Bilt shows another cold period centred at 1720, which is neither apparent in the Central England record nor in the Swiss record. The Swiss record also shows a cold period centred in the 1690s, but it only ranks fourth. Therefore, in Europe, the 19th century was characterised by the repeated occurrence of cold climatic conditions which peaked in the 1880s. On the basis of those records, which begin prior to 1800, one may then conclude that the 19th century was colder than previous centuries. When comparing temperature trends between the 19th century and the present day (see e.g. Hansen and Lebedeff, 1987; Houghton et al., 1990; Bloomfield, 1992) the tendency has been to choose the coldest periods of the 19th century.

The three warmest periods are generally centred in the 1940s, the 1980s and in the late 1820s. For records to 1820, a warm period was the 1790s. By and large, the 1940s was the warmest period, followed by the 1980s (at those stations with records ending in the early 1990s) and the 1820s (or 1790s). The Swiss record shows the period centred at 1540 as the third warmest period (see Table 3).

The 20-year averages of the rural/small town stations beginning in 1781 - 1880 show the periods 1841 - 1880 and 1881 - 1900 as the coldest. Both were significantly colder than 1821 - 1840.

Considering the longer-term averages of the Swiss record, the cold periods in the 19th century were the coldest during the 460 years between 1525 and the present (see also Fig. 2). The periods 1801 - 1900 (-.59°C) and 1841 - 1890 (-.59°C) were both significantly colder than the average 1525 - 1800 (-.25°C) at or above the 99 per cent level of statistical significance.

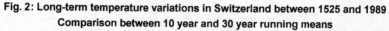

Fig. 2: Long-term temperature variations in Switzerland between 1525 and 1989
Comparison between 10 year and 30 year running means

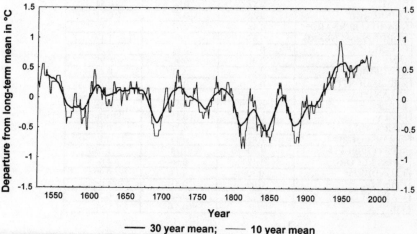

The temperature departure of the last 20 years of record i.e. 1970 - 1990 with respect to the averages for 1841 - 1860, 1881 - 1900 and 1781 - 1980 is given in Table 4, which shows that the temperature departure of the last 20 years compared to the long-term average 1781 - 1980 was only about one-half to two-thirds of the difference to the period 1841 - 1860 or 1881 - 1900. When considering European temperature records, the choice of either one of the periods in the 19th century as a base period would lead to significantly larger estimates of the temperature increase from "pre-industrial" times.

THE GLOBAL WARMING DEBATE

Tab. 4: TEMPERATURE DIFFERENCES FOR 1971 - 1990 COMPARED TO THE AVERAGES FOR
A: 1841 - 1860
B: 1781 - 1980
C: 1881 - 1900

	(a) 1841 - 1860	(b) 1781 - 1980	(c) 1881 - 1900
BASEL	1.26	0.77	1.07
BERGEN	0.38	0.24	0.50
BERLIN	0.37	0.14	0.04
BRESLAU	0.17	0.04	- 0.20
BUDAPEST	0.58	0.44	0.93
CENTRAL ENGLAND	0.48	0.34	0.50
COPENHAGEN	1.53	0.85	1.14
DE BILT	0.57	0.50	0.54
EDINBURGH	0.20	0.27	0.21
GRAND St.BERNARD*	0.48	0.02	0.17
HOEHNPEISSENBERG	0.67	0.49	1.17
INNSBRUCK	0.67	0.31	0.57
JENA *	0.91	0.49	0.95
KLAGFURT	0.80	0.51	0.86
KREMSMUNSTER	0.77	0.53	0.98
MILAN (*)	1.11	0.59	0.73
PARIS	0.62	0.25	0.56
ROMA	0.63	0.21	0.36
STOCKHOLM	0.93	0.72	0.81
STRASSBOURG	0.82	0.24	0.59
St.PETERSBURG	1.13	1.13	1.13
SWISS RECORD	1.12	0.66	1.04
TRONDHEIM	0.30	0.14	0.29
UPPSALA	0.99	0.41	1.05
WARSAW	0.72	0.42	0.24
VIENNA	1.0	0.57	0.90

REGIONAL AVERAGES:

CETEMP (*)	0.81	0.58	0.72	0.67
EASEUR (*)	0.54	0.31	0.57	0.41
EURAL (*)	0.70	0.31	0.44	0.65
EURCITY(*)	0.75	0.47	0.66	0.59
EURSMT(*)	0.46	0.29	0.63	0.57
NEUROP (*)	0.68	0.57	0.84	0.69
SEUROP (*)	0.53	0.15	0.28	0.21
WEUROP (*)	0.43	0.30	0.70	0.43

* AVERAGE 1971 - 1980

124

Tab. 5: SEASONAL TEMPERATURE TRENDS BETWEEN 1780 AND 1980. IN °C PER 100 YEARS.

STATION	Winter	Spring	Summer	Fall
BASEL	0.8	0.28	0.1	0.54
BERGEN	0.24	0.27	- 0.03	0.56
BERLIN	0.63	0.66	- 0.35	0.12
BUDAPEST	0.65	- 0.01	- 0.53	0.06
CENTRAL ENGLAND	0.30	0.11	0.04	0.41
COPENHAGEN	0.94	0.79	0.35	0.54
DE BILT	0.59	0.21	0.01	0.21
EDINBURGH	0.48	0.05	- 0.20	0.52
GRAND St.BERNHARD	0.04	0.26	0.35	0.68
INNSBRUCK	0.54	0.10	0.14	0.22
JENA	1.05	0.43	0.25	0.49
MILAN	0.95	0.55	0.40	0.54
PRAGUE	- 0.15	- 0.26	- 0.53	- 0.29
ROME	0.28	- 0.19	- 0.05	0.39
SWISS RECORD	0.58	0.25	0.17	0.53
STOCKHOLM	0.77	0.72	- 0.00	0.29
St.PETERSBURG	1.09	0.74	- 0.26	0.69
STRASSBOURG	0.57	0.29	0.27	0.43
TRONDHEIM	0.72	0.39	- 0.40	0.46
UPPSALA	0.43	0.35	0.00	- 0.04
WARSAW	1.06	0.66	- 0.39	0.42
VIENNA	0.29	- 0.33	- 0.91	- 0.23

Trends in Sub-periods

The question whether or not there has been a trend in global and regional temperature records since the middle or the end of last century has received a large amount of attention. The unequivocal opinion seems to be that there has been a global temperature increase of about 0.5°C since the middle of last century (e.g. Houghton et al., 1990). However, the analysis of regional temperature records in the USA does not show an overall temperature increase since the 1890s.

Since it has been established in the previous paragraph that European temperatures reached their lowest values around the middle or the end of last century and their highest 20-year averages in either the 1940s or 1980s, it appears obvious that there should be a positive temperature trend between either the middle or the end of last century and the end of this century. At most stations, there has been a significant increase of between 0.05 to 1.19°C for the past 100 years. However, some regional differences should be noted: a cooling of about 0.5°C occurred over parts of East Central Europe (Berlin, Breslau, Warsaw). Since temperature records of these cities between 1880 and 1990 are in good agreement, the cooling in that region seems to have been a real phenomenon.

The small town/rural stations average is judged to be the most reliable. Over the past century, it increased by 0.74°C. It should also be pointed out that the smallest positive trends occurred in coastal regions (Trondheim, Bergen, De Bilt, Central England) and the largest in South Central Europe.

There have generally been negative trends between 1781 and 1880, which by and large have lower significance levels attached to them. Larger differences appear between both rural and urban and among regional records. Urban stations generally warmed, such as Western Europe, with the exception of stations in Southeast Central Europe, which experienced a pronounced, albeit smaller, cooling than the surrounding rural stations. In contrast to that.

Cooling between 1820 and 1880 is more pronounced and more significant at a number of rural and small town stations. It was further regionally more pronounced over Northern, Central and South-Eastern Europe where the magnitude of the cooling between 1780 and 1980 reached the same magnitude as the warming between 1880 and 1980. From Eastern Europe, only urban records are available which may either not show the climatic cooling visible at other stations between 1780 and 1880 due to urban growth, or that a different regional trend prevailed there. The overall cooling at non-urban European stations between 1780 and 1880 is roughly one-third of the warming between 1880 and 1980.

Taking the Swiss record as an indicator of continental European climate variations, which appears justified on the basis of the correlations shown in Table 2, long-term trends in the Swiss record are calculated between 1880 and 100-year time steps in the past. Cooling has been present in every such time interval, generally in the order of 0.1°C per century. The total cooling between 1525 and 1880 amounted to 0.38°C. It is interesting to note however, that during the interval 1680 and 1880, there has been 0.09°C per 100 years cooling in the Swiss record but 0.16°C of warming in the Central England record. This result re-emphasises the conclusion that there have been more regional differences in European temperature trends, with the Swiss data being more representative of continental Europe. It further shows that the 19th century appears cold compared to any of the preceding centuries at least since 1525.

On the other hand, the 20th century was the warmest of the last five centuries. When calculating an overall trend beginning in 1525, there was a cooling of 0.02°C per century. Only the last 100 years made a warming contribution and reversed the cooling trend of the preceding 350 years.

Seasonal Differences in Trend

Depending on data availability (see Table 1), seasonal trends were calculated for the length of the record. The results are shown in Table 5. The following features are noteworthy:

At most stations, large seasonal differences in trend appear. Most common and significant is a wintertime warming, a warming in fall, lesser warming in spring, little warming or even cooling in summer. Where it occurred, this cooling appears to be most significant in trends beginning in the second half of the 18th century in Northern and South East Central Europe. Fig. 3 shows the combined average summer temperature of nine representative European stations between 1780 and 1980. The two warmest 20-year periods occur in the 1940s and in the 1790s.

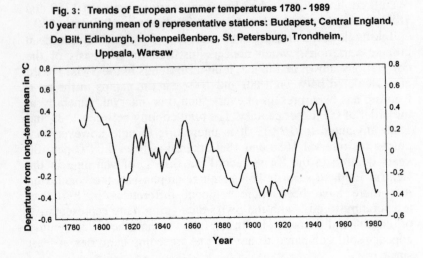

Fig. 3: Trends of European summer temperatures 1780 - 1989
10 year running mean of 9 representative stations: Budapest, Central England,
De Bilt, Edinburgh, Hohenpeißenberg, St. Petersburg, Trondheim,
Uppsala, Warsaw

Magnitude of Natural Variability

In this section, consideration shall be given to determining two questions: in which periods of the last few hundred years did warming and cooling episodes occur on climatically relevant long-time scales; and how large was the magnitude of this warming.

In order to do this, 20-year averages were derived, these being considered to reflect a climatically relevant average. 20-year periods were chosen to avoid non-climatic background noise which affects 10-year time scales. A longer average than 20 years may hide possible greenhouse warming effects, which may be present towards the end of the period.

Warming: 1820s, 1900s, 1940s and 1980s

Cooling: 1810s, 1840s, 1880s and 1960s.

In every European record, the major warming was in the first half of the 20th century. At most stations, the warming was a two-part event with the first substantial warming – and in some cases the largest of the entire record – occurring around the turn of the century. An analysis of seasonal trends of that period shows that this warming was entirely a warming of the winter half of the year. Summers actually cooled during that period. The second stage, on the other hand, with largest warming rates ending in the 1940s, was a warming of the summer half of the year. The magnitude and

128

the duration of those events were the main contributors to the positive temperature trends derived for the entire period 1881 - 1980. The cooling observed between c.1950 and 1970 was at most stations, and particularly the continental European ones, a major event by historical standards. The warming since 1970 shows up only in the longest records used here ending in the 1990s. This warming was roughly of the same magnitude as the cooling between the 1940s and the 1960s.

Table 6 shows that the observed maximum range of warming and cooling between 20-year periods was generally between ±0.7°C at a standard deviation of 0.3. It was larger at northern and continental European stations than at Western European stations.

It can therefore be concluded that the magnitude of climate fluctuations on 20-year time scales observed in Europe during the last few decades was not outside of the range observed in the last few centuries.

The warming episode in the first half of the century was also not unusual in terms of peak warming rates per 20 years, but it was unusual because of its duration, which resulted from the juxtaposition of two warming peaks in the 1900s and the 1940s and the lack of an intervening cooling period. When using longer-term averages to compute warming rates, the warming rates in the first half of this century are the largest in the entire records. When using 50-year averages in the Swiss record, the largest warming peak occurred in the 50-year period ending in 1939. One of the coldest 20-year periods in the Swiss record was centred in 1887 and the warmest period in 1944.

The following major cooling and warming episodes occurred in longer-term European records between 1525 and 1800.

Cooling: 1570s, 1690s and 1760s

Warming: 1610s, 1720s - 1730s and 1780s

Therefore, the period between the late middle ages and the present has been characterised by a succession of cooling and warming periods, which generally led to the largest negative temperature departures in the middle of the 19th century and to the largest positive temperature departures around the middle of the 20th century.

Tab. 6: MAXIMUM WARMING / COOLING RATES IN 20 YEAR PERIOD (°C / 20 YEARS) AT SMALL TOWN AND RURAL LOCATIONS.

STATION	WARMING		COOLING	
		PERIOD ENDING IN:		
BERGEN	0.66	(1942)	- 0.37	(1974)
	0.30	(1904)	- 0.28	(1872)
	0.24	(1866)	- 0.20	(1846)
CENTRAL ENGLAND	0.69	(1718)	- 0.66	(1749)
	0.50	(1828)	- 0.48	(1887)
	0.47	(1907)	- 0.46	(1847)
	0.40	(1867)	- 0.42	(1688)
	0.36	(1942)	- 0.35	(1972)
	0.17	(1981)		
DE BILT	0.76	(1828)	- 0.65	(1794)
	0.42	(1739)	- 0.53	(1749)
	0.39	(1981)	- 0.35	(1889)
	0.36	(1867)	- 0.35	(1847)
	0.35	(1942)	- 0.29	(1964)
EURAL	0.50	(1944)	- 0.60	(1846)
	0.45	(1907)	- 0.39	(1887)
	0.26	(1867)	- 0.32	(1964)
EURSMT	0.47	(1827)	- 0.52	(1847)
	0.45	(1943)	- 0.33	(1963)
	0.40	(1904)	- 0.31	(1883)
GRAND ST. BERNHARD	0.56	(1952)	- 0.62	(1847)
	0.53	(1930)	- 0.57	(1972)
	0.52	(1871)	- 0.29	(1887)
	0.21	(1903)		
HOHENPEISSENBERG	0.90	(1811)	- 0.80	(1822)
	0.78	(1908)	- 0.73	(1887)
	0.56	(1953)	- 0.54	(1847)
	0.47	(1984)	- 0.44	(1972)
INNSBRUCK	0.61	(1907)	- 0.53	(1809)
	0.39	(1952)	- 0.39	(1885)
	0.34	(1930)	- 0.38	(1848)
	0.34	(1866)	- 0.23	(1972)
	0.29	(1829)		
JENA	0.67	(1907)	- 0.73	(1846)
	0.61	(1944)	- 0.34	(1886)
	0.33	(1866)	- 0.20	(1964)
	0.31	(1968)		
KLAGENFURT	0.52	(1920)	- 0.71	(1847)
	0.41	(1968)	- 0.34	(1889)
	0.38	(1952)		
	0.23	(1869)		
KREMSMÜNSTER	0.58	(1952)	- 0.63	(1847)
	0.42	(1908)	- 0.47	(1888)
	0.28	(1979)	- 0.36	(1964)
	0.21	(1867)		

STATION	WARMING		σ	COOLING	
		PERIOD ENDING IN:			
SWISS REC	0.69	(1869)	σ = 34	- 0.83	(1815)
	0.59	(1946)		- 0.75	(1888)
	0.59	(1720)		- 0.65	(1696)
	0.51	(1612)		- 0.62	(1574)
	0.48	(1908)		- 0.55	(1848)
	0.42	(1779)		- 0.35	(1628)
	0.38	(1830)		- 0.31	(1744)
	0.21	(1982)		- 0.27	(1969)
TRONDHEIM	0.82	(1936)	σ =30	- 0.58	(1809)
	0.64	(1828)		- 0.51	(1846)
	0.40	(1892)		- 0.45	(1964)
	0.20	(1799)		- 0.37	(1870)
UPPSALA	0.74	(1942)	σ =35	- 0.83	(1847)
	0.67	(1828)		- 0.58	(1872)
	0.59	(1905)		- 0.56	(1962)
				- 0.46	(1809)

Tab. 7: COMPARISON OF OBSERVED AND ESTIMATED MODEL PREDICTED TEMPERATURE DEPARTURES AT EIGHT EUROPEAN LOCATIONS. AVERAGES 1971 - 1990 (IN °C)

	MODELLED	OBSERVED	Δ MODELLED - OBSERVED(1)
CENTRAL ENGLAND	1.3	0.34	0.96
DE BILT	1.4	0.50	0.90
JENA/BERLIN	1.6	0.49	1.11
PARIS	1.3	0.25	1.05
ROME	1.4	0.21	1.19
SWISS REC/BASEL	1.6	0.66	0.94
TRONDHEIM	1.5	0.14	1.36
UPPSALA	1.7	0.41	1.29

(1) average of GFDL, GISS, NCAR (Luther and McCracken, 1985)

THE GLOBAL WARMING DEBATE

The relevance of European temperature variations prior to the year 1900 with respect to global climate fluctuations

It has been shown that there is a good correlation between European and global temperature variations in the period 1850 - 1990. European temperature variations prior to 1850 might also be compared to variations in other parts of the world.

The major problem that arises here is that instrumental observations prior to 1850 are available from only a few stations in North America, but there is secondary data from different geographic regions of the world.

The conclusion drawn here that the period 1850 - 1890 was one of the coldest of the last 460 years is supported by the work of Borisenkov (1992), who showed that in central Russia the coldest spring, summer and fall temperatures occurred in that period as well. Further, the warmest summer temperature occurred around 1800, and this was also the case at a number of European stations.

Wang et al. (1992) showed that in Beijing, China, the warmest summers of the last 250 years were observed around 1740. For eastern China, the second half of the 19th century and the second half of the 17th century appear to have been the coldest periods of the last 500 years and the middle of the 18th century was significantly warmer.

The Swiss record was also characterised by above-average summer temperatures for the period 1710 - 1730. Above-average temperatures in the late 18th century also occurred over the Southwestern USA, but not in the period 1820 - 1840, which was one of the coldest there, but a relatively warm period in Europe.

Above-average summer temperatures over the western USA in the 18th century and below-average temperatures in the late 19th century were also derived by Briffa et al. (1992) on the basis of tree-ring density reconstruction.

A reconstruction by Wang and Wang (1991) for two different regions of China also shows the years around 1850 were relatively cool and the coldest of the entire record since 1350.

Serre-Bachet et al. (1992) conclude that the coldest longer-term periods occurred in the second half of the 17th century (for the grid point 50°N 20°E) and from the latter part of the 18th to the early part of the 19th century. In South East Central Europe, the latter part of the 18th century could be identified as a warm period, and the 1840s and the 1880s as being colder than the 1810s in the rural records. This discrepancy might be due to urban warming in the records of Warsaw, Breslau and Berlin in the 19th century, which may not have been accounted for in Serre-Bachet et al. (1992).

Likewise, the cooling between the late 18th and the late 19th century documented here cannot be derived from the European reconstructions of Greveman and Landsberg (1979) or from Hanse and Lebedeff (1987). The reason for this may again be the use of urban records which warmed relative to rural records between the late 18th and the late 19th century.

Although not conclusive, there are therefore, some indications that longer-term European climate variations have been synchronous with climate variations in other parts of the world. However, the cool periods in the 19th and latter part of the 17th and 16th centuries seem to have been global events, and some of the intermediate warm periods of the 18th century are also synchronously documented in other parts of the world.

Given the quality of data coverage in the Swiss record, with its broad spectrum of data sources from all seasons, (i.e archival, phenological, lake-freezes, harvest yields etc.) plus a high correlation with global/hemispheric temperature variations since 1850, it seems realistic to use it as an indicator of global/hemispheric temperature variations prior to 1850.

European temperature trends and global warming

Do temperature variations observed in Europe support the model-predicted temperature increases which are thought to occur as a result of the build-up of greenhouse gases?

A number of studies have already been devoted to that issue (e.g. Sneyers, 1992, v. Rudloff, 1991, Coops, 1992) and have been mostly inconclusive. Coops (1992) sums up his statistical analysis of 13 long-term European temperature records: "So far, there is no definite evidence that the increasing concentration of greenhouse gases is affecting the climate of Europe."

Assuming that longer-term European temperature variations prior to c.1900 are truly indicative of global/hemispheric temperature variations, one may conclude that the global temperature rise to the year 1990 would be about one-third less than the figure of 0.45°C given in e.g. Houghton et al. (1990). If this increase might then – wholly or partially – be due to the enhanced greenhouse effect resulting from the emission of radiatively active trace gases is still a different matter (see e.g. Houghton et al., 1990, p.203). It may be recalled that the warming since c.1880 can almost entirely be accounted for by a warming between c.1900 and 1940, which cannot be ascribed to an enhanced greenhouse effect.

Even though it is not yet possible to test, contention that "there is or will be a climate warming of the magnitude that climate models predict", it should be possible to consider the question of whether the magnitude of the temperature increase predicted by computer models appears plausible.

Rather than using an arbitrary time scale, it is best to compare the magnitude of the average temperature departure of the last 20 years from the long-term average with model-predicted departures of the last 20 years. This procedure circumvents the problem that the warming of the first half of the century is being counted as a contributor to the warming towards the end of the period in a statistical trend analysis even though that warming can be interpreted as a natural fluctuation. Moreover, the recent temperature departure is then not being compared to an unusually cool period, but to a representative long-term average instead.

It could obviously be argued that natural climatic fluctuations have occurred during those last decades to counteract a greenhouse-induced warming, making it therefore useless to compare that average to a model-predicted average. Since this may be the case, the estimates of natural variability on 20-year time scales derived from long-term observations may be applied to predicted temperature in order to determine if the observed temperature falls within the range of natural fluctuations of the model-predicted temperature increase.

For this analysis, temperature departures from the long-term mean of the last 20 years have been estimated for those eight European locations in the following way, which should be considered a rough estimate at best.

The combined effect of the increase of all greenhouse gases is assumed to have resulted in an additional greenhouse effect of 2 W m^{-2} as an average 1971 - 1990 (Houghton et al. 1990), which is approximately equal to half the additional greenhouse forcing of a CO_2 doubling.

For various estimates, the modelled equilibrium warming resulting from a CO_2 doubling of the models of the Geophysics Fluid Dynamics Laboratory (GFDL), the Goddard Institute of Space Studies (GISS) and the National Center of Atmospheric Research (NCAR) was derived from Luther and McCracken (1985; their Fig. 4.38, 4.39). It was thereby assumed that the annual average was the average of summer and winter warming. In addition, estimates were also derived from Fig.12 in Manabe et al. (1991). Despite its simplicity, this procedure might nonetheless give a rough idea of magnitude. The model-predicted temperatures for Europe during the last few decades are shown in Table 7.

The differences between the figures thus derived and those derived from Manabe et al. (1991) are less than 0.2°C at each station. They are in a range between 1.3 and 1.7°C, compared to an average of 0.4°C for the observed increase. Therefore, the model predictions, minus the observed warming, amount to roughly 0.9°C to 1.4°C, with an average of 1.1°C. They fall outside the range of observed fluctuations, which has only been approximately 0.7°C per 20 years. Using the figures derived from Manabe et al. (1991), the average difference between modelled and observed figures would amount to 1.0°C, which would also be outside the range of natural fluctuations. Thus, were those differences due to natural climatic fluctuations, a cooling must have occurred during the last few decades which not only falls outside of the 99.73 per cent confidence interval (three standard deviations) of observed climate fluctuations on this time scale, but it must have been larger than any cooling observed before in the documented climate history of Europe.

Clearly, this is an unlikely event. As an alternative, the possibility might be considered that the predicted temperature increases used here are too large, even if the positive temperature departures observed during the last few decades are due to the additional greenhouse effect.

On the other hand, the observed positive temperature departures may just as well be the sum of a natural warming and the greenhouse effect, in which case the magnitude of the greenhouse-induced warming would have been very small compared to the model-predicted warming. Therefore, depending on the true magnitude of the natural fluctuations which have occurred in the last few decades, the greenhouse effect could have contributed anywhere from 0.0°C to 0.4°C to the positive temperature departures observed in Europe during the last 20 years.

It is conceivable that all of the warming has been due to natural variability, in which case the contribution of the greenhouse effect has been zero.

On the other hand, the greenhouse effect may have been responsible for the entire warming, while a cooling of the largest observed magnitude could have occurred at the same time. In that case, the greenhouse warming has been approximately 0.4 + 0.7 = 1.1°C instead, which amounts to about 75 per cent of the predicted warming. Therefore, the limits of greenhouse-induced warming in the last decade lie somewhere between zero and 75 per cent of the computer-modelled predictions.

References

Boden, T. A., R. J. Sepanski, F. W. Stoss 1991: Trends '91: A Compendium of Data on Global Change. Publication No. ORNL/CDIAC -46, Carbon Dioxide Information Analysis Center, Oak Ridge, TN, USA; 665 pp.

Borisenkov, Y. P., 1992: Documentary evidence from the U.S.S.R. in: Climate since A.D. 1500. Bradley, R. S. and P. D. Jones, Eds., 246-268. Routledge, London and New York.

Briffa, K .R. and P. D. Jones, F. H. Schweingruber, 1992: Tree-Ring Density Reconstructions of Summer Temperature Patterns across Western North America since 1600. Journal of Climate, Vol. 5, 735-754.

Coops, A. J., 1992: Analysis of Temperature Series in Europe in Relation to the Detection of the Enhanced Greenhouse Effect. Theor. Appl. Climatol. 46, 89-98.

Dronia, H., 1967: Der Stadteinfluß auf den weltweiten Temperaturtrend (The urban influence on world-wide temperature trends). Inst. f. Meteorol. und Geophysik der Freien Universität Berlin, Meteorologische Abhandlungen, Vol. LXXIV, No. 4.

Groveman, B. S. and H. E. Landsberg, 1979: Simulated Northern Hemisphere Temperature Departures 1579-1880. Geophysical Research Letters, Vol. 6. No. 10, 767-769.

Hansen, J. and S. Lebedeff, 1987: Global Trends of Measured Surface Air Temperature. Journ. of Geophys. Res., Vol. 92, 13,345-13,372.

Houghton, J. T., G. J. Jenkins and J. J. Ephraums, 1990: Climate Change: The IPCC Scientific Assessment. Cambridge University Press, 365 pp, plus xxxiv pp Policymakers Summary.

Jones, P. D. and T. M. L. Wigley, 1991: Global and Hemispheric Anomalies. In: Trends '91, pp512-517, Ed. T. A. Boden et al.

Karl, T. R., 1988: Multi-year fluctuations of temperature and precipitations: the Gray area of climatic change. Climate Change, 12, 179-197.

Lamb, H. H., 1988: Weather, Climate and Human Affairs. Routledge, London and New York, 364 pp.

Lauscher, F., 1981: Säkulare Schwankungen der Dezennienmittel und extreme Jahreswerte der Temperatur in allen Erdteilen. Publ. 252, Zentralanst. f. Meteorol. imd Geodyn., Vienna, Austria.

Luther, F. M. and M. C. McCracken, 1985: Projecting The Climatic Effects of Increasing Carbon Dioxide. United States Department of Energy Research, DOE/ER-0237.

Manabe, S., R. J. Stouffer, M. J. Spelman and K. Bryan, 1991: Transient Responses of a Coupled Ocean-Atmosphere Model to Gradual Changes of Atmospheric CO_2. Part I. Annual Mean Response. Journal of Climate, Vol. 4, pp785-818.

Rudloff, v., H., 1967: Die Schwankungen und Pendelungen des Klimas in Europa seit dem Beginn der regelmäßigen Instrumentenbeobachtungen (1670). Friedrich Vieweg u. Sohn, Braunschweig, 370 pp.

Rudloff, v., H., 1991: Klimaschwankungen in Europa, Stadteinfluß und Treibhaus-Effekt. Z. Meteorol., Vol. 41, 3, pp216-226.

Schönwiese, C. D., J. Malcher and C. Hartmann, 1990: Globale Statistik langer Temperatur-und Niederschlagsreihen. In German. Report No. 65, Institute of Meteorology and Geophysics, University of Frankfurt, Germany, 301 pp.

Serre-Bachet, F., J. Guiot and L. Tessier, 1992: Dendroclimatic evidence from southwestern Europe and northwestern Africa. In: Climate since A.D. 1500. Bradley, R. S. and P. D. Jones, Eds., 349-365. Routledge, London and New York.

Sneyers, R., 1991: On the use of statistical analysis for the objective determination of climate change. Meteorol. Zeitschrift N.F. 1. J.g, H.5, 247-256.

Wang, S. W., and R. S. Wang, 1991: Little Ice Age in China. Chinese Science Bulletin, Vol. 36, No. 3, 217-220.

Gerd-Rainer Weber

Gerd-Rainer Weber undertook undergraduate and graduate studies in atmospheric sciences at the Free University of Berlin, during which time he was a Fulbright and Indiana University Scholar. Further study in America gained him an MSc degree in atmospheric sciences from the University of Michigan. He returned to the Free University of Berlin to study for his Meteorology PhD in conjunction with the Max-Planck-Institute of Aeronomy.

Since 1985, Dr Weber has been a scientist with the German Coal Mining Association. He is presently responsible for scientific research, analyis and consultancy in the field of environmental impact of coal burning, particularly problems related to acid rain and global warming.

Since 1993, he has been the head of the environment section of the German Coal Mining Association, responsible for the supervision and co-ordination of research in those areas as financed by the coal industry. He is a member of various environmental working-groups within German industry and international agencies. He carries out independent research on climate-related issues, has had publications in the peer-reviewed literature, and made contributions to a number of conferences. He has recently published a book on the greenhouse effect (in English and German editions).

Random Natural Global Temperature Changes Superior to Anthropogenic Signals

Asmunn Moene
Norwegian Meteorological Institute, (retired)
Norway

Summary

It follows from the first law of of thermodynamics that the large time-scale fluctuations of the annual global surface air temperature are solely determined by the fluctuations in the heat energy content of the world's oceans through the sea-surface temperature.

The disturbances of the thermal heat energy balance at the sea-surface are caused by the great range of annual average values of the rate of solar energy inflow through the sea surface, caused by the variable cloudiness over tropical oceans, and the great range of the rate of heat loss by evaporation at the same low latitudes.

These continuous random perturbations explain the observed stochastic white noise nature of global temperature fluctuations. The range of the rate of thermal energy flow of these random perturbations is shown to be as much as two orders of magnitude greater than a disturbance caused by a CO_2-doubling in the atmosphere.

Introduction

A thorough understanding of the natural variability of the global temperature is a necessary condition for separating an anthropogenic signal, (e.g. from a CO_2-doubling in the atmosphere), from the natural variability. As the observed natural variability is stochastic white noise, (the variance is independent of the length of the period), it can, for decades or centuries, mask deterministic forced global signals. It is therefore of decisive

139

importance to evaluate the magnitudes of the different natural perturbations of the thermal energy balance.

As no external work is performed at the top of the atmosphere and at the bottom of the oceans, the first thermodynamical energy equation of the total solar heat absorbing mass (M) of the earth is given as

$$cMdT/dt=R' \qquad (1)$$

where c is the specific heat and T the spatial mean annual temperature of the mass units and t the time.

The net annual radiation balance at the top of the atmosphere is given as $R=Q(1-\alpha)-I$ where Q is the total mean annual incoming solar radiation, α the albedo and -I the infrared heat loss to space. R is the quantity that induces the ensuing global climatic change i.e. the change in the mean global surface temperature. R can be written as the long-term average plus the deviations R'. As we have a long-term radiation balance we have R= R'.

If τ is the response time needed to obtain a temperature change, ΔT, with a given impulse R', we get by time integration of (1)

$$\tau=cM\Delta T(R')^{-1} \qquad (2)$$

i.e. the thermal response time τ is proportional to the heat capacity C=cM.

The internal energy is additive and we get from (1)

$$C_l T_l dt + C_a dT_a/dt + C_o dT_o/dt = R', \qquad (3)$$

where l, a and o represent the crust of the surface of land areas, the atmosphere and oceans respectively.

Equation (3) is the basic energy equation for global climatic changes. Since C_l and C_a are several orders of magnitude smaller than C_o the basic equation is reduced to

$$C_o dT_o/dt= R'. \qquad (4)$$

The main conclusions drawn from (4) is that the derivable large time-scale fluctuations of the annual global surface temperature are determined solely by the fluctuations in the heat content of the world's oceans through the sea-surface temperature fluctuations.

Because of the small heat capacity with corresponding small response time of the atmosphere, the surface air must, in a statistical sense, be in thermal equilibrium with the surface of the oceans. The observed global mean sea-surface and surface air temperatures are both near to 15°C.

The negligible accumulation of heat energy absorbed by an earth without oceans, and consequently without water vapour, would cause the surface to warm up until it radiated to space as much energy as it absorbed. The equilibrium temperature of such an earth would be about -18°C. The inclusion of the present amount of CO_2 in this dry atmosphere increases the temperature at the surface by only 0.5°C according to Ramanathan (1981).

It follows from Equation (4) that is must be an energy balance determining the global mean temperature near 15°C at the surface of the oceans.

Table 1 is given by Pickard and Emery, (supplied with a $2xCO_2$-effect)

Typical Values (W/m^2) World annual		
	Average	**Range**
S	+150	+80 to +200
L	-50	small ($2xCO_2$: +4)
E	-90	-50 to -160
H	-10	0 to -40

Table 1:
  S = rate of inflow of solar energy through the sea surface
  L = net rate of heat loss by the sea as long-wave radiation to the atmosphere and space
  E = rate of heat loss by evaporation
  H = rate of heat loss through the sea surface by conduction

The most important conclusion drawn from Table 1 is that the range of the net rate of heat loss as a long-wave radiation to the atmosphere and space is kept to a minimum. This is obviously an important minimum principle in the global climate system.

The perturbation-forcing of S appears through the albedo term, α, in Equation (1). Most of the oceans within 40° of the Equator have, according to satellite measurements, a minimum albedo below 0.1, but the average albedo is about 0.25. The variable cloudiness is therefore a very important factor, as the main accumulation of solar heat takes place in the given oceanic area.

141

THE GLOBAL WARMING DEBATE

The perturbation input must, in a statistical sense, be a continuous sequence of perturbations of global energy balance, i.e. the white noise thermal input confirmed by the observed changes in the global sea surface temperature. The stochastic variability of the other dominating term, E, also contributes to random perturbations of the energy balance.

The magnitude of the perturbations caused by the terms S and E is given in Table 1 by the associated ranges. The continuous random variability of these terms must account for the observed natural random changes of the global air-surface temperature in the time scales of decades to centuries.

It is of interest to compare the ranges of S and E with the reduction of the term L caused by a doubling of the CO_2-content in the atmosphere. The magnitude of this reduction amounts to $4 Wm^{-2}$, (according to e.g. Ramanathan). This amount is two orders of magnitude smaller than the ranges of S and E given in Table 1. The natural random changes therefore have the capability to mask any signal in the global temperature changes caused by a CO_2-doubling.

References

Moene, A. 1991: On the oceanic control of the global surface air temperature. Norwegian Journal of Geology, Number 3, Vol. 71, pp195-197.

Pickard, G. L. and W. J. Emery. 1982: Descriptive Physical Oceanography, 54-76. fourth edition, Pergamon Press.

Ramanathan, V. 1981: The role of ocean-atmosphere interactions in the CO_2 climate problem. J. Atmos. Sci., 38, pp913-930.

Asmunn Moene
Asmunn Moene was educated by Professor Dr H Solberg and graduated with a Master's degree in meteorology from the University of Oslo. He was a meteorologist for the Norwegian Meteorolgical Institute for many years, and the chief of the Institute's forecasting centre from 1971 to his retirement in 1988. Asmunn Moene has published several articles on the interaction of the oceans and atmosphere.

Section 3

Models, Forecasts and Uncertainty

A Preliminary Critique of IPCC's Second Assessment of Climate Change

S.Fred Singer
Director, Science & Environmental Policy Project
Virginia
USA

Summary

Global warming is rapidly becoming a non-problem. The latest climate model calculations predict a much-reduced temperature rise for the next century of as little as 0.5 degrees C, about the size of recent natural fluctuations. Such a minor warming by the year 2100 would be broadly consistent with an extrapolation of current temperature observations from satellites; but it would be barely detectable and certainly inconsequential. Why then should we trust any of the forecasts about future warming, sea level rise, and other claimed impacts, or use them as the basis for costly policies? The UN-sponsored Intergovernmental Panel on Climate Change (IPCC) appears to be intent on keeping the good news from leaking out to policymakers and the public.

The present article is a preliminary (but not comprehensive) critique of the summaries of the report of IPCC Working Group 1 (WG1 – climate science) and of the so-called Synthesis Report (based on the reports of all three IPCC working groups). Of necessity, this critique addresses the draft documents available at the Madrid and Rome meetings in Dec. 1995; the final versions have not been completed but will likely differ only in detail.

Introduction

The UN-sponsored Intergovernmental Panel on Climate Change (IPCC) serves as the scientific advisory body to the governmental parties of the Global Climate Treaty, the UN Framework Convention on Climate Change (FCCC). The IPCC, composed of three working groups, is run by a small group of scientist-administrators, aided by a Geneva-based secretariat. It is this steering group that prepares the drafts of the summaries and the later press releases, while teams of

146

mainly academic scientists prepare the technical chapters of the basic IPCC report. Needless to say, it is only the summaries and press reports that are read by policymakers.

In November and December 1995, I attended the Madrid and Rome meetings of the IPCC on behalf of The Science & Environmental Policy Project, a non-profit, non-partisan research group. We wanted to document how the nearly 200 governmental delegates from some 120 nations went about fashioning a Summary from an underlying scientific report.

The IPCC has now completed its Second Assessment of Climate Change, to be published in 1996. It is being portrayed as, in effect, a confirmation of the First Assessment (of 1990 and 1992)[i] that led to the Global Climate Treaty. As was the case for the earlier assessments, the 1995 *summaries* bear only a passing resemblance to the body of the report; they play down uncertainties and emphasize that which lends credence to a major future warming. The IPCC does not tell any untruths, yet it misleads by presenting only selected facts and omitting important information that could dispel the perception of impending catastrophe. The IPCC seems to follow Oscar Wilde's dictum: "Truth is the most precious commodity we have; let's not waste it."

Are the Climate Models Validated?
This is certainly the crucial question. How else can we know which model to trust – or indeed any model – when their forecasts differ by as much as 300 percent? The 1995 summaries claim a range of warming of from 1.0 to 3.5°C by 2100 (relative to 1990). In 1990 and 1992, the IPCC had claimed that model calculations (predicting from 1.5 to 4.5°C by 2050) were "broadly consistent" with the climate data since 1880. The 1995 summaries try to maintain this fiction in the following ways:

• The IPCC reports (correctly) that climate has warmed by 0.3 to 0.6 °C in the last 100 years, but neglects to mention that there has been little warming if any (depending on whose compilation is used) in the last 50 years, during which time some 70 percent of the total anthropogenic greenhouse gases have been added to the atmosphere.

• The Summary completely ignores the undisputed fact that the satellite data – the only truly global measurements, available since 1979 – show no warming at all but actually a slight cooling of 0.05°C per decade, although compatible with a zero trend.

Real atmospheric cooling should be compared with what climate models predict: a "best" warming rate of 0.3°C per decade, according to IPCC's 1992 Summary – recently reduced to 0.2°C per decade in the 1995 Summary. This is the clearest demonstration of the lack of validation of the models.

- The Summary doesn't make it explicit that the IPCC time scale for warming has now been stretched out – doubled, in fact, from 2050 to 2100 – making any possible impact less dramatic.

- The Summary does not mention the report of the European Climate Support Network (the co-ordinating organ of the European meteorological institutes), presented at the UN Climate Convention in Berlin, March-April 1995. The report concluded that the observed temperature changes in Europe and the North Atlantic from 1951 to 1990 were within the range of natural variation, and that anthorpogenic climate change is expected to be detectable only "in the course of the next century, but probably not before 2010, 2020, or 2030."[xv]

The Summary also ignores an authoritative US government statement (of May 22, 1995, responding to a General Accounting Office report critical of climate models)[ii]; it quotes a "further global warming" from as low as 0.5 to 2.0°C by 2100 – only about half of the IPCC's 1995 prediction.

A value of only 0.5°C by 2100, while just compatible with current observations, would, however, be inconsequential, and even difficult to detect in view of the large natural fluctuations of the climate. Global warming would become a non-problem. The mystery is why some still insist on making it a problem, a crisis, or a catastrophe – "the greatest global challenge facing mankind"[1].

Effects of Aerosols
A new feature of more advanced climate models is the inclusion of the radiative effects of atmospheric sulfate aerosols (see Dr Robert Balling's paper in this book). But the new computer studies fail to "validate"; they are still not "broadly consistent" with climate data.

- The IPCC Summary fails to mention explicitly that, thanks to the inclusion of previously neglected aerosols in Global Circulation Models (GCMs) – its 1995 temperature forecasts are one-third less than the range of values endorsed just three years ago. Yet statesmen signing a Global Climate Treaty in Rio, including George Bush, were assured that the IPCC forecasts represented a "scientific consensus" and were "of the highest quality"[1].

- The IPCC puts a great deal of reliance on a new computer study carried out at the British Meteorological Office's Hadley Centre. Preliminary results were circulated to delegates in Berlin in April 1995 at the first full governmental meeting of signatories to the 1992 Climate Treaty. It was explained to them, politicians all, that this new scientific result "validated" the computer models by producing a simulated temperature rise over the last 130 years that matched closely the observed surface air temperature changes.

A note in the journal *Nature*[iii] claimed that the model calculation, which included the effects of sulfate aerosols, matched closely the observed climate record. This claim has turned out to be premature. When the paper "Climate response to increasing levels of greenhouse gases and sulphate aerosols" by J.F.B. Mitchell et al. finally appeared in *Nature* in August 1995, the story looked rather different.[iv] The paper made a number of assumptions. It assigned a somewhat arbitrary albedo (reflecting power) to the sulfate layer; more important, it assumed a variation with time that appears unrealistic, by ignoring the effects of pollution. For example, the European land mass shows a sharp increase in aerosols between 1950 and 1970, followed by a more gradual increase up to 2050. The North American land mass shows a much smaller increase between 1940 and 1970, followed by a constant value through 2050. The global mean shows an increase to 2050 (and beyond).

The results following from these assumptions are not really surprising: "a future global mean warming of 0.3 K per decade for greenhouse gases alone, or 0.2 K per decade with sulphate aerosol forcing included." There are two things wrong with this "prediction": global temperature data from earth satellites since 1979 show no increase whatsoever, rather than the predicted value. In fact, if one takes into account the reduction in sulfates brought about by pollution control in the last thirty years, one should have observed an even greater increase than 0.3°C per decade – a rise of at least 0.5°C since 1979. (Even a constant level of aerosols in the presence of increasing greenhouse gases should lead to a warming of more than 0.3°C per decade – contrary to observations.)

The Mitchell paper is revealing however, because it contradicts the widely publicized 1990 and 1992 assessments of the IPCC, which have always claimed that the climate record over the past 100 years is "broadly consistent" with the model calculations. Here is what the Mitchell paper states in the first sentence of its abstract:

"Climate models suggest that increases in greenhouse-gas concentrations in the atmosphere should have produced a larger global mean warming than has been observed in recent decades."

The cooling effects of aerosols have been well recognized for some thirty years and invoked by climate scientists, such as Murray Mitchell and Reid Bryson, to explain the climate cooling observed between 1940 and 1975.[v] Yet only when the discrepancies between observations and model calculations became too obvious were aerosols incorporated into General Circulation Models (GCMs)[vi] – and only imperfectly.

- Manmade aerosols encompass a wide variety of particulates – sulfates from the emission of SO2 in fossil fuel combustion to smoke and soot from forest clearing and other biomass burning. Since these have quite different optical properties, their climate effects will also be quite different.

GCMs consider only the "direct" effects that involve scattering of solar radiation and thus an increase in albedo. It is generally acknowledged, however, that the indirect effects, involving the nucleation of cloud droplets, are more important and far-reaching.[vii] Unfortunately, these are also difficult to model reliably.

- To the extent that pollution control by major emitting nations is reducing the creation of sulfate aerosols, one would expect to see enhanced regional differences, as well as a *current* average warming rate higher than 0.3°C per decade – making the disagreement with observations even greater.

Detection and Attribution of an Anthropogenic Effect on Climate

The IPCC, having failed to resolve the never-mentioned discrepancy between model calculations and the temperature data of the past century, now claims that historic temperature data "point towards a detectable human influence on climate." (Draft Summary of 9 Oct. 1995). This statement was toned down somewhat in the draft of 5 Dec. 1995: "...balance of evidence suggests that there is a discernible human influence on global climate."

The IPCC statement is based on a claimed statistical correlation of observed and calculated temperature patterns, published by Santer et al. in an internal report at Livermore Lab under the above title[viii].

The adoption of this position by IPCC can be faulted on both procedural and substantive scientific grounds.

- Procedurally, the IPCC should not use – never mind quote in a Summary – a report that has not been published in the peer-reviewed literature, where it can be scrutinized and if necessary corrected or replaced.

- Substantively, Santer et al., in the abstract of their report, do not claim what IPCC asserts. They say only: "This analysis supports but does not prove that we have detected an identifiable anthropogenic signal..."

In fact, they have not detected such a signal. The claim that "pattern correspondences increase with time" (IPCC draft of Dec.5, p.2) is not supported by the evidence. Santer's claim that "the pattern of near-surface temperature change in response to combined sulfate aerosol/CO_2 forcing shows increasing similarity with observed changes over the last 50 years" is belied by their Fig.11, which shows no pattern of *increasing similarity.*[ix]

In view of the above, it is difficult to give credence to any claim that "over recent decades the observed spatial pattern of temperature change *increasingly* resembles the expected greenhouse-aerosol pattern." (emphasis added) There has not been time for an independent scrutiny to see, for example, whether the resemblance really "increases," irrespective of the GCM and aerosol scenario used.

Other Misleading Information and Omissions (Summary of WG1; draft of Oct.9, 1995)

The IPCC summary document makes unjustified statements in an effort to portray the consequences of any greenhouse warming as threatening. For example:

- Sea level rise over the past 100 years is related to a "concurrent rise in global temperature."

  – But there has been essentially no temperature rise since 1940, and certainly none at all since 1979. Does this mean that the observed sea level rise in recent decades is due to entirely different causes? What does this say about the models that were used to calculate sea level rise? And what about the observations of a thickening of the Greenland ice cap[x] and recent NCAR model calculations[xi] that would permit a *drop* in sea level with rising sea surface temperature? None of these are mentioned in the summaries.

151

- "The behaviour of the El Nino-Southern Oscillation (which causes droughts and floods in many regions) has been unusual since 1989."
  − Maybe so, but IPCC claims this as evidence for an "important systematic change" − subtly suggesting a human-related cause. So what about previous episodes of "unusual" ENSO activity?[xii] And why frighten policymakers by trying to relate what is most likely a natural climate variation to a temperature increase that is not even observed?

- Finally, the summary of WG1 plays down the large existing uncertainties in observations and theoretical models, especially in the radiative forcing of aerosols. It does not mention the possible influence of solar variability or other natural factors in the pre-1940 global temperature increase; nor the possible climate effects of increasing high-altitude air traffic; nor the uncertainty about atmospheric lifetime of CO_2 and its effect on the importance of other greenhouse gases, such as methane.

Unjustified Claims and Selective Use of the Truth

The WG1 Summary starts inauspiciously by proudly listing "significant new findings since IPCC 1990" − of which one is rather obvious ("greenhouse gases have continued to increase"), and the others are debatable or wrong. Namely:

- "recent years" have been among the warmest"[*]
  − could mean anything, since according to at least one published global temperature record (by Prof. Reid Bryson) the warmest years occurred around 1940.

- "climate models have improved [since 1990]"
  − one would hope so considering the vast sums spent on global change research − up to $2.1 billion per year in the US alone.

- "evidence points to detectable human influence on climate"
  − on local climate certainly, through deforestation and the growth of both agriculture and cities as a result of population increase. But the "evidence " relating to global climate does not

---

[*] A front-page story in the 'New York Times' (Jan 4 1996) claimed that 1995 was the hottest year in recorded human history, based on a release issued by the British Meteorological Office. The story's implication was that there exists a warming trend, thus validating IPCC predictions. On closer examination, it was discovered that the release was based on data of only the first 11 months of 1995, plus an educated guess about December, which was subsequently found to be wrong.

yet exist and is based on model calculations not validated by actual data.

- "The radiative forcing of CO_2, CH_4, and N_2O can be calculated with confidence"
  – Yes, but that of the much more important H_2O, aerosols, and clouds cannot. Small changes in their quantities (or altitude or location), or in the way they are modeled, can change the magnitude and even the sign of the radiative forcing and therefore of the temperature change.

Comments on the IPCC Synthesis Report
(SR draft of 11/3/95)

The announced purpose of the SR, based on the individual reports of the three IPCC working groups, is to supply the technical (scientific and economic) information that will permit addressing Article 2 of the Climate Treaty (UN-FCCC), namely "...stabilization of greenhouse gas (GHG) *concentrations*...to prevent *dangerous* interference with the climate system." (emphases added).

- A temperature increase of only 0.5°C by the year 2100, the most likely outcome based on the satellite data, would be well within the range of temperature fluctuations experienced historically. Unfortunately, the SR never explains this point; nor for that matter does the Summary of WG1 (Climate Science).

- WG2 (Impacts of Climate Change) can be criticized because it gives far too little weight to the real benefits of a modest warming; it fails to decompose the (misleading) *average* rise as being due mainly to a nocturnal warming. The benefits to agriculture and to human existence generally should be clear.

WG2 also fails to explore the abundant literature on the beneficial effects of climate warming from the historical record.[xiii]

Finally, WG2 neglects completely the ability – and likelihood – of humans to adjust and compensate for any adverse changes – should they occur. This is most definitely the case for disease, where good nutrition, sanitation, medical drugs, and insecticides are certainly more important than merely temperature. If human lives are at stake because of a possible geographic spread of tropical diseases, then DDT may be more effective than reducing emissions of GHG.

- The conclusions of WG3 (Response Strategies) can be faulted because, as admitted, they are based on outdated temperature data from the 1990 and 1992 IPCC reports. The expected modest warming should produce *positive* benefits rather than damages. In that case, there is no need for a cost-benefit analysis that implies a need to balance mitigation costs against avoided damages.

- A case in point: One of humanity's real concerns should be how to stave off or at least ameliorate a coming ice age – a near certainty within the time frame considered in the IPCC deliberations. There is little question that such a climate *deterioration* could be a disaster for much of mankind – unless there is sufficient resilience and sufficient wealth.[xiii] Any manmade climate warming could certainly be helpful, but the best preparation would be vigorous economic growth.

Economic growth requires an increased use of energy for most of the world – whether fossil-fueled or nuclear; there are no current alternatives in the short term, as Third World leaders are beginning to realize.

- Energy efficiency and conservation are most desirable – and so are other "no-regrets" policies that make economic sense. But WG3 merely nibbles at the problem when discussing only stabilizing *emissions* or reducing them by 20 percent or so. As is well recognized, stabilization of *concentrations* requires that GHG emissions *worldwide* be reduced by 60 to 80 percent[1] – and emissions of carbon dioxide alone by even more. Worse still, if one allows modest growth for the developing countries, the industrialized nations must effectively cease to burn fuels for power plants, heating, and transportation. WG3 fails to deal with the cost of an emission control program that addresses this daunting issue.

- The IPCC is now caught in a logical trap. It must argue that even if an increasing level of greenhouse gases does not raise temperatures appreciably, there is always the danger of unanticipated climate changes due to instabilities, nonlinearities etc. But the IPCC is not willing to include a full range of stabilization scenarios for carbon dioxide – realizing their complete political infeasibility.

At the Rome meeting, Greenpeace International argued correctly, but unsuccessfully, that the SR emission scenarios should include also the present CO_2 level of 350 ppmv. We agree, but believe that – logically – it is essential to include also the pre-industrial level of 280 ppmv. Our reasons are as follows:

Article 2 of the FCCC does not define a "dangerous level" of GHG concentration – nor does the IPCC do so. While maintaining the present level may not increase average global temperature of the *atmosphere* appreciably, one cannot be sure that the ocean circulation and the cryosphere will remain stable over the long term. As pointed out in the SR, surprises may occur and one cannot logically predict a surprise. Hence, returning to the pre-industrial GHG levels is an option that must at least be investigated, if not actually pursued, since one cannot define a "safe" level of GHG concentration. But doing so would expose the futility of trying to stabilize the concentration even at the present level.

The Broader Political Picture

Many activists, politicians, and some scientists have by now acquired a vested interest in a climate catastrophe. Consider that the US government budget for global change research has reached the amazing sum of $2.1 billion a year; even the National Cancer Institute doesn't quite match this figure. Europe is displaying similar largesse. In addition, the supranational European Union is trying to foist a carbon tax and other nonvoluntary schemes on its member countries in order to restrict the use of energy and the emission of the greenhouse gas carbon dioxide from the burning of fossil fuels.

The Global Climate Treaty, signed at the 1992 Rio de Janeiro "Earth Summit," has spawned a permanent bureaucracy and several international bodies that keep meeting endlessly to discuss what to do about a threat that has not been shown to exist and may not become apparent for a century – if ever. International symposia are proliferating. Even the mayors of cities are meeting to hold hands – in early 1995 in Berlin, then in Tokyo, and who knows where next.

By now, well over a hundred countries are involved in these exercises, keeping thousands of well-paid functionaries busy and spending some tens of millions of dollars on meeting and planning – funds that could be devoted to solving real environmental problems. That's bad enough. But what is unfortunate is that the measures contemplated are likely to ruin national economies and would certainly stifle economic growth and reduce the standard of living of a large part of the global population.

Predictably, global warming has become the forum where developing nations attack the industrialized countries – playing upon guilt. In 1972, in Stockholm, it was the wealthy nations that were using up all the world's oil; today it's carbon dioxide into a common atmosphere. Nothing much seems to have changed.[xiv]

References

i.   Houghton, J.T., Jenkins, G.J. & Ephraums, J.J. (eds) *Climate Change. The IPCC Scientific Assessment.* Cambridge Univ. Press, 1990.

Houghton, J. T.,Callander, B. A. & Varney, S. K. (eds) *Climate Change 1992. The Supplementary Report to the IPCC Scientific Assessment.* Cambridge Univ. Press, 1992.

ii.   "Combined DOC/NOAA, DOE, EPA, NASA and NSF Comments on the April 1995 Draft GAO (US General Accounting Office) Report on Factors Limiting the Credibility of GCMs" [Enclosure to Letter of May 22, 1995 to Mr. Peter Guerrero, Director, Environmental Protection Issues, GAO/RCED from Robert W. Corell, Assistant Director for Geosciences (National Science Foundation) and Chair, Subcommittee on Global Change Research]. Appended to: "Limitations of General Circulation Models and Costs of Modeling Efforts" U.S. General Accounting Office Report GAO/RCED-95-164, July 1995

iii.   Nature vol. 374, p. 487, 6 April 1995

iv.   Mitchell, J.F.B., et al. *Nature* **376**, 501-504, 1995.

v.   See chapters in *Global Effects of Environmental Pollution* (S.F. Singer, ed.) Reidel Publishers, Doordrecht, 1970

vi.   Taylor, K. & Penner, J.E. *Nature* **260**, 311-314, 1993

vii.   Charlson, R.J. et al. *Tellus* **43AB**, 152-163, 1991. Hobbs, P. V. (ed.) *Aerosol-Cloud-Interactions.* Academic Press, San Diego, 1993.

viii.   Santer, B.D. et al. *Towards the Detection and Attribution of an Anthropogenic Effect on Climate.* PCMDI Report No. 21, Livermore National Laboratory, January 1995; submitted to *Climate Dynamics*

ix.   Ellsaesser, H.W., private communication; submitted to *Climate Dynamics*

x.   Zwally, H.J. *Science* **246**, 1589-1591, 1989.

xi. Thompson, S. & Pollard, D. *Eos* **76**, No. 46, p. F104, 7 Nov. 1995 (Supplement)

xii. Quinn, W.H. et al. *J. Geophys. Res.* **92**, 14449-14462, 1987

xiii. Moore, T.G. "Global Warming: A Boon to Humans and Other Animals," Hoover Institution, Stanford Univ., 1995

xiv. To quote that great baseball player (and amateur philosopher) Yogi Berra: "It's *deja vu* all over again."

xv. Schuurmans, C. J. E., et al. *Climate of Europe: Recent Variation, Present State and Future Prospects.* Royal Netherlands Meteorological Institute, De Bilt, 1995.

The United Nations Intergovernmental Panel on Climate Change and the Scientific "Consensus" on Global Warming

Patrick J. Michaels
Department of Environmental Sciences
University of Virginia
USA

Paul C. Knappenberger
Technical Director
New Hope Environmental Services
USA

Summary

Climate data support the moderate prediction of climate change (1-1.5° C increase) rather than the more extreme scenario (4° C or more) The moderate point of view was originally marginalised in the IPCC "consensus" process in both the 1990 First Assessment on Climate Change and in the 1992 Update prepared specifically for the Earth Summit and to provide backing for the Rio Framework Convention on Climate Change.

It is now accepted, based on ground-based data, that the errors in those models are currently between 160% and 360%. If one compares them to the satellite data combined with the land record, the error rises to a maximum of 720%.

In some recognition of this massive error, the 1995 IPCC "consensus" is that warming has been mitigated by sulphate aerosols. However, when that hypothesis is specifically tested, it fails. Further, data required to test the validity of the sulphate enhanced greenhouse models was withheld by the IPCC, despite repeated requests.

Introduction

In June 1992, the Framework Convention on Climate Change, also known as the "Rio Treaty" was signed at the United Nations Earth Summit in Rio de Janiero. In order to provide a scientific basis for the treaty, the United Nations commissioned its "Inter-governmental Panel on Climate Change" (IPCC) to produce a first "Scientific Assessment of Climate Change" (IPCC, 1990), in 1990, and then to update that Assessment in a volume specifically created for the 1992 Summit (IPCC, 1992). These reports, and a recent "Second Assessment" in 1995 are promoted by IPCC as representing the "consensus" of scientists.

The major scientific difference between the 1990 and 1992 reports is that the latter employed climate projections that gradually increased the greenhouse effect. The 1990 report used projections that unrealistically and "instantaneously" doubled the natural carbon dioxide greenhouse effect, and therefore produced untestable hypotheses.

It is now generally accepted that the models on which the 1992 treaty were based were grossly in error, predicting between three and four times as much global warming as had occurred. It seems inescapable that this error was known by the IPCC at the time the treaty was signed. Was the "consensus" of scientists really that they knew there was a large forecast error that needed to be covered up in order to promote the signing of the Treaty?

Some reviewers of the original 1990 report had indicated that the projections made at that time were too warm, and that one explanation was that other emissions due to human activity were reducing the warming. This view was marginalised by IPCCs "consensus" process, but turns out to now be championed in its 1995 Second Scientific Assessment. Thus the IPCC process is capable of discounting scientists who in fact turn out to be far ahead of the IPCC consensus, and yet in less than six years they come to accept their point of view.

Ironically, the new "consensus" established by the IPCC – that manmade sulphate emissions have muted the warming to the extent that their 1992 models were in drastic error – is itself subject to question. IPCC (1995) emphasises a climate model that appears to be making the same type of errors as the 1990 and 1992 models, even though it is forecasting a reduced warming.

By now choosing to espouse climate projections that are less severe than those of its original reports, the IPCC is slowly changing its consensus from an extremist view of climate change to one that is much more moderate. However, the process whereby this takes place remains critically flawed. The documentation of the change in position and the nature of that process is the subject of this paper.

History of the Global Warming Issue
The fact that certain gases in the atmosphere absorb infrared radiation--the type that emanates from the warmed surface of the earth--was first described by John Tyndall in 1868. His laboratory experiments demonstrated that if one were to increase the concentration of such gases, that more of this type of radiation would be absorbed and therefore re-emitted to the lower atmosphere. Undoubtedly this would lead to some change in the earth's climate, though the amount and type of change remained to be quantified.

Arrhenius (1896) published the first quantitative analysis of how global climate would change as the natural carbon dioxide greenhouse effect was enhanced by the industrial combustion of fossil fuels. He calculated that doubling the CO_2 greenhouse effect would raise global temperature by 5.2° C, and that going half-way to a doubling, which is where we are today, would produce a net surface warming of 3° C.

Environmental activists often cite Arrhenius' work because the net warming predicted is so close to the average of the computer models of IPCC (1990, 1992), which, in aggregate predicted a warming of 4.2° C for a doubling. This neglects other important aspects of Arrhenius' calculation. He wrote:

"The influence is in general greater in the winter than in the summer...The influence...is in general somewhat greater for the land than ocean. On account of the nebulosity [cloudiness] of the southern hemisphere, the effect will be less there than in the northern hemisphere. An increase in CO2 will of course diminish the difference in temperature between day and night. A very important...effect will probably remove the maximum effect...to the neighbourhood of the poles".

Arrhenius' forecast is clearly for a high latitude, night warming. Due to the length of night during winter in the polar regions, he is clearly also forecasting a warming primarily confined to that season.

As we shall see, Arrhenius forecast turned out to be correct in all but one aspect: he overestimated warming by approximately 400%. But he was correct concerning where it would be concentrated and how it would be expressed.

Importance of Winter Warming

Virtually all of the apocalyptic scenarios that accompany the extremist vision of global warming--massive sea level rise caused by the melting of large areas of high-latitude ice, burning forests, starvation from global crop failures, and general ecological collapse--are fuelled by a dramatic warming of the summer days. It is, in fact, impossible to melt the polar ice during any other season; warming polar winter temperature merely results in a wetter atmosphere which produces more snow and enhances the icepack.

Modelling Climate Change

The climate change problem ultimately is one of local effects caused by larger-scale atmospheric disturbance. Thus the only serviceable analyses of the true meaning of the issue must be resolved at the regional level. While this has been recognised for a long time, the generation of reliable regional simulations, or "models" has remained a daunting task.

Nonetheless, and in spite of the repeated protestations of many of the involved scientists, these models--called General Circulation Models (GCMs)--have been used by the IPCC from their earliest reports. For example, the 1990 report describes "Estimates For Changes by 2030" for Central North America, Southern Europe, Australia, and other regions; even though IPCC wrote that "confidence in these regional estimates is low", they created the impression to those unfamiliar to the models that there was a measure of scientific validity. In fact, the 1990 models had *never* passed a rigorous test to determine whether they were realistically simulating regional climate; the first test of this type was published by Michaels et al. (1994), and it was found that the regional simulations, with one small exception, did not resemble the real climate.

The obvious effect of these regional scenarios was to cause a number of alarmist stories in the popular press. In fact, Michael Manton of the Australian Bureau of Meteorology, told an assembled audience at the Tasman Institute in Melbourne on July 13, 1995, that the regional projections were indeed included for political considerations.

Virtually every scientist who was conversant with this field knew that these projections were highly dubious and that they would nonetheless have an incendiary effect. How, then, could such an obvious ploy survive through the ostensibly thorough IPCC peer review process? The fact is that neither the 1990 IPCC report nor the subsequent ones were subject to a rigorous, anonymous peer review process.

Summary of the IPCC Process

In each of the IPCC reports, portions of the climate change problem (such as "climate models", or "sea level rise") are assigned to a small group (usually three to five) of "lead authors". These individuals then solicit small contributions--two or three pages--from a larger number of experts within a narrower range of subject matter. The reports are then compiled and included or excluded at the discretion of the lead authors. For example, Robert Davis, of University of Virginia, one of the world's experts on atmospheric circulation changes, states that of his contribution "zero" was included in this subject area. (It is a fact that Davis's published research demonstrates changes in the jet stream that are counter to what would be expected from GCMs.)

The "draft" report is then submitted to the contributing authors and a series of reviewers. (This author was *both* a contributor and a reviewer, an incestuous relationship that is inimical to any semblance of objectivity). Again, the lead authors then decide which reviewers' comments to keep and which to disregard. I submitted 4,639 words of review comment on the 1995 Second Assessment on Climate Change but could not find one substantive change in the resulting text.

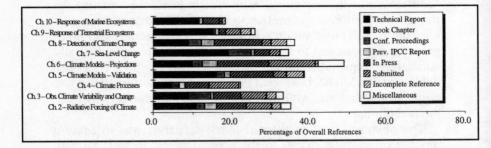

Fig 1:   Number of improper citations in the IPCC draft Second Scientific
          Assessment (1995) sent for review.

An additional problem is that contributing authors often cite their own work not yet published; in general this is not available to reviewers. Robert Davis in *World Climate Report* (1995) conducted a study of the "references" sections of IPCC drafts that were sent out for review. He found that 648 of the listed 1969 references in the 1995 Second Scientific Assessment were "improper- ... [compared to] ... the standards used by top-ranking scientific journals". Figure 1 shows the magnitude of this problem.

In summary, the IPCC forms its view of "consensus" by selecting lead authors who then select contributors of their own choosing, and then arbitrarily decide which of their contributions to retain or discard. They also send the documents out to reviewers, often to the same authors, and again arbitrarily decide which reviews to retain. Aubrey Meyer recently noted in *Nature* that, in the chapter on economic aspects of climate change, four of the seven authors were the same names that wrote the majority of references in the report. "How can this be an objective process when the authors spent so much of the time reviewing each other's work"? (Massood and Ochert, 1995).

Validity of the IPCC Consensus

Perhaps the best example of the problems in trying to define a "consensus" with this process is the long-running battle over the validity of the GCM forecasts. The 1990 First Scientific assessment that the author was sent for review stated that there was "substantial confidence that models can predict at least the broad-scale features of climate change". IPCC (1990) stated that, unless greenhouse emissions were curtailed, the increase in global temperature in 2025 be "about 2° C above that in the pre-industrial period", which implies a warming of 1.5° C between 1990 and 2025, or a remarkable 0.42° C per decade. Yet the accompanying text in the same paragraph gave a figure of 0.3° C per decade.

Along with several other reviewers, I wrote that such statements were incorrect, in large part because of the developing discrepancy between modelled and observed temperatures, especially in the Northern Hemisphere. Additionally, the propensity for warming to appear at night and in winter, rather than by day and in summer, argued that even the seasonality was inaccurate.

One possible explanation tendered at the time was that sulphate aerosols, or some other "anti" greenhouse compound, was preventing much of the warming and also redirecting its seasonality by changing atmospheric cloudiness. After all commentary was in, however, the entire *Policymakers Summary* contained one paragraph on manmade aerosols in which they stated that they might lead to "significant regional cooling", but they nonetheless published the 0.3° C per decade as their "best guess" estimates for climate change.

This had the effect of marginalising any scientist who did not espouse the 0.3° C per decade (or possibly the 0.42° C per decade) warming, because they would automatically be labelled as "outside the consensus" or not "mainstream".

The 1992 *Update*, prepared specifically for the Earth Summit and as the scientific backing for the Framework Convention on Climate Change emphasised that the major conclusions of the 1990 report remained intact:

Findings of scientific research since 1990 do not affect our fundamental understanding of the science of the greenhouse and either confirm or do not justify alteration of the major conclusions of the first IPCC [1990] Scientific Assessment...

But it also stated that:

The consistency between observations of global temperature changes over the past century and model simulations of warming due to greenhouse gases over the same period is improved if allowance is made for the increasing evidence of a cooling effect from sulphate aerosols.

However, by not changing the expected climate sensitivity from the 1990 report (1.5–4.5° C, the IPCC still succeeded in marginalising scientists who disagreed with the original estimate of 0.3° C per decade, even though it now allowed that sulphates were responsible for some cooling.

The 1992 report was clearly a bridge to the 1995 second assessment, which repeatedly cites a model by Mitchell et al. (1995) that incorporates both the effects of sulphate aerosols and the greenhouse enhancement. This paper, published in *Nature*, begins with the statement that the earlier (non-sulphate) models "have produced a larger mean warming than has been observed", a clear statement that the "consensus" of "broad agreement" between the models and observed climate, as stated in IPCC (1990), must have been in error.

TABLE 1: "BEST ESTIMATE" OF WARMING TO 2100 GIVEN IN IPCC REPORTS

REPORT	WARMING	% OF IPCC 1990
1990	3.2° C	100
1992	2.5° C	78
1995	2.15° C	67

The final section of this paper will discuss in more detail this particular model and the review process for the 1995 IPCC Assessment. Suffice it to say, at this point, that the warming predicted in this model is less than one-third of the mean of the models heavily cited in IPCC 1990.

Clearly, what has resulted in the new "consensus" (that the rate and magnitude of climate change was over-predicted), is a careful analysis of the historical climate records. Ironically, a graphic in IPCC (1990) demonstrates that if one ascribed all of the observed temperature change of the 20th century to changes in the greenhouse effect, the net warming for a doubling would be 1.3° C, which is precisely the amount remaining in the Mitchell et al. (1995a) model.

The Observed Record of Climate Change

The importance of historical climate change to the validity of the models cannot be overestimated. Thus it seems worthwhile to summarise that data at this point. We present here two different ways of looking at historical temperatures.

The first is the combined land-ocean temperature record of Phil Jones and Tom Wigley of the University of East Anglia (Department of Energy, 1993 and updates), and is the record that is most cited by scientists in their research on climatic change. This history has an unknown small amount of "urban" warming (as opposed to global, i.e. "true" warming), because of the fact that cities develop around their weather stations. This biasing effect should be greatest in the most recent years, as the number of stations that are surrounded by enough people increases proportionally with global and regional population.

The method employed to eliminate this effect is likely to miss urban warming that occurs in the more recent years. In the Jones and Wigley analysis, neighbouring stations are examined for warming trends that appear in only one record. If there is a trend, then this station is either removed from the record or the data is adjusted downward.

The problem is that urban warming that occurs at the end of the record will not be evident for enough years for a statistically significant (but artificial) trend to develop *at individual locations*, and therefore these data will remain in the global records. *In aggregate*, a large number of these types of records could induce an overall (global) warming signal that is both statistically significant while being at least in part artificial.

The second record combines the Jones and Wigley history with temperatures sensed by orbiting satellites, which begins in 1979. While the satellite data is obviously not contaminated by urban warming, it is also not a true ground-based temperature, but rather is an average for roughly the bottom 15,000 feet of the atmosphere. This measurement is very precise and thought to be accurate within ± 0.01° C. It was first published by two NASA scientists, Roy Spencer and John Christy, in 1990.

The satellite record matches in a virtually perfect fit with the mean column temperature measured between 5,000 and 30,000 feet by the global weather balloon network that is launched twice daily (Figure 2). These calibrated balloon thermometers are highly accurate and therefore indicate that the satellite data are representative of most of the lower atmosphere.

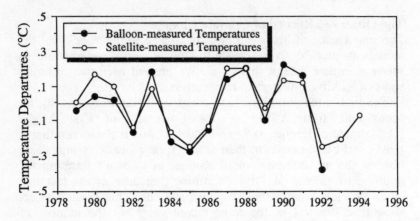

Fig 2: Mean global satellite temperature versus mean 5,000-30,000 foot temperature measured by calibrated weather balloon.

Observed Climate Changes: Century and Half-Century Scales
Each of our plots is also presented as the century (since 1900) record, and that for the last fifty years. This comparison is interesting inasmuch as almost all of the alteration of the natural greenhouse effect has been since 1945, as shown in an accompanying figure. One would expect any trends that began in the early part of the century to become more pronounced since World War II due to the increasing emission of greenhouse gases.

NET TEMPERATURE CHANGE
The first figure is the Jones and Wigley combined land-ocean record (ending in 1993), and the second figure merges this record with the satellite data that began in 1979. (Statistically insignificant changes are listed as 0*)

REGION	CENTURY	LAST 50 YEARS
Globe	+0.50°/0.25° C	+0.30/0*
Northern Hemisphere	+0.40/0.20	+0.20/0*
Southern Hemisphere	+0.50/0.30	+0.45/0*

Global Temperature

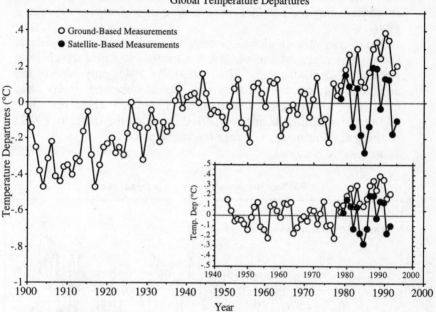

Fig 3: Global Temperatures including both ground-based and ground-based + satellite data. Inset: Last 50 years.

In the land-based record, there is a statistically significant warming of 0.5° C during the last century. This is far beneath the value that was forecast to be observed by now as a result of the greenhouse enhancement. In the models that were highlighted in the 1992 IPCC update prepared specifically for Earth Summit, Mitchell et al. (1995b) state that the range of observed warming to date in those types of models should have been 1.3-2.3° C, meaning that the over-prediction was between 0.8° C and 1.8°C (errors of 160% and 360%, respectively). Adding the satellite data further reduces the century warming, to approximately a quarter of a degree, and renders the prediction error a rather remarkable 320 to 720%!

In the last fifty years there has been a global trend of +0.3° C for the entire period over the ground-based network . This is not an appreciably different warming to that which occurred in the first half of the century, in spite of the fact that the changes in the greenhouse effect have primarily been since World War II. When

167

satellite data are added in for 1979 onwards, the trend of the last fifty years becomes statistically indistinguishable from zero. In this representation *there is no significant warming in the combined surface-satellite record of global temperature since 1943.*

Trend analysis of global records demonstrates, in a statistical sense, that much of the observed warming was already realised prior to 1945 (Balling and Idso, 1989). By 1945, only 30% of the enhancement of the greenhouse gases observed today had occurred, which implies that there has been relatively little additional warming during the period in which the majority (70%) of the greenhouse effect change has taken place.

Hemispheric Records

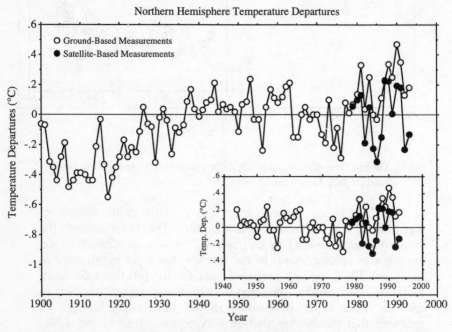

Fig 4: Same as Figure 3, except for Northern Hemisphere

Virtually *all* of the warming of the Northern Hemisphere was prior to the major post-war emissions of the greenhouse gases; a linear trend through the data since 1935* is statistically indistinguishable from zero. In addition, the "water" (Southern) hemisphere, which should warm up least and slowest, in fact shows the more "greenhouse-like" signal, albeit muted, with a relatively steady, but small, warming through the century. While most of the Southern

Hemisphere stations are on land, the fact that so much of the hemisphere is water results in more oceanic influence on the record than occurs in the Northern Hemisphere, and this should serve to retard warming.

Southern Hempishere Temperature Departures

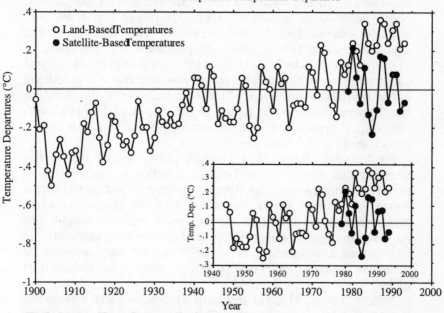

Fig 5: Same as Figure 3, except for Southern Hemisphere

Most of the long-term temperature histories originate in the northern half of the planet, and this ground-based record shows a warming of 0.5° C this century and only 0.2° C since 1943. Addition of the satellite data in 1979 results in no net warming since then. In fact, the satellite data wipes out any statistically significant warming trend back to 1914. In other words, *the satellite-plus-ground-data record shows no statistically significant warming of the Northern Hemisphere over the period 1914-1993, or the last 80 years.*

Analyses such as these have been repeatedly demonstrated in scientific papers and public presentations by many scientists (including this author) who espouse the theory of "moderate" greenhouse warming rather than the more extreme position advocated by the suite of models showcased in IPCC 1992. (*The records we used for these analyses end in 1993. The 1995 finalised data are not available as of the time of this writing.) The currency of arguments against IPCC 1992 was sufficiently strong so that the new (1995) "consensus" is that the old models were indeed wrong, because of the cooling effects of sulphate aerosols.

Details of the Sulphate/Greenhouse Model in IPCC 1995

The prominence of the UK Meteorological Office transient sulphate/greenhouse model in the draft versions of the Second (1995) assessment of Climate Change required that it be very critically examined in the review process. The precursor model, which did *not* include sulphate compensation, was published by Murphy and Mitchell early in 1995. Examination of critical components of its output force one to conclude that it is producing rather substantial warmings of the high latitudes of the Northern Hemisphere. Because this region is virtually devoid of sulphates, one might hypothesise that an analogous sulphate/greenhouse model would suffer from a similar error.

Further, the Murphy and Mitchell (1995) model clearly has warming that derives primarily from reduction in the intensity of the cold anticyclones that form over Siberia and northwestern North America in winter. Formation of these airmasses, which takes place primarily during the long polar night or twilight, will be only minimally effected by sulphate aerosol, especially in models, such as Mitchell et al. (1995a), that only included its reflective property: one cannot reflect away solar radiation at night.

Mitchell et al. (1995a) ran both greenhouse and greenhouse enhanced sulphate models. (Sulphate + greenhouse) They found the following important results:

1. The sensitivity of the greenhouse-only model to a doubling of CO_2 at equilibrium (total warming) is 2.5° C. But the paper states that this model is "significantly different" from the observed climate since 1970; i.e., it predicts too much warming, like the other models of the type that formed the foundation of the 1992 IPCC update prepared for the Earth Summit.

    It is notable that the net warming for doubling CO_2 in those models averaged around 4.2° C. The fact that Mitchell's (1995a) model, with only 2.5° of warming for a doubling, was still overestimating warming is testimony to the validity of the "moderates" view of global warming.

2. The model that combines sulphates and greenhouse gases is *not* significantly different from observations since 1950.

170

3. The percent of warming "forcing" in the sulphate + greenhouse model at time of CO_2 doubling is 67% of that of the greenhouse model alone. Therefore the equilibrium warming is roughly 67% of 2.5° C, or 1.7° C.

The claim that the observed global temperatures "from the 1940s" were correctly captured by the sulphate enhanced greenhouse models implies that 0.4° C (the linear warming trend in the Jones and Wigley record since 1945 is 0.39° C) of the 1.7° C has already occurred. Therefore the future total warming for a doubling of CO_2 is 1.3° C. This is a very low number, which greatly supports the global warming "moderates" and argues against the extreme view. The latest draft of IPCC 1995's "summary" document, available at the time this paper was written, forecasts an increase of average temperature between now and 2100 of 0.8° C to 3.5°. The mean of this range is 67% of what was given as the "best estimate" in IPCC 1990 and 78% of the value in IPCC 1992.

Do Sulphates Explain the Lack of Warming?

Our section on observed temperatures histories makes it abundantly clear that the models on which IPCC 1990 and 1992 were based were predicting far too much warming to have already occurred, and this is verified by recent modelling studies (Mitchell, 1995b), showing the current error from those models is at least 0.8° C and possibly as large as 1.8° C. The addition of *any* parameter to a model that reduces the net incoming surface radiation will result in a greater match to the historical record, as the mean temperature rise will be lessened. Because sulphates are primarily in the Northern Hemisphere (where current errors are the greatest), any "sulphate" solution will cool the hemisphere more and make the simulation appear to be spatially correct. Thus the question arises: is it sulphates, or is it just the fact that the old models were too hot?

Clearly, the way *not* to answer this question is to put some increased reflective process in the Northern Hemisphere into the model. That model will certainly resemble reality better, but the cause of the error may not be corrected. Rather, the way to determine if sulphates are the cause of the error, is to test the old (sulphate-free) models and see how they perform in areas that are known to be sulphate-free and those that are sulphate-rich.

Such a test was performed by Michaels et al. (1994) on the model most featured in the IPCC 1992 update prepared for the Earth Summit. We examined the patterns of climate change that were projected by the model of Manabe et al. (1991), and compared them mathematically to the observed patterns. The Manabe et al. (1991) model is sulphate free. Michaels et al. (1994) hypothesised that, if sulphates are the cause of the error in the model, then the model should perform significantly better in the southern hemisphere, which is virtually sulphate-free, and in the polar regions. Using the same reasoning, we hypothesised that the model would perform worst in the sulphate dominated regions of eastern North America, Europe, and Asia.

Each one of the hypotheses was rejected. Perhaps more ominous was that the model performed best where the sulphates effect was supposed to be greatest, and the model performance was worst in the sulphate-free regions. This was especially notable in the polar regions (particularly in the Northern Hemisphere), where the largest errors were found between observed and predicted climate.

Figures 6 and 7 detail the results of our test for two regions.

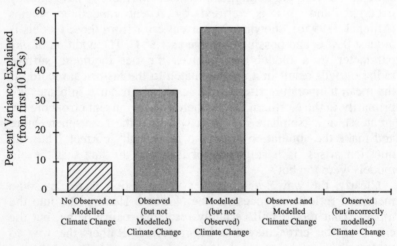

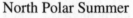

Fig 6: Performance of the sulphate-free model in a sulphate-free region. See text.

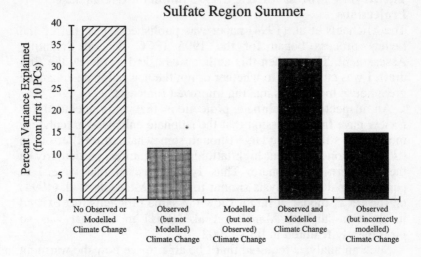

Fig 7: Performance of the sulphate-free model in sulphate-rich regions. See text.

There are five possible outcomes:

1. Neither the observed pattern or predicted pattern can change,

2. There can be a change in observed climate which was not predicted,

3. There can be a change in the predicted climate which was not observed,

4. The patterns of observed and predicted change can be correctly modelled, and

5. The patterns of observed and predicted change can be in opposite directions.

Outcomes 1 and 4 constitute "correct" forecasts, while 2 and 3 are classical Type I and II errors. Outcome 5 is the worst possible case: the directions of observed change is opposite to what was predicted.

Our figures show performance of the IPCC 1992 type models for the North Polar Summer--a sulphate free simulation, and for summer in the sulphate regions of the world. Clearly the model performs worst where there are fewest sulphates and best where there are the most. This does not bode well for the hypothesis that sulphates were the cause of the failure of the models that were the basis of the Rio Treaty.

THE GLOBAL WARMING DEBATE

The Review Process for IPCC 1995 Sulphate-Greenhouse Projections

The Michaels et al. (1994) paper was published a year before the review process began for the 1995 IPCC Second Scientific Assessment. Thus, when this author was asked to review the first draft, I was curious as to whether or not the new sulphate enhanced greenhouse model was making improved forecasts.

An inspection of climate projections that were included for review gave the impression that the sulphate enhanced greenhouse model was still making large (though somewhat reduced) errors in its estimation of current high latitude temperatures, particularly in the Northern Hemisphere. Thus I hypothesised that were I to perform a pattern analysis similar to that of Michaels et al. (1994) on the IPCC model, it might show the same problems that existed in the non-sulphate Manabe et al. (1991) model that was so prominently featured in IPCC 1992.

Such an analysis required that I be able to see how the warming evolved as the carbon dioxide increased in the model.

Mitchell, who developed the sulphate enhanced greenhouse model that was featured in the 1995 draft, was also a lead author of the chapter on future climate projections, that I was sent for review. This conveniently meant that he was both in charge of the review process and the model in question simultaneously. I therefore sent an electronic mail message to him, on May 10, 1995, that read in part:

"In writing my review of the draft of the 1995 IPCC assessment, I need to examine the transient latitude-longitude gridded output of the models...I am particularly interested in certain spatial characteristics of this model that I thank may be exceedingly germane to the 1995 assessment."

Mitchell replied on May 11:

"In view of the interests of my collaborators, who have invested a lot of effort in producing these results, I feel it inappropriate to send you gridpoint data at present."

This was answered by Michaels to Mitchell, as follows (on the same day):

"I do not understand your statement...Science is a co-operative effort in which information should be freely shared...While I understand your feelings about the proprietary nature of results that are not yet published, your Nature paper [Mitchell et al., 1995a, was published in August, months before the review process was complete] will clearly be published long before reviews of IPCC are integrated. It is, in my mind, not proper to withhold scientific information to a colleague who has been asked by the IPCC itself to review its own work...I therefore ask you to reconsider your decision not to send me the gridded output from the models."

Mitchell then responded by forwarding two manuscripts, but not the data requested. Therefore on May 12, Michaels sent to Mitchell:

"It is apparent that you are not sending me the time series of the gridded latitude-longitude output from the models. I respect your decision, although I do not agree with it."

After receiving no reply, I attempted on May 16 to appeal to Mitchell's scientific curiosity and career interests:·

"The reason I am so interested in the gridded data stems from [a portion of your manuscript that states that the sulphate model may still be producing too much warming]...consequently, it would be my working hypothesis that even a sulphate modified GCM would still be producing a large (and erroneous) Arctic winter warming...perhaps you can see why I am so interested in the gridded time series. Maybe you'll reconsider? I am sorry to trouble you but I hope you agree that the credibility of the Atmospheric Sciences – everything we have worked for – lies in the global warming issue."

When the data were still not forthcoming, I attempted to have them sent to a "neutral" party, Roy Jenne of the U.S. National Center for Atmospheric Research, who would logically need them for his archive of climate model results. May 17, 1995:

"Roy Jenne says he would be very pleased if you would promptly send him a high latitude sample of the 1.5m temperature transient output from the sulphate/greenhouse model, say, gridpoints north of 60 degrees...Roy would be very careful about sending it out."

No further communication was received from UK Meteorological Office.

However, in the meantime, I telephoned Dr. Michael MacCracken, head of the U.S. Global Change Research Program, and the head of the "Country" [U.S. government] review team for IPCC. MacCracken said he would mention the matter to John Houghton, head of the IPCC. Despite this, the data have never appeared.

On November 16, 1995, I related these events to the Subcommittee on the Environment of the U.S. House of

THE GLOBAL WARMING DEBATE

Representatives. A report describing the incident in *Nature* said that as a result this and related issues, global warming policy was "getting out of hand".

References

Arrhenius, S., 1896. *Philosophical Magazine* **41**, 237.

Balling, R. C., Jr., and S. B. Idso, 1989. *Environmental Conservation* **17**, 165.

Intergovernmental Panel on Climate Change (IPCC), 1990. *Scientific Assessment of Climate Change*. World Meteorological Organization, United Nations Environment Programme. 360pp summary report .

_____, 1992. *The Supplementary Report to the IPCC Scientific Assessment*. 200pp summary report.

_____, 1995 (draft). *Second Scientific Assessment of Climate Change*.

Manabe, S., et al., 1991. *J. Climate* **4**, 785-818.

Massed, E. and A. Ochert, 1995. *Nature* **378**, 119.

Michaels, P. J., Knappenberger, P. C., and D. A. Gay, 1994. *Technology: Journal of the Franklin Institute* **331A**, 123-133.

Mitchell, J. F. B., et al., 1995a. *Nature* **376**, 501-504.

Mitchell, J. F. B., et al., 1995b. *J. Climate* **8**, 2364-2395.

Murphy, J. M. and J. F. B. Mitchell, 1995. *J. Climate* **8**, 57-80.

Spencer, R. W. , and J. R. Christy. 1990. *Science* **247**, 1558.

Tyndall, J. 1868. *Heat as a Mode of Motion*, London, Longmans, Green.

U.S. Department of Energy, 1994. *Trends '93: A Compendium of Data on Global Change*. 984 pp.

World Climate Report, 1995. Climate Policy of the "Anointed": The Avoidance of Peer Review. Vol. 1, No. 3.

THE GLOBAL WARMING DEBATE

Patrick J. Michaels

Patrick J. Michaels is Associate Professor of Environmental Sciences at the University of Virginia and is the Virginia State Climatologist. Dr Michaels is a past President of the American association of State Climatologists and Program Chair for the Committee on Applied Climatology of the American Meteorological Society. His AB and SM degress are in Biological Sciences and Plant Ecology from the University of Chicago, and he received a PhD in Ecological Climatology from the University of Wisconsin-Adison in 1979. Dr Michaels is internationally recognised as an expert on the problems of global warming and man's effect on the atmospheric environment. He has published over 150 scientific, technical and popular articles on climate and its impact on man, and is a contributing author to the United Nations Intergovernmental Panel on Climate Change. He is the author of *Sound and Fury: The Science and Politics of Global Warming,* published in 1992 by Cato Institute.

The Great Greenhouse Controversy

Fred Hoyle
UK

Summary

*Understanding the Earth's greenhouse effect does not require
complicated computer models in order to calculate useful numbers
for debating the issue. A solution of the greenhouse problem – if
it is a problem – is suggested which does not require industry to
reduce its carbon dioxide emission, so avoiding the economic
strain this would have, and the socially unwelcome consequences
that would follow from it.*

Introduction

Sunlight falling on a plane area facing directly into the Sun, at the
Earth's distance from the Sun but out in space, provides an energy
flux of 1.36×10^6 erg cm^{-2}s^{-1} (10^7 erg s$^{-1} \equiv 1$ Watt). A rotating
sphere without atmosphere instead of a plane area receives on the
average per unit area one quarter of this incident flux, 3.4×10^5 erg
cm^{-2}s^{-1}. (The factor ¼ arises because the projected area of the
sphere is π times the square of the radius, whereas the actual area
receiving the sunlight is 4π times the square of the radius.) If the
sphere were perfectly black the whole of the latter flux would be
absorbed and would then be re-radiated as infrared radiation. For a
sphere like the Earth with an atmosphere, a fraction of the flux of
sunlight is reflected back into space and this fraction does not go
into infrared. The problem of determining the fraction reflected
back into space, the so-called albedo, is particularly difficult in the
case of the Earth, because, of course, the Earth's surface is
extremely patchy, as is its atmosphere, which has clouds in some
places and not in others. So, one is thrown back at the outset on
averages, which is to say on a approximation to the real situation.

Working downwards from the high atmosphere to the Earth's
surface, there is molecular scattering (the blue-sky effect), there is
dust scattering, there is ozone absorption (which takes place so

high in the atmosphere that it hardly affects the greenhouse problem), there is cloud reflection and ultimately, there is reflection from the surface, which can vary from only about 3% from the oceans up to 80% or more from fresh snowfields. The following table gives averages for this hugely complicated situation:

Table 1: Percentage Average Reflectivities from Various Causes.

Source	Percentage Reflectivity
Molecular scattering, dust scattering and ozone	7
Average reflectivity at surface	5
Cloud reflectivity	33

To raise a delicate point, it really isn't very sensible to make approximations like those of Table 1 and then to perform a highly complicated computer calculation, while claiming the arithmetical accuracy of the computer as the standard for the whole investigation. Once the precise detail of the Earth's reflectivity has been lost, the investigation has been so degraded that merit cannot be recovered by attention to arithmetic. Indeed, it seems to me that one cannot then do much better than what now follows.

The absorbed flux of light is re-radiated, mostly at the surface, in the infrared range and approximates a 'black-body' frequency distribution. In this approximation, and calculating without any greenhouse effect for the moment, the re-radiated energy flux is $\frac{1}{4}$ a c T^4 erg cm^{-2}s^{-1}. Here, T is the black-body temperature in degrees absolute, c is the speed of light, and a is the so-called radiation density constant with a known numerical value (7.565 x 10^{-15} erg cm^{-3} deg^{-4}). The factor $\frac{1}{4}$ arises because the infrared is radiated at all angles to the vertical. By equating $\frac{1}{4}$ a c T^4, using the known values of a and c, to 1.87 x 10^5 erg cm^{-2}s^{-1} (which balance is required once a steady condition has become stabilised) one easily obtains T = 239K or -34°C.

This is the base level from which later calculations have to be made. It differs from the temperature the Earth would have in the absence of the Greenhouse in that the value in Table 1 for cloud reflectivity would have to be reduced at such low temperatures. A total reflectivity of perhaps 25 percent, rather than 45 percent would then be appropriate. When the incident sunlight going into heat would be 2.55 x 10^5 erg cm^{-2}s^{-1} rather than 1.87 x 10^5 erg cm^{-}

$^2s^{-1}$. A similar calculation then leads to 259K or -14°C. This would be the Earth's overall temperature in the absence of the Greenhouse, calculated to a reasonable degree of approximation.

We have the greenhouse to thank, not to decry, that we do not live in such petrifying conditions. So, turning now to the greenhouse, the necessary data for getting to grips with it was published long ago by C. W. Allen (Athlete Press, Astrophysical Quantities, many editions). Instead of setting out the data in tables, which are hard to digest, Allen displayed it in a diagram whose study is greatly repaying. Figure 1 has been redrawn from his diagram.

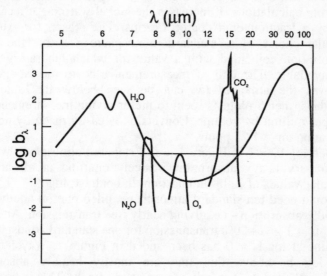

Figure 1

Wavelength λ in microns (μm) is given on the abscissa scale. The ordinate scale is the logarithm (base 10) of a quantity which Allen calls b_λ, defining b_λ as the reciprocal of the number of standard atmospheres that give 50% absorption and 50% transmission (in a standard atmosphere each cubic centimetre contains 2.69×10^{19} molecules). Thus, 1 on the left-hand scale means $\log b_\lambda = 1$, $b_\lambda = 10$, and only one tenth of a standard atmosphere is needed to give 50% absorption. (As well as having a defined molecular density, a standard atmosphere has a defined molecular composition. In Allen's case, the standard molecular composition is such that a whole atmosphere contains 1 gram of precipitable water per cm^2, and 220 atmo-cm of CO_2 per cm^2. The latter quantity means that the number of CO_2 molecules contained in the atmosphere per cm^2 of base area is the same as one gets in 220 cm^3 of pure CO_2, with each cubic centimetre containing 2.69 x 10^{19} molecules. That is to say, a total of 220 x 2.69 x $10^{19} = 5.92$ x 10^{21} molecules of CO_2 per base area of the atmosphere, equivalent to a mass of about 0.12 gram of carbon per cm^2 of base area. Or a total carbon mass of 6.05 x 10^{17} grams for the whole atmosphere, the atmosphere have a base area of 5.1 x 10^{18} c^{m2}.)

These CO_2 values used by Allen in his standard atmosphere are about 20 percent lower compared to the actual present day atmosphere, something which makes little difference to the high CO_2 peak in Figure 1, and which has no significant effect on the following calculations. It increases the global warming effect, but only by a fraction of a degree Celsius. The reason for Allen's particular choice of a 'standard' atmosphere was that the CO_2 concentration coincided with a value for which laboratory data were available. The unit of measurement used in the laboratory data was the atmo-cm (as can be seen below in Table 1). Nowadays, meteorologists seem to prefer giving measurements in parts per million by volume. Conversion is easily made by noting that 1 atmo-cm $\equiv 1.25$ ppmv.

When $\log b_\lambda = 1$ in Figure 1, a full standard atmosphere would give a very heavy absorption, scarcely emitting at all at the particular values of λ, b_λ, in question. In contrast, $\log b_\lambda = -1$, $b_\lambda = 0.1$ would need ten standard atmospheres piled one on another to give 50% absorption - i.e. giving nearly free transmission. And $\log b_\lambda = 0$, $b_\lambda = 1$ gives 50% transmission for one standard atmosphere.

A line at $\log b_\lambda = 0$ has been added in Figure 1. Wavelengths with $\log b_\lambda$ above this line are mostly heavily absorbed. Wavelengths below it mostly escape nearly freely. This is because the opacity curves for the main greenhouse gases, CO_2 and H_2O, cut the line at considerable angles. This circumstance suggests as an approximation that at all wavelengths for which b_λ is greater than unity (above the line) infrared radiation be taken as so heavily absorbed that nothing at those wavelengths escapes through the greenhouse. And by a like token, at all λ for which b_λ is less than zero (below the line) radiation be taken to escape freely. This way of calculating the greenhouse contains the essence of the matter. Since the treatment of the albedo is already approximate, it makes little sense, in view, not to take advantage of this immense simplification of the problem. The approximations has the effect of giving free transmission in a band from 8 μm to 13μm about, and from a weak spot at 17.5 μm to about 22.5 μm in the drier regions of the Earth. And also for infrared radiation generated at any appreciable height in the atmosphere. It can be adequately approximated as an escape band from 17.5 μm to 20 μm.

For black-body radiation at the Earth's actual mean temperature of about 290K, the percentages of the total radiation in these two wavebands are 32% and 8% respectively. Thus about 40% of the infrared radiation escapes freely in the above simplified model, and 60% is totally blocked from escape. This forces a return to an infrared temperature T such that 40% of ¼ a c T^4 equals the energy flux of the absorbed incident light, 1.87 x 10^5 erg cm^{-2}s^{-1}. Giving T = 301K, a remarkable increase of 42°C due to the greenhouse.

This is an overshoot when compared to the actual Earth. An overshoot by about 10°C, and the cause of it is not hard to find. It has been assumed that in the blocked wavebands, λ less than 8 μm, λ between 13 μm and 17.5 μm, and λ greater than 20 μm, energy is not carried up through the greenhouse by the motion of the air. Since the heat energy of the air molecules exceeds more than ten thousand millionfold, the energy resident as radiation, this is an assumption not likely to be wholly true, And in at least one respect it is certainly incorrect.

Rainfall implies some vaulting of energy up through the greenhouse, weakening its effect to some degree. Latent heat of evaporation of water is carried up, sometimes to considerable heights, and is released again when droplets condense. Travellers by air, particularly in the tropics, will be familiar with the immense clouds that boil up to the tropopause, or heights above 35,000 feet. The latent heat of condensation of water droplets in those clouds has vaulted much of the greenhouse. The amounts of energy so involved are by no means small. Thus the energy needed to evaporate 1 inch of rain is equivalent to about three days of sunshine. In regions of high rainfall there may be as much as 100 inches of rain annually, so in those region as a considerable fraction of the energy of the incident optical light goes into evaporation of water, and thence evades at least some of the greenhouse. The outcome being for the free band from 17.5 μm to 20 μm to be widened at its upper bound – the lower bound of 17.5 μm is less affected since the core of the carbon dioxide absorption extends well above the tropopause. The nett effect is to lower the calculated 301K towards 290K.

I come next to the effect of varying the CO_2 concentration. The calculation now requires the data set out in Table 2. The second column of the table is adequately close to where we are today, while the first column is where the atmosphere will be if fossil-fuel consumption continues at the present rate to 2050. The numbers in the second column show that the free band from 8 μm to 13 μm, used in the above calculation, would be more accurate if taken from 8 μm to 13.1 μm. And for the first column taken from 8 μm to 12.93 μm, thereby narrowing the band slightly in the ratio (12.93-8)/(13.1-8) = 0.9667. Previously, we had a 32% transmission through this band. But with the enhanced CO_2 concentration of 500 atmo-cm, the transmission would then be close to 32 x 0.9667 = 30.93%, slightly less that before. And similarly, the other free band from 17.5 μm to 20 μm would be narrowed so as to carry 7.69% instead of 8%. These percentages being of the energy in the whole infrared spectrum. For a total transmission of 38.3% instead of 40% Thereby increasing the calculated temperature by the difference between $239/(0.383)^{\frac{1}{4}}$, which is 3K. It is well-known that difference calculations of this kind are usually more accurate than either calculation is separately. This is because the errors are essentially the same and therefore cancel when the difference is taken. It is also well-known that manifest calculations like this are likely to be broadly trustworthy in their results, whereas sometimes one can be deceived by inaccessible, extensive computer calculations, especially if the computer belongs to someone else.

Table 2: Transmittance Values for Various Wavelengths and Concentrations of CO_2

Wavelength (μm)	CO_2 concentration in atmo-cm					
	500	200	100	50	10	2
18.18	.809	.914	.956	.978	.996	.999
16.67	.063	.165	.282	.421	.707	.888
15.38	.000	.000	.002	.009	.008	.335
14.29	.000	.003	.013	.039	.189	.492
13.33	.199	.341	.466	.594	.824	.941
12.50	.824	.921	.959	.979	.996	.999
11.76	.775	.875	.927	.960	.991	.998
11.11	.929	.966	.981	.990	.998	1.000
10.53	.949	.978	.989	.994	.999	1.000
10.00	.972	.988	.994	.997	.999	1.000

The result of 3K actually agrees quite well with computer calculations, indeed with what are supposed to be the best of them. The advantage of overtness is that we see immediately that the 3K result is contingent on nothing but the CO_2 concentration being changed. Which is certainly not correct. A raising of the Earth's mean temperature from 290K to 293K would inevitably produce more evaporation of water vapour from the oceans. The saturation vapour pressure of water rises by as much as 20% between these temperatures. Inevitably then, there would be more cloud and more reflection of sunlight by clouds, lowering the flux of sunlight getting through to the Earth's surface and consequently increasing the Earth's albedo. Taking account of this effect, it is not hard to see that an increase of cloud reflectivity by 2%, from 33% in Table 1 to 35%, would cancel a half of the enhanced greenhouse, cutting the above rise of 3K to 1.5K. (And of course, cutting the rise in the saturation pressure of water vapour from the above 20% to 10%.) To argue that a 10% rise in the water content of the atmosphere would not generate a 2% rise in cloud reflectivity seems to me hazardous. And yet this is what the computer enthusiasts seem to have done. The lesson, in my own experience, is that while one can safely leave arithmetic to a computer, one should never leave physics to it.

So, it is necessary to split the calculated greenhouse enhancement of 3°C into a part that is a genuine rise and a part that is self-cancelling. The way I like to proceed in a situation like this is to follow the judgement of Solomon: to split things down the middle, 1.5°C self-cancelling, 1.5°C a genuine rise. Leaving me to continue with a little sociology, which frankly, is not my subject, but it is one that we all get tempted into from time to time. Given the choice, I imagine nobody would opt for a world without any greenhouse, that is, a world with a mean temperature of about 259K. And probably few would opt for an ice-age world with a mean temperature of 275K to 280K. To this point the greenhouse is seen as good. Further still, a majority clearly continues to see the greenhouse as good up to the present-day mean of about 290K. But, at the next 1.5K a drastic change of opinion sets in: the greenhouse suddenly becomes the sworn enemy of environmental groups, world-wide, to the extent where they rush of to Rio and elsewhere and make a great deal of noise about it. I find it difficult to understand why. If I am told that computer calculations show immensely deleterious consequences would ensue, then I have a good laugh about it. In private, of course, since I am always careful to be polite in public.

I have also found it good policy, whatever one might feel about something in private, to take up a humble attitude about it in public. So I will assume from here on that those who feel that, while a 35°C greenhouse effect is cornucopian, a rise by *37°C* would be tantamount to Armageddon, are correct in their views. The inference then is that something must be done to stop the CO_2 concentration from rising in the atmosphere from its present-day value of about 250 atmo-cm to its projected value of 500 atmo-cm in the year 2050. My purpose being to show that such an objective can be achieved without ruining the world's industries and so bringing on a situation which potentially could have the eventual effect of returning us all to the Dark Ages.

If CO_2 is to continue to be emitted into the atmosphere and yet not to accumulate there, it must be stored in some way as it is produced. A physically possible storage place would be the cold waters of the deep ocean, but his does not seem seriously practicable, at any rate at the present time. Storage in trees has also been considered, but this does not work out too well either, when the details are considered.

Densely-packed, spindly forest trees have a rather low mass of about 10^5 grams, a tenth of a ton. They each occupy two or three square metres of ground area, for a mass surface density of a few grams per cm^2, about 1 g cm^{-2} of which is atomic carbon. The amount of atomic carbon in the present atmosphere was noted above to be 6.10^{17}g, and a similar quantity is required to be stored up to the year 2050. This would require a forested area of spindly trees amounting to about 6.10^{17} cm^2, which is not far below the whole land area of the Earth north of latitude 55°.

Going from spindly trees to stately parkland trees does not help. Stately trees have masses that are an order of magnitude or more greater than spindly trees, but what they gain in individual mass, they lose in the ground area required for their roots and for access to sunlight. The conclusion is, therefore, that trees will not do: the required area of forest is too large.

Deep bogs, swamps and marshes contain at least one hundred times more carbon per unit area than dense forests, with peat deposits running to depths of up to 10 metres, such as can be found in the great bog of central Ireland.

The carbon stored in deep bogs, swamps and marshes, is of the order of 199 gram cm^{-2}. At this area density about 1% of the land area north of latitude 55° would need to be set aside as wetlands in order to take up the industrial emission of CO_2, with plenty of time before the year 2050 to get it done. The essential point being to ensure that the chosen areas are sufficiently badly drained to prevent oxidation of carbon back into the atmosphere, and to take such steps as would encourage the growth of vegetation in those areas.

My last question is whether such a degree of carbon storage has ever actually happened. The present-day existence of the remains of deep bogs suggests that is might have done. With the effect of taking down the atmospheric concentration of CO_2 to the region of 50 atmo-cm. Something of the sort was suggested long ago by Svente Arrhenius as the cause of the ice-ages.

Were all CO_2 removed from the atmosphere, the escape band for infrared would go the whole way from 8 μm to 20 μm, which would cover a fraction 0.6 of the infrared. The greenhouse would then produce a temperature rise, assuming the H_2O greenhouse was not concurrently affected, from 239K to $239/0.6^{1/4} = 271.6$K.

This would overshoot the lowering of temperature required for an ice-age. However, bogs could never grow to the extent of entirely taking out all CO_2 from the atmosphere. Some CO_2, about 50 atmo-cm, would remain essential for biological activity to continue, giving a greenhouse producing a temperature intermediate between 271.6K and 290K. Explaining perhaps, why typical mean temperatures in the ice-ages were around 280K.

It is known that the last ice-age ended with great rapidity in the Allerød/Bølling about 13,000 years ago. Thus a viable theory of the cause of ice-ages must explain why, after ice-age conditions had persisted for most of the preceding 100,000 years, the ice-age was suddenly gone in less than a millennium. Possibly even in a few centuries. The answer, I suspect, was that CO_2 stored in deep bogs was rapidly returned to the atmosphere by oxidation, by fires. Peat bogs are unstable against fire. This is because the energy from the combustion of an appreciable volume of bog is considerably greater than the energy needed to dry out a similar volume, which then continues the burning.

So, what could cause such fires? It is attractive, it seems to me, to suggest the arrival of a giant comet in a suitable orbit, as proposed by Clube and Napier. With the fires started by tunguska-like bolides impacting areas of high carbon storage.

This view has the advantage that it explains why, in the remote past, ice-ages have generally persisted for long periods of the order of 100,000 years. Then they have disappeared suddenly, only to reappear after a few thousand years of warmer interglacial conditions. Because suitable giant comets are generally interspersed by intervals of the order of 100,000 years. In past times, it was necessary to wait 100,000 years before such a comet arrived. But then, once the comet was broken up and its pieces gone, the bogs slowly returned, abstracting the CO_2 from the atmosphere once again, in an irregular progression as drainage conditions influencing bog formation fluctuated.

This seems to make sense in a way that I have never found other theories of ice-age do. It implies that, so long as man remains able to control drainage patterns, there will be no further ice-age.

It should be noted, however, that the deep cold waters of the ocean contain enough dissolved CO_2 to supply the present atmospheric amount more than thirty times over. Moreover, there is an interchange of deep water with surface water, usually supposed to be too slow to affect the global warming controversy, but relevant on the time-scale of an ice-age. Unless the ice-ages were also associated with an interruption of this circulation. Or unless CO_2, once dissolved in the deep ocean, diffuses so as to remain there whatever the water may do. Because CO_2 is significantly more soluble in cold water than it is in warm could be the reason why the CO_2, once it gets deep, stays deep, not being stirred up again.

References

Allen, C. W., Astrophysical Quantities, The Athlone Press, London, 3rd Edition, p 130.

Houghton, J. T., Jenkins, G. J. And Ephraums, J. J., eds, Climate Change: The IPCC Scientific Assessment, 1990, Cambridge University Press.

Biography
Professor Sir Fred Hoyle was knighted in 1972, has been a Fellow of The Royal Society since 1957. His long and distinguished career began at Bingley Grammar School and Emmanuel College, Cambridge, of which he was made an Honorary Fellow in 1983. Among many official appointments, he was Professor of Astronomy, Royal Institution of Great Britain from 1969-72; and President of The Royal Astronomical Society from 1971-73. He has been awarded many prizes and distinctions, including the Royal Astronomical Society Gold Medal in 1968, and the Dag Hammerskjöld Gold Medal, Académie Diplomatique de la Paix, 1986.

He has published over 100 books, including, *The Nature of the Universe, 1951; A Decade of Decision, 1953; Astronomy, 1962; Star Formation, 1963;* numerous novels including *The Black Cloud, 1957; A for Andromeda, 1962;* and two volumes of autobiography, most recently, *Home is Where the Wind Blows, 1994.*

Section 4

The Sun's Rôle in Climate Change

Evidence from the Scandinavian Tree Line Since the Last Ice Age

Wibjörn Karlén and Johan Kuylenstierna
Department of Physical Geography
Stockholm University
Sweden

Summary

The focus of this paper is to investigate the possible correlation between changes in the Scandinavian climate and solar activity. Information about climatic changes in Sweden and Norway has been obtained from three sources: the carbon-14 dating of pine wood retrieved from above the present pine tree limit, studies of glacial sediments and the carbon dating of alpine glacier moraines. Alpine tree limits reveal that summer temperatures in general were warmer during the millennia following the last ice age. Superimposed on this general trend are fluctuations of a few hundred years duration. A period probably as cold as the last several hundred years occurred around 8200 years ago. Other severe cooling took place around 4500, 2200 and 1200 years ago. The timing of major climatic events has been compared with solar activity as measured by carbon-14 changes and shows a good correlation with cold periods in Scandinavia for most of the last 8000 years. Deviations between carbon-14 anomalies and the climatic record may be due to volcanic eruptions increasing the concentration of sulfate aerosols in the atmosphere.

A similarity between the periods of cold climate and carbon-14 levels indicates that solar variability may be an important factor for climate change.

Introduction

An accurately-dated timescale of climatic changes in Scandinavia, based on carbon dated samples of wood retrieved from sites above the present pine tree limit, shows that the climate of Scandinavia has fluctuated considerably since the last ice age. Several cold periods occurred around 8800, 8200, 7300, 6100, 5800, 4900, 3300, 3000-2000, 1100 years ago as well as during the last 400 years, the so-called Little Ice Age. During the warmest events the pine tree limit was located about 200 m above the present pine tree limit in Lapland, which indicates a summer temperature about 1.2 ^{o}C warmer than at present although about 0.8 ^{o}C of this may be due to the land mass being lower than at present. However, around 9300, 8400, 7700, 6800, 5600, 4200, 3200, 1600 and 800 years ago there were warmer summer periods than at present.

The so-called holocene climate of the past 10,000 years can be reconstructed from studies of glacier fluctuations, the distribution of alpine forests, lake levels in semi-arid areas and analysis of ice cores drilled at the poles. Because many of these environmental records are based on a small number of dates, the periods and extents of climatic changes are not always well defined.

Global climatic changes are currently the key question, and the answers require *global* changes happening at the same time, such as changes in greenhouse gases, volcanic activity, aerosols and solar output (Berger and Labeyrie 1987). If such changes are not synchronous, what we may be seeing is just a redistribution of heat and the impact of such global factors may be of limited importance.

Records of the atmospheric content of carbon dioxide, obtained from an Antarctic ice core and from peat studies, indicate only small changes in CO_2 concentration during the past 10,000 years implying that CO_2 can have had little effect on climate. On the other hand sulfate aerosols from volcanoes as measured from Greenland ice cores, have varied considerably, and this has been claimed to be the major cause of climatic change in this period. However, although volcanic aerosols may have affected short term climatic events, it is unlikely that they could have caused changes in the climate lasting several hundreds, let alone several thousands, of years. Solar variability remains the one factor which may have caused large scale and long-term climate changes.

Direct observations during one 11-year sunspot cycle showed a change of only 0.07 % in solar energy output, which is considered too little to cause the observed variations in temperatures on Earth. Wigley and Kelly compared climatic records from both north and south hemispheres with carbon-14 levels, which yields a measure of solar activity, and found a significant correlation, but this fell short of scientific proof. This correlation might have been more convincing if a better record of global climatic record was available.

We have studied tree line variations in the Scandinavian mountains and compared the climatic record with carbon-14 variations and linked them to the solar output. Studies of glacier moraine and sediments, and fluctuations in the alpine tree limit at several sites in the Scandinavian mountains have been used to construct a timescale of regional climatic change.

The western section of the Scandinavian peninsula is largely mountainous with several peaks reaching an altitude of over 2000m. High mountains, relatively cool summers and a large amount of precipitation contribute to favourable conditions for glacier formation. Birch (*Betula alba* and *Betula tortuosa*) and pine (*Pinus silvestris*) form the alpine tree limits. Variations in glacier size and in the altitude of the pine tree limit permit dating of climate changes over hundreds of years.

The land mass of Scandinavia has risen appreciably since the last ice age and this will have changed the local climate. The total uplift of the mountains in northern Scandinavia is believed to have been around 150 m, much of this occurring soon after deglaciation. Over the last 5000 years land uplift is believed to have been around 75m.

Continuous records of glacier fluctuations have been obtained from sediment studies. Changes in glacier size cause changes in the movement of glacial silt, and this is reflected in sediments and peat deposits flooded by meltwater streams. Samples dated by radiocarbon measurement of organic debris from beneath moraines have yielded maximum ages of glacier advances, which even if not close to the actual date of occurrence, nevertheless add support to information obtained from dates on sediments.

Dates on pine wood found above the present tree limit in Scandinavia show that the tree limit was high shortly after the last ice age and remained high until about 5000 years ago. The earliest date, 8660±80 years before the present (B.P.) was obtained from wood in southern Norway. From 5000 years B.P. to the present the general trend has been a decrease in the tree line altitude. At present the tree limit is 200 - 300 m lower than it was, although part of this lowering is a result of upward movement of land mass, and part due to climatic factors.

The information obtained on climatic changes in Scandinavia has been summarised in Figure 1. Radiocarbon dates on pine wood from northern Sweden and southern Norway were plotted against altitude (m) above the present pine limit. A few dates are considered unreliable, as they indicate an anomalously high altitude compared to the majority of dates. Because the land uplift is not known in detail, no correction has been made for it in Figure 1.

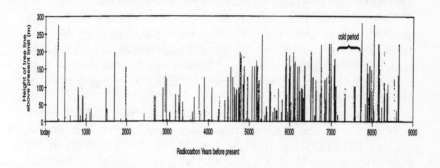

Figure 1. Radiocarbon dates on pine wood found above the present pine tree limit in Scandinavia.

The earliest major cold period has been dated to around 7400 years B.P. - marked in Figure 1. A large number of dates on pine wood from above the present pine tree limit indicates that for most of the time between 7200 and 4400 years B.P. the limit was higher than at present, often reaching an altitude corresponding to 200 m above the present tree limit, although this high altitude was partly a result of incomplete rising land mass. Nevertheless we can infer that this epoch lasting around three thousand years was much warmer than the years since then. However, there was at least one period, lasting between 100 and 200 years, during which the pine tree limit was below the present (6400 years B.P.). In addition, tree limit was less than 100 m above the present tree limit on two occasions (5800 and 5400 years B.P.). Between 4400 and 2800 years B.P., scattered dates indicate that the tree limit was as much as 100 m above the present on a number of occasions. A final period, marked by a cluster of dates on pine wood found up to 100 m above the present tree limit, has been dated to between 1100 and 800 years B.P.

The climate timescale for Scandinavia used in this study is mainly based on carbon-dated pine wood found above the present tree limit. Because pine germination is largely determined by summer temperature, the summer temperature is likely to have been relatively high during periods in which a large number of pine wood dates have been obtained. We believe that the number of samples for the period 8500-4500 years B.P. is large enough to allow changes in climate to be depicted with accuracy. For the period 4500 years B.P. to the present, only a relatively small number of dates have been obtained, which means that interpretations from this period must be considered less reliable.

If there are no dates, or only scattered dates within a period, it is an indication that the climate was unfavourable for the germination of pine above the present pine tree limit and that the summer temperature was low. These conclusions about cold climate are supported by evidence obtained from our studies of glacier fluctuations.

Periods during which glacier advances occurred, and for which there are only a few scattered pine dates, may have been at least as cold as the climate during the late 1800s, for which there are scientific records. During this period, average summer temperature in northern Scandinavia was close to 1 $^{\circ}$C colder than it was around 1940. Tree ring studies indicate that during the 1600s, when glaciers advanced everywhere, the climate was approximately as cold as it was during the late 1800s. However, the earlier cold period lasted longer than the latter one did, which resulted in more extensive glacier advances at that time. Since the extent of a glacier advance depends on the severity and duration of the cold event as well as the initial size of the glacier, it is difficult to estimate the severity of the event in the first instance from glacier changes. It is only after a few hundred years that a glacier will respond to a climatic change with an extensive advance, whereas in a warm period pine germination will most likely occur within a few years. Considering the fact that land mass recoil was close to complete 1000 years ago, the difference in summer temperature between the warm events around 5000 years B.P. and the latter warm period is small. However, if continental recoil is not considered, the local temperature was 1.2 $^{\circ}$C higher 5000 years B.P. than at present.

Most periods marked by a climate cooler than the present are matched by increases in radioactive carbon-14. This means that most cold events occurred close to periods of increased production of carbon-14 in the atmosphere, in other words when solar radiation has been weak.

The cold events around 7300, 5000-4000 and 3000-2000 years B.P., as well as during the last 300 years, are separated by periods of 2000-3000 years, a spacing similar to that of the records in the

Greenland ice core records. This similarity in pattern follows directly on the changes in climate recognised in earlier ice cores, indicate that the current fluctuations may be a continuation of the much more pronounced events.

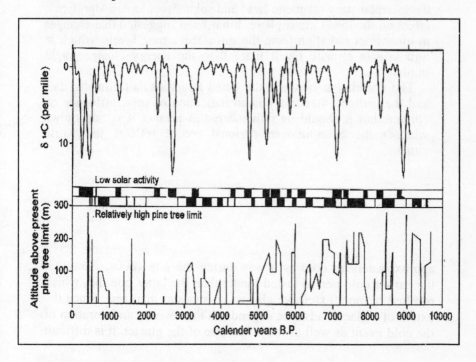

Figure 2. Summary of information about Holocene alpine
tree limit change in Scandinavia.

As mentioned above, the trend towards colder climate in Scandinavia since the last ice age is to some extent a result of land uplift. However, it is paralleled by similar trends elsewhere e.g. North America and the Caribbean, where land uplift has been minor or non-existent and can therefore not explain the whole trend alone. Therefore, it is likely that the Earth's orbit has changed causing a decrease by about 35 Wm^{-2} of incident solar radiation in midsummer in Scandinavia in the past 10,000 years and this may explain at least some of this trend. This change in summer sun light would cause a long term trend towards cooler summer climate in the northern hemisphere during this period.

The correlation observed between carbon-14 dates and climate has previously been considered accidental because no physical explanation has been found to link the two factors. Recently

197

possible links have been suggested and these include changes in cloud cover, affected by the global magnetic field, which in turn responds to solar activity. Even small changes in cloud cover will have a considerable effect on climate. It has been suggested that the interplanetary magnetic field and solar flares have a significant effect on the lower atmosphere. It has been suggested that changes in ultraviolet radiation from the sun affect ozone levels, which in turn affects climate much more than the energy change might imply.

The correlation between the dated Scandinavian climatic data and the carbon-14 anomaly is an indication of solar influence on climate, but it should be remembered at present it is not known whether the Scandinavian regional record reflects the world climate.

References

Aas, B. and Faarlund, T., 1988: Postglaciale skoggrenser i sentrale sörnorske fjelltrakter. 14C-datering av subfossile furu- og björkerester. *Norsk geografisk Tidskrift* **42,** 25- 61. Oslo.

Alexansersson, H. and Eriksson, B., 1989: Climate fluctuations in Sweden 1860-1987. SMHI Reports *Meteorology and Climatology*, No. **58**. Norrköping, 54 p.

Berger, W.H. and Labeyrie, L.D. 1987: Abrupt climatic change - an introduction. In, Berger, W.H. and Labeyrie, L.D. (Eds.), *Abrupt Climatic Change*, D. Reidel Publishing Company (425 p.), 3-22.

Berger, A., 1994: The Earth´s past and future climate. *European Geophysical Society Newsletter* **53**, 1-8.

Bond, G., Broecker, W., Johnsen, S., McManus, J., Labeyrie, L., Louzel, J. and Bonani, G., 1993: Correlation between climate records from North Atlantic sediments and Greenland ice. *Nature* **365,** 143-147.

Bond, G.C. and Lotti, R., 1995: Iceberg discharges into the North Atlantic on millenial time scales during the last glaciation. *Science* **257,** 1005-1015.

Briffa, K.R., Jones, P.D., Bartholin, T.S., Eckstein, D., Schweingruber, F.H., Karlén, W., Zetterberg, P. and Eronen, M., 1992: Fennoscandian summers from A.D. 500: Temperature changes on short and long timescales. *Climatic Dynamics* **7,** 111-119.

Denton, G.H. and Karlén, W., 1973: Holocene climatic variations - their pattern and possible cause. *Quaternary Research* **3**(2), 155-205.

Foukal, P., 1994: Study of solar irradiance variations holds key to climate questions. EOS, *Transactions, American Geophysical Union* **75**(33)**,** 377-382.

Grönlie, A., 1981: The late and postglacial isostatic rebound, the eustatic rise of the sea level and the uncompensated depression in the area of the Blue Road Geotraverse. *Earth Evolution Sciences* **1**: 50-57.

Hammer, C.U., Clausen, H.B., and Dansgaard, W., 1980: Greenland ice sheet evidence of post-glacial volcanism and its climatic impact. *Nature* **288,** 230-235.

Hodell, D.A., Curtis, J.H., Jones, G.A., Higuera-Gundy, A., Brenner, M., Binford, M.W., and Dorsey, K.T., 1991: Reconstruction of Caribbean climate change over the past 10,500 years. *Nature* **352**, 790-793.

Hood, L.L., Jirikowic, J.L. and McCormack, J.P., 1993: Quasi-decadal variability of the stratosphere: Influence of long-term solar ultraviolet variations. Journal of the Atmospheric *Sciences* **50**(24), 3941-3958.

Houghton, J.T., Jenkins, G.J. and Ephraums, J.J. 1990: Climatic change. The IPCC scientific assessment. *World Meteorological Organization/United Nations Environment Programme*, Cambridge University Press, 365 p.

Hustich, I., 1958: On the recent expansion of the Scotch pine in northern Europe. *Fennia* **82**(3), 1-25. Helsinki.

Johnsen, S.J., Clausen, H.B., Dansgaard, W., Fuhrer, K., Gundestrup, N., Hammer, C.U., Iversen, P., Jouzel, J., Stauffer, B. and Steffensen, J.P., 1992: Irregular glacial interstadials recorded in a new Greenland ice core. *Nature* **359**, 311-313.

Karlén, W., 1976: Lacustrine sediments and tree-limit variations as indicators of Holocene climatic fluctuations in Lappland: Northern Sweden. *Geografiska Annaler* **58**A(12), 1-34.

Karlén, W., 1981: Lacustrine sediment studies. *Geografiska Annaler* **63**A(3-4), 273-281.

Karlén, W., 1993: Glaciological, sedimentological and paleo-botanical data indicating Holocene climatic change in Northern Fennoscandia. In, Frenzel, B. (Ed.): Oscillations of Alpine and Polar tree limits in the Holocene (234 p.), *Paleoclimate Research* **9**, 69-83.

Karlén, W. and Matthews, J.A., 1992: Reconstructing Holocene glacier variations from glacial lake sediments: studies from Nordvestlandet and Jostedalsbreen-Jotunheimen, southern Norway. *Geografiska Annaler* **74**A(4), 327-348.

Karlén, W., Bodin, A., Kuylenstierna, J. and Näslund, J.-O., in press: Climate of northern Sweden during the Holocene. *Journal of Costal Research* Special Issue **17**.

Kullman, L., 1980: Radiocarbon dating of subfossil Scots pine (*Pinus sylvestris* L.) in the southern Swedish Scandes. *Boreas* **9**: 101-106. Oslo.

Kullman, L., 1987: Sequences of Holocene forest history in the Scandes, inferred from megafossil *Pinus sylvestris*. *Boreas* **16**, 21-26. Oslo.

Kullman, L., 1994: Palaeoecology of pine (*Pinus Sylvestris*) in the Swedish Scandes and a review of the analysis of subfossil wood. *Geografiska Annaler* **76**A(4), 247-259.

Lundqvist, G., 1959: C14-daterade tallstubbar från fjällen. *Sveriges Geologiska Undesökning,* Ser. Ba, No. **18**, 147 p. Stockholm.

Lundqvist, J., 1969: Beskrivning till jordartskarta över Jämtlands län. *Sveriges Geologiska Undersökning, Ser. Ca.* No. **45**, 418 p. Stockholm.

Magney, M., 1993: Solar influence on Holocene climatic changes ilustrated by correlations between past lake-level fluctuations and the atmospheric ^{14}C record. *Quaternary Research* **40**, 1-9.

Matthews, J.A., 1985: Radiocarbon dating of surface and buried soils: Principles, problems and prospects. In: Arnett, R.R. and Ellis, S. (Eds.), *Geomorphology and Soils*, p. 87-116. Allen and Unwin, London.

Matthews, J.A. and Karlén, W., 1992: Asynchronous neoglaciation and Holocene climatic change reconstructed from Norwegian glaciolacustrine sedimentary sequences. *Geology* **20**:991-994.

Moe, D., 1979: Tredgrense-fluktuasjoner på Hardangervidda etter siste istid. In: Nydal, R., Westin, S., Hafsten, U. and Gulliksen, s. (Eds.), *Fortiden i sökerlyset, Datering med 14C metoden gjenom 25 år*, p. 199-208. Trondheim.

Neftel, A., Oeschger, H., Staffelbach, T. and Stauffer, B., 1988: CO2 record in the Byrd ice core 50,000-5,000 BP. *Nature* **331**, 609-611.

Nesje, A. and Dahl, S.O., 1991: Holocene glacier variations of Blåisen, Hardangerjökulen, central south Norway. *Quaternary Research* **35**, 25-40.

Nesje, A. and Kvamme, M., 1991: Holocene glacier and climate variations in western Norway: Evidence for early Holocene glacier demise and multiple Neoglacial events. *Geology* **19**, 610-612.

Nesje, A. and Johannessen, T., 1992: What were the primary forcing mechanisms of high-frequency Holocene climate and glacier variations? *The Holocene* **2**(1), 79-84.

Nesje, A., Dahl, S.O., Lövlie, R. and Sulebak, J., 1994: Holocene glacier activity at the southwestern part of Hardangerjökulen, central-southern Norway: evidence from lacustrine sediments. *The Holocene* **4**(4), 377-382.

Nesje, A. and Dahl S.O., 1991:Holocene glacier variations of Blåisen, Hardangerjökulen, central southern Norway (Ca. 3200-1400 BP). *Quaternary Research* **35**, 25-40.

Oeschger, H. and Beer, J., 1990: *Philosophical Transactions of the Royal Society of London.* A **330**, 471-480.

Östrem, G., Haakensen, N. and Melander, O., 1973: Atlas over breer i Nord-Skandinavia. *Norges Vassdrags- og Elektrisitetsvesen, Hydrologisk Avdeling, Meddelse* 22, 315 p.

Östrem, G., Dale Selvig, K. and Tandberg, K., 1988: Atlas over breer i Sör-Norge, *Norges Vassdrags- og Elektrisitetsvesen, Hydrologisk Avdeling, Meddelse* 61, 180 p.

Pearson, G.W., Becker, B. and Qua, F., 1993: High-precision measurement of German and Irish oaks to show the natural ^{14}C variations from 7890 to 5000 BC. *Radiocarbon* 35(1), 93-104.

Platt, C.M.R., 1989: The role of cloud microphysics in high-cloud feedback effect on climatic change. *Nature* 341, 428-429.

Pudovkin, M.I. and Babushkina, S.V., 1991: Effect of electromagnetic and corpuscular solar flare radiations on zonal atmosperic circulation intensity. *Geomagnetism and Aeronomy* 31(3), 388-392.

Ramanathan, V., Cess, R.D., Harrison, E.F., Minnis, P., Barkstrom, B.R., Ahmad, E. and Hartman, D., 1989: Cloud-radiative forcing and climate: Results from the earth radiation budget experiment. *Science* 243, 57-63.

Rind, D., Peteet, D. and Kukla, G., 1989: Can Milankovitch orbital variations initiate the growth of ice sheets in a general circulation model? *Journal of Geophysical Research* 94, 12851-12871.

Rochefort, R.M., Little, R.L., Woodward, A. and Peterson, D.L., 1994: Changes in sub-alpine tree distribution in western North America: a review of climatic and other causal factors. *The Holocene* 4(1), 89-100.

Roeckner, E., Schlese, U., Biercamp, J. and Loewe, P., 1987: Cloud optical depth feedbacks and climate modelling. *Nature* 329, 138-140.

Selsing, L. and Wishman, E., 1984: Mean summer temperatures and circulation in a south-west Norwegian mountain area during the Atlantic period, based upon changes of the alpine pine-forest limit. *Annals of Glaciology* 5, 127-132.

Smith, H., 1911: Postglaciala regionförskjutningar i norra Härjedalens och södra Jämtlands fjälltrakter. *Geologiska Föreningen i Stockholm, Förhandlingar* 33(7), 503-530.

Sonett, C.P. and Finney, S.A., 1990: The spectrum of radiocarbon. *Philosophical Transactions of the Royal Society of London* A 330, 413-426.

Stuiver, M., Braziunas, T.F., Becker, B. and Kromer, B., 1991: Climatic, solar, oceanic, and geomagnetic influences on Late-Glacial and Holocene atmospheric ^{14}C/^{12}C change. *Quaternary Research* 35, 1-24.

Stuiver, M. and Becker, B., 1993: High-precision decadal calibaration of the radiocarbon time scale, AD 1950-6000 BC. *Radiocarbon* **35**(1), 35-65.

Stuiver, M, and Reimer, P.J., 1993: Extended ^{14}C data base and revised CALIB 3.0 ^{14}C age calibration program. *Radiocarbon* **35**(1), 215-230.

Svensson, N.-O., 1991: Late Weichselian and early Holocene shore displacement in the central Baltic sea. *Quaternary International* **9**, 7-26.

Tinsley, B.A., 1994: Solar wind mechanism suggested for weather and climatic change. EOS, *Transactions, American Geophysical Union* **75**,(32), 369-370.

White, J.W.C., Ciais, P., Figge, R.A., Kenny, R. and Markgraf, V., 1994: A high-resolution record of atmosperic CO_2 content from carbon-14 isotopes in peat. *Nature* **367**, 153-156.

Wigley, T.M.L. and Kelly, P.M., 1990: Holocene climatic change, ^{14}C wiggles and variations in solar irradiance. *Philosophical Transactions Royal Society London* A **330**, 547-560.

Zielinski, G.A., Mayewski, P.A., Meeker, L.D., Whitlow, S., Twickler, M.S., Morrison, M., Meese, D.A., Gow, A.J. & Alley, R.B. 1994, Record of volcanism since 7000 B.C. from the GISP2 Greenland ice core and implications for the volcano-climate system. **Science 264**, 948-951.

Wibjörn Karlén
Msc from University of Maine, USA, PhD from Stockholm University, Sweden.
Dr Karlén has been Professor of the Department of Physical Geography at Stockholm University since 1985. He is the President of the Swedish Society for Anthropology and Geography; The Swedish National Committe for Geography and is closely associated with a wide range of national and international committees. Dr Karlén's research interests are the holocene climatic changes and glacial chronology and deglaciation chronology; and has been the field leader of numerous research projects in four continents over the past 25 years. He is on the edictorial advisory board of *The Holocene* and *Antarctic Science*, and has made a large contribution to the literature.

THE GLOBAL WARMING DEBATE

Johan Kuylenstierna
MSc in earth sciences at Stockholm University. PhD student and teacher at the Department of Physical Geography.
Areas of study: the holocene climate in northern Sweden and Tierra del Fuego, Chile. Has also worked in Antarctica and Franz Josef Land, Russia.

Variations in the Energy Output of the Sun

Genrik Nikolsky
Institute of Physics,
St Petersburg University
Russia

Summary

The Earth's climate is controlled by radiofrequency radiation and high-speed flows of cosmic rays from active regions of the Sun and by a flux of particles at the moments when flares occur.

Variations in the spectral radiation from facula fields surrounding sun spots control the ozone mechanism of climate forcing and the condensation mechanism of cloud formation.

Our observations show the following:

- *Solar radiation impacts on the climate, and this depends on variations in its spectral composition in the 400-600 nm spectral range.*

- *The most significant indices of solar activity are the area occupied by facula fields (S_f) and location of the active regions on the Sun's equator.*

- *The discovery and identification of the key radiations is difficult because the phenomenon is sporadic and brief and appears as a burst in the spectral ranges. We have observed it at 340-410 nm, 440-485 nm, 500-510 and other wavelengths.*

The atmosphere of the Earth is subjected to powerful electromagnetic (wave) radiation from the Sun over a wide range of wavelengths from radio waves down to X-rays. Much research has been done on solar radiation in the ultraviolet range (UV) as well as bursts of X-rays from active regions of the Sun. Variations in these types of radiation are responsible for disrupting the various components and thermodynamic equilibrium of the upper atmosphere.

In our studies of solar activity and its impact on climate, we (at the Institute of Physics) focused on the Sun's spectrum – from 340 nm to 3500 nm – which covers three-quarters of the total output of the Sun. The spectral maximum of solar energy occurs in the narrower wavelength range of 450 to 650 nm. Variations of solar energy in these ranges (radiation) can have a pronounced effect on the Earth's climate. From 1981, our group undertook spectral observations of solar radiation, first in the range 340-530 nm and later extended this to 110 nm. To avoid the distortions of the lower turbid layer of the troposphere, our measurements were made at mountain reading stations in the North Caucasus region and at heights of 2100 metres.

We studied variations in spectral solar radiation at different phases of solar activity with the aim of discovering the effect of brief changes in spectral radiation when there are flares and radiobursts, and particularly when these active regions pass through the equator/ central meridian of the Sun.

Observations over many years suggest the need to study the range of 450-750 nm at high resolution if we aim to observe the energetic significance and physical nature of variations in the Sun's radiation. It has been claimed in a visible range of the spectrum that this is more or less stable and free from "explosive" variations. This erroneous view is the consequence of averaged values of the total solar irradiance (I_0) obtained from satellite measurements. Recently the satellite experiment, SOVA, came into operation and it can measure the wavelengths of 335, 500 and 862 nm using a three-channel radiometer. We should point out that with fewer channels and because of damage to their interference filters, these observations are of limited value.

Our observations, as well as the SOVA ones, suggest that there is an influence of solar radiobursts in the centimetre range (Nikolsky, 1994) of water vapour in the troposphere. The changes reveal themselves as variations of atmosphere transmission in the UV and near-IR ranges, where water clusters absorb.

A number of events observed by our group (Kondratyev and Nikolsky, 1995) and by other scientists (For example, Schuurmans, 1965) are connected with the intrusions into the atmosphere of energetic particles ejected from active regions of the sun, flaring regions in particular. On 20th October 1989 at the mountain station, we observed the effect of a strong proton flare on the lower tropospheric water vapour and the transformation of this into clouds. Soon after the proton flare, we were able to follow the development of the process of vapour condensation – first in nearby canyons until the station was enveloped in cloud and then, within an hour, the entire sky was covered with cloud. We also obtained data which showed great changes in water vapour content in the troposphere over the western part of the Pacific at the time of the proton flare. This was observed by Tiros-N satellite measurements of outgoing IR-radiation made on 19th-21st October 1989. We found that the total spectroscopy content of water vapour in the troposphere fell by over 50%. It should be mentioned that in the region of the Pacific Ocean covered by Tiros-N observations, heat liberation, due to the water vapour condensation, should have been as high as $600Wm^{-2}$ per day (20th October 1989).

As mentioned, observations of solar radiation and its penetration through the atmosphere were carried out over the period starting from the maximum of the 21st cycle (1981) of the Sun's activity through to the subsequent minimum and maximum phases of the 22nd cycle (1994).

In more than ten cases, we found extremely puzzling high values of transparency of the atmosphere in UV and the violet-blue ranges of the visible spectrum. We discovered that, as a rule, anomalies in transparency arise when an active region on the Sun is passing through the central meridian and are observed at local noontime. One should keep in mind that when measuring through the thickness of the atmosphere, the increase in solar spectral intensity is revealed by comparing the spectral transparency excess with the calculated (model) value characteristic of a clear and dry atmosphere, with air pressure and temperature profiles on the troposphere over the station at the moment of observations.

Further study showed that an apparent increase in transparency occurs when the Earth is illuminated by radiation coming from an active region on the Sun, and is characterized by an intensity maximum near 410 nm, and by specific spectral variation. These kind of solar radiation bursts cannot be explained by the increase in atmospheric transparency, because when they occur, the transparency of the atmosphere would have coincided with the values characteristic of the ideal atmosphere at the station level (2100m) and in some cases would have reached values corresponding to the ideal atmosphere at 3400m level.

Comparison of the energy contribution from such "explosive" variations of the Sun's solar radiation with the total solar constant given by Nimbus-7 data showed that the excessive radiation is generated by less than a millionth part of the Sun's surface.

THE GLOBAL WARMING DEBATE

Technical Details

An UV-spectrometer was the principal instrument in our optical measuring complex - a small-size double monochromator DH 10 UV supplied with an aperture tube with a milky diffuser and placed on a Sun-tracking device which provided continuous and controlled pointing at the Sun. When input and output slits are of identical width equal to 0.05 mm, and a dispersion is equal to 4 nm/mm (gratings with 1200 lines/nm), the resolution is 0.4 nm. A stepping motor provided scanning to 0.1 nm/step. A wavelength scale of the spectrometer was easily controlled by Fraunhofer lines. Recording time of the spectrum for the wavelength region 330 - 430 nm (1000 steps) was 1.5 min. Sensitivity was controlled 3-5 times a day.

To make statistical significance of the characteristics of extraterrestrial solar spectral intensity bursts more reliable, the spectrometer was supplemented with a two-channel filter photometer for 405 nm and 630 nm wavelengths. This instrument also proved to be necessary for estimating the degree of spectral compensation of bursts in the total flux of solar radiation. On 10th November 1992, at about 9h30m UT a sharp rise in the intensity of solar radiation for 405 nm-channel was recorded, but the data for 630 nm-channel did not confirm the occurrence of this variation. Since measurements in each channel were made every 2 minutes and the irradiance rise was very short. the precise determination of its beginning proved to be impossible - it was defined as 9h33m±1min.UT. The intensity drop at 11h07min±1min.UT was also very sharp. The mentioned circumstances indicate that the divergence of the blue ray is small; according to the duration of illumination one may estimate the divergence as equal to 0.9°. Hence it follows that in the solar atmosphere physical mechanisms of collimation of spectral radiation beams are widely spread. One of the possible reasons of collimated beam occurrence is the generation of nonequilibrium (induced) super-emission in a column of hydrogen-helium plasma enclosed in a magnetic envelope - magnetic power flux tube (MPFT) - with an effective diameter about 250 km and some, thousands of kilometres in length. MPFTs of greater diameters (up to 1500 km) are less effective as sources of electromagnetic (e.m) radiation, but nevertheless because of widespread occurrence in the chromosphere (spicules), they throw out a great amount of electromagnetic energy in the upper chromosphere.

The estimations of super-emission from a large number of "effective" magnetic power flux tubes (MPFT) leads to a change in luminosity value of 3×10^{-3} per cent at the solar activity maximum (for example in October 1981). Based on average values of experimentally-obtained estimations of energy excess in the blue region of the spectrum, the solar constant variations in October 1981 would possibly reach an intensity change of 0.3%. The increase is explained by a concentration of "effective" MPFTs in the "royal", or uppermost latitudes of the Sun. Hence, we have support for the hypothesis of the way that excessive bursts of solar radiation affect the atmosphere and for considering temporary variations in spectral and total radiation.

The work by Loginov and Sazonov (1971) also treats causes of nonlinear dependence between the "solar constant" and solar activity and considers consequences of this non-linearity. When analysing the link between the decrease in radiation caused by Sun spots and its increase in faculae (two mutually-compensating processes), Loginov and Sazonov found that for an 11-year cycle, the correlation between spots and faculae differed greatly from cycle to cycle. To eliminate factors obscuring links between these parameters, they averaged several hundred monthly mean values for areas of faculae (S_f) and of sunspot umbrae (S_μ) taken from the Greenwich catalogues of solar activity for 1874-1963. As a result, they discovered a close link between values of S_f and S_μ which appeared to be non-linear: when S_μ increase was more than 200 parts per million of visible hemisphere area of the Sun (ppmvh), the rate of S_f increase was diminished by an order of magnitude, and when S_μ values were >500 ppmvh there appeared a tendency of S_f to decrease. This implies that the cycle of variations in S_f does not coincide with the cycle of Sun spot numbers (Wolf numbers - R_z - relative numbers of solar spots) and that the link of the "solar constant" with solar activity is non-linear. These data imply that the relation between R_z and mean surface air temperature, T_s (which would be particularly evident in summer months in subtropics where the direct heating effect is great enough) is non-linear as well.

Before proceeding to discuss the connection of solar activity with variations in surface air temperature, we had to consider another aspect, i.e. total ozone content (TOC) looking at the sources of short-term variations of TOC. The data of high-altitude observations of solar activity impact on optically-active components of the atmosphere, by Nikolsky and Shultz (1995) as well as by Steblova (1968) show that 30 minutes before the chromospheric flare there is a smooth rise of TOC by 6-8% which then undergoes a smooth drop. By the beginning of the flare the excess of TOC value is no more than 2%. The subsequent phase of declining TOC occurs immediately. The explanation of the TOC response to an event in the chromophere was proposed by us while studying pre-flare processes of energy accumulation in the active regions of the Sun. It turned out that near the region of the flare the brightness of a facula ring began to increase quickly about 26±8 min before the flare occurred (Chistyakova and Chistyakov, 1975). The similarity of the time taken for the increase in the brightness on the facula ring and the increase in TOC makes it possible to explain the phenomena as follows: the last phase of accumulation and transformation of magnetic energy in the flare is accompanied by an increase in the intensity of ozone-producing UV-radiation of wavelength less than 242 nm and hence, by synchronous increase of ozone concentration in 35-55 km layer. It is as if the flare has drained electromagnetic energy from its environment, resulting in a drop in the short-wavelength UV-radiation which then affects the TOC.

Clearly, there is a connection between the phenomenon which shows that these facula rings emit very short UV-radiation from the flare as well. Undoubtedly, UV-radiation flux is most effective when the active regions occur on the equator of the Sun. The total area of faculae (S_f) located on the visible hemisphere of the Sun may be related to the power of solar activity to affect the ozone layer.

It should be kept in mind that facula magnetic structure produces not only hard UV-radiation but also intensive polychromatic radiation with the maximum in the blue spectral range. Loginov and Sazonov (1971) and Foukal (1994) considered the connection between facula areas (S_f) and spot umbra areas (S_μ) for 1874-1963 period using monthly average and yearly average values respectively. It was found that the connection for monthly average values as well as for yearly ones is substantially non-linear.

The parameters S_f, S_μ and T_s are of interest when averaged over successive solar cycles, from the 12th to the 19th (see Fig. 1). Variations in T_s are obtained from a weather network located at Northern latitudes between 30- 40°. Data for three summer months of each year within every solar cycle over the years 1880-1963 were averaged and deviations from average T_s were calculated. S_f and S_μ values are also referred to the three summer months. Data for changes in total solar irradiance were obtained from Reid (1991).

According to Figure 1, the correlation between S_μ and changes in T_s turn out to be less strong than between S_f, and changes in T_s. Attention is drawn to the different tendencies of variations in S_μ and in all other parameters over the 19th cycle. Since S_μ values increase while T_s values decrease, we conclude that it is not compensated by faculae S_f increase which is responsible for T_s decrease. Dyakonova and Chistyakov (1993) analysed long-term observations of phenomena which followed Sun flares, and Chistyakova and Chistyakov (1975) observed the increase in brightness (to around 30%) and areas (by 100-200%) of a faculae ring around the sunspot which took place about 30 minutes before the flare occurred. Of great importance is evidence concerning after-flare pulsations of facula rings and the angular radius of the Sun. These results are similar to the series of oscillations of solar radiation in our observations (Kondratyev and Nikolsky, 1995).

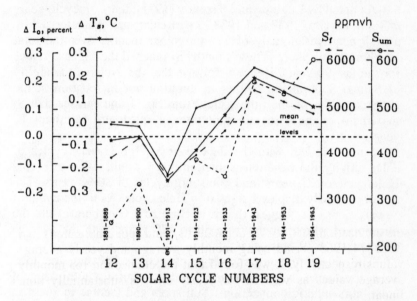

Fig.1. Comparison of solar cycle mean values for deviations of surface air temperature (T in the belt of 30 - 40 N) with areas of faculae (S) and spot umbra (S) as well as with variations in "the solar constant" (I) over the period 1881-1963. S - and S - values are plotted in ppmvh (parts per million of a visible hemisphere area of the Sun). To mark the scale for I -curve the relation between I and T (according to Reid, 1991) was taken into account. An optimum of a link between I and T was estimated near a lower limit by Reid, that is T 0.5 C corresponds to I 0.4%. I -curve itself repeats in general S -run.

Fig. 1 shows the close correlation between S_f and T_s while the area of umbra spots and other parameters correlate less well. This suggests a non-linear connection between T_s and solar activity: the latter is usually represented by areas of solar spots or umbra spots. One can see from Fig. 1 that when the value of S_f changes during 32 years from 3500 to 5300 ppmvh (parts per million visible hemisphere area of the Sun) the change in surface air temperature is 0.45°C. According to Reid (1991), such a change should take place when I_0 varies by 0.4 - 0.9%. Because there is no information of the time of stabilisation of T_s - equilibrium state following a

Sun flare, we had to use the lower limit of correlation, i.e. the change in $T_s = 0.45°C$, and the change in $I_0 = 0.4\%$. This value for the change in I_0 is in a good agreement with Smithsonian data (Hoyt, 1979) as well as with the data of long-term measurements of variations in luminosity of stars, the mass and age of which are close to the Sun's (Lockwood et al., 1992).

As noted by Loginov and Sazonov (1971), the 17th cycle-years of solar activity (1937 and 1938 in particular) are characterised by a high positive anomaly of T_s in summer months over the total Northern hemisphere. These months S_f reached the highest values for the last 90 years. Hence it follows that the cycle of variability of S_f and S_μ coincide neither in duration nor in location at the extreme values on the time scale. From Fig. 1 one can see that S_f maximum is ahead of sun spot number maximum by about 10 years.

Since we deal with the data averaged for 11-year cycles of solar activity, the variations shown in Fig. 1 would rather refer to a Hale cycle of 22 years, and Gleisberg cycles of 80-90 years. The S_μ curve clearly displayS signs of a Hale cycle. As to the cycle of S_f variations, we suggest that it is close to a Gleisberg cycle, the duration of which ranges from 30 to 120 years, with the average value equal to 79 years.

The above features showing connections between the total solar irradiance, with spots and faculae, require a rethinking of solar–atmospheric connections. Sun spots and faculae increase in undeniable solar cycles and these impact strongly on the Earth's climate.

References

Chistyakova, K.G., and Chistyakov, V.F. (1975) Chromosphere flares and fast changes of sunspots. Problems of Cosmic Physics. Vizchashkola, Kiev, 10, pp 108-118 (in Russian).

Dyakonova, V.D. and Chistyakov, V.F. (1993). On oscillations of the solar radius for the duration of one day. Global Variations of the Sun and Physics of Active Regions, V.F. Chistyakov (Ed.) Dal'nauka, Vladivostock (in Russian).

Foukal, P. (1994). On stellar luminosity variations and global warming. Science, 264, pp 238-239.

Hoyt, D.V. (1979) The Smithsonian Astrophysical Observatory solar constant program. Rev. Geophys. Space Phys. 17, pp 427-458.

Kondratyev, K.Ya., and Nikolsky, G.A. (1995) Solar activity and climate. 2. Direct impact of extra-atmospheric spectral distribution of solar radiation variations. Earth research from space, 6, in press (in Russian).

Lockwood, G. W., Skiff, B.A., Baliunas, S. L. and Radick, R.R. (1992) Long-term solar brightness changes estimated from a survey of Sun-like stars. Nature, 360, pp 653-655.

Loginov, V.F., and Sazonov, B.I. (1971) Solar constant and Earth climate, Izvestya of All-Union Geograph. Society. 3, pp 229-233 (in Russian).

Nikolsky, G. A. (1994) Consequences of the solar event 2 November 1991. Proceedings of the 1992 STEP Symposium/5th COSPAR Colloquium, D. Barker, V. Papitashvili, M. Teague (Eds.) pp 591-595, Pergamon Press.

Nikolsky, G. A., and Shultz, E. O. (1995) Anomalies of aerosol optical thickness in UV-spectral range in mountains. Problems of atmospheric physics, 20, in press. St Petersburg University (in Russian).

Reid, G. C. (1191) Solar total irradiance variations and the global sea surface temperature record. J. Geoph. Res. 96, 2835-2838 (D2).

Schuurmans, C.J.E. (1965). Influence of solar flare particles on the general circulations of the atmosphere. Nature 205 pp 167-169.

Steblova, R. S. (1968). Effect of solar flares in the ozonosphere. Geomag and aeronomy, 8, pp 370-372 (No 2) (in Russian).

THE GLOBAL WARMING DEBATE

Genrik Nikolsky
Dr. Nikolsky is qualified in physics, mathematics and sciences. He is head of a sector of radiative energetics of the atmosphere at the St. Petersburg University.
His area of scientific work is the physics of solar-atmospheric relationships. From 1961 to 1970 he studied balloon-borne observations (up to a height of 31-33km) of radiation-balance components. Since the late 1970s he has performed a series of mountain observations of spectral variations of atmospheric transparency and solar irradiance variability in the basic range of spectrum. The data of 16 years of research made it possible to reveal direct impact of variations of solar emission ozone and tropospheric water vapour and their consequences for weather and climate. The results are outlined in a series of papers, reports and co-authored monographs.

A Two-Century Comparison of Sunspot Cycle Length and Temperature Change - the Evidence from Northern Ireland

C.J. Butler
Armagh Observatory,
College Hill,
Armagh
UK

Summary

It has been shown by Friis-Christensen and Lassen (1991) that there is a close inverse correlation in the behaviour of the mean northern hemisphere air temperature and the length of the sunspot cycle, over the period 1861-1990; higher temperatures being observed during shorter cycles. This result would appear to be of considerable importance for studies of both past and future climate and suggests that, as the solar dynamo speeds up, it causes, by some process as yet unknown, an increase in the temperature of the Earth's troposphere. In this paper we extend the comparison between sunspot cycle length and temperature back to the late 18th century using data accumulated at Armagh Observatory since 1795. Our data support the contention that solar variability has been a major cause of temperature changes over the past two centuries.

Introduction

With ever more detailed study of the Earth's atmosphere we have become more acutely aware of the changing climate. This is not to suggest that the climate was ever stable and static; it has been well known for over a century that it is variable on time scales of decades, centuries, millennia, tens of millennia etc. What worries present day scientists, and indeed the general public, is that progressive industrialization could lead to a change in the composition of the Earth's atmosphere that might ultimately result in a catastrophic change in global climate. However, before we can assess the likely influence of human activities on climate, we need to have a much more precise understanding of the underlying, naturally variable, phenomena that have driven climate change over previous centuries and millenia. Foremost on our list of possible natural causes of climate change are: firstly, the erratic volcanic explosions that occasionally spread vast quantities of dust and aerosols in the stratosphere, thus blocking out incoming radiation from the Sun, and secondly, the variability of the Sun itself.

Volcanoes and Solar Activity as agents of Climate Change

The IPPC Scientific Assessment (1990) identified volcanic eruptions as one of the likely causes of change in climate. It concluded, however, that there would be some compensation for the blocking of solar radiation by an increase in diffuse radiation, and the overall effects should be relatively short-lived compared to the response time of the ocean-atmosphere system (of the order of decades). Just such a short departure to cooler conditions, lasting 2-3 years, did in fact recently take place following the eruption of Mt Pinatubo in the Phillipines in 1991. There is, nevertheless, some indirect evidence from the acidity of precipitation in ice cores that volcanic eruptions may have more lasting effects on climate (see Bradley and Jones, 1993). However, the chemistry of the atmosphere is not simple and we cannot be sure whether the acidity is the result of volcanic activity, or is a consequence of climate change caused by another mechanism.

Amongst the candidates for causing climatic change, the Sun, the power house of the solar system, must figure prominently. It is the Sun which drives the weather patterns of the Earth's atmosphere and maintains the constant circulation of its ocean currents. It is now widely accepted that it is the changing characteristics of the Earth's orbit around the Sun and the consequent variation in the amount of solar radiation received by the Earth at different seasons, that initiates the Ice Ages, (the Milankovic Effect). Though we know that over hundreds of millions of years, the Sun will gradually increase its brightness, as the hydrogen burning core of the Sun gets larger, we have come to believe that on shorter time-scales, stars such as the Sun, maintain a relatively constant luminosity. But are we justified in this assumption? In the pre-satellite era, it was not possible to measure the luminosity of the Sun to the requisite accuracy, due partly to the difficulty in obtaining a convenient standard comparison

Butler

source. In the last two decades, however, the position has improved markedly with several satellites providing independent measurements of the total solar radiative output. The results show that, indeed the Sun is variable in its brightness, though in overall energy terms and over recent decades, only by a fraction of one percent.

For many centuries, observers of the Sun have been aware of its varying physical appearance. The most prominent changes relate to the periodic appearance of dark spots on the surface of the Sun which last for several days to several weeks. They are now known to be regions of strong magnetic fields which appear dark because their temperature is lower than that of the surrounding area. Generally speaking, their number increases and decreases, cyclically, with a period which averages at eleven-years, but which may vary from less than ten to greater than twelve years. They are just one manifestation of what is normally referred to as *solar activity* and may be accompanied by *flares*; dramatic outbursts which also characterise the active Sun.

For well over a century, scientists have tried to relate the changes in the weather on Earth to the appearance of sunspots. Their efforts have met with varying degrees of success: sometimes a reasonably convincing correlation would appear to hold for a succession of solar cycles (say rainfall with sunspot number), only to be confounded by subsequent observations. Many of these attempts to prove a connection between solar activity and climate have looked for the tell-tale sign of an eleven year cycle. However, probably more than anything else, it was the approximate coincidence of the Little Ice Age in the 17th and early 18th centuries with the prolonged period when sunspots were almost absent, known as the Maunder Minimum, that sustained an underlying conviction held by many people that a link between solar variability and climate would eventually emerge.

In their now well-known paper, Friis-Christensen and Lassen (1991) appeared to make a breakthrough, with fresh evidence to support the long-held suspicion that solar activity was an important contributor to climate change. Their results showed that it was not so much the amplitude of the sunspot cyle that was important as its length for when they plotted the length of the cycle against time, they found a strikingly similar behaviour to that of the Northern Hemisphere Mean Temperature, with higher temperatures coinciding with with shorter periods of the sunspot cycle and lower temperatures with longer periods, (see Figure 1). Understandably, and because of previous failed attempts to link climate and solar activity, these results met with some scepticism from the meteorological community.

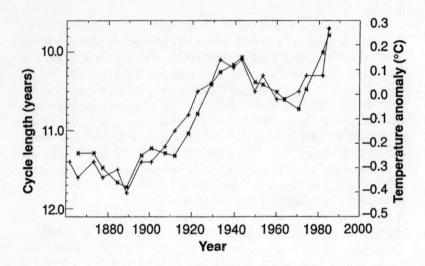

Figure 1 The variation of the sunspot cycle length since 1860, (*) superimposed on the variation in the mean air temperature for the northern hemisphere (+), (from Friis-Christensen and Lassen, 1991).

The Friis-Christensen and Lassen result applied only to the period since 1861, during which temperature measurements have been made in a reasonably reliable way over an area well distributed over the Northern Hemisphere. What was the position earlier in the 19th, and in the 18th centuries? In particular, we would like to know if the short sunspot cycle lengths that prevailed in the mid-19th and mid-18th centuries were also accompanied by higher than average temperatures.

Unfortunately, there are very few reliable temperature series which cover this period and those that do exist are often from sites which have been affected by urban encroachment. Friis-Christensen and Lassen (1991) used records of sea ice around Iceland as a proxy for temperature at high northern latitudes to give some confirmation that the effect they found in the mean Northern Hemisphere temperature from 1861-1992 continued back to the early 18th century. However, some other proxy indicators (see Bradley and Jones, 1992), do not give such good agreement. It is evident that thermometer temperature measurements would provide a more convincing justification of a connection between sunspot cycle length with temperature.

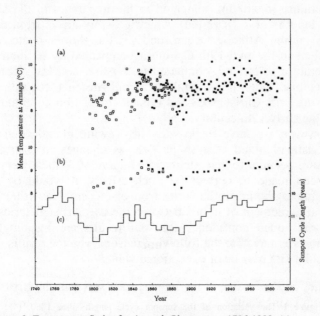

Figure 2. Temperature Series for Armagh Observatory, 1796-1992; (a) annual mean temperature, (b) eleven year means centred on years of sunspot minimum and maximum, (c) sunspot cycle length (inverted). Filled squares are from maximum and minimum temperatures, open squares - from *spot* temperatures.

A Long Temperature Series for Armagh Observatory

In cataloguing historical documents at Armagh Observatory, (Butler, 1987), we became aware of a largely untapped source of early meteorological data, that had been maintained since 1795. Two series were investigated, one of maximum and minimum temperatures from 1843 to present, and the other a series of *spot* temperatures from outside a north facing wall. There was sufficient overlap between the two series, and a further series during which hourly temperatures were recorded automatically (1869-1882), that it was possible to establish corrections required due to changes in the recording times and equipment, (Butler, 1995). In Figure 2, we show the annual mean temperature for both

219

series, the eleven-year means centered on years of sunspot maximum and minimum, and the sunspot cycle length. It is immediately evident that: (1) there is a close correspondence between the sunspot cycle length and the mean temperature at Armagh, (2) that there is a slight delay of about ten years in the temperature maximum compared to the maximum in the sunspot cycle length curve (inverted), which possibly arises from thermal inertia of the Atlantic Ocean, and (3) the shorter cycle lengths prevalent in the mid-19th C were accompanied by an increase in temperature in Ireland, compared to the first and last decades of the century. Thus the Armagh data confirms that, for this site at least, the Friis-Christensen and Lassen correlation continues back until the early 19th century.

However, we have to be wary of drawing global conclusions from data obtained at a single site, as changes in instrumental exposure peculiar to that site may be important. Whilst every effort has been made to correct for such effects, it would be highly desirable to obtain similar series from elsewhere. Nevertheless, the general agreement of trends between the two Armagh series gives us some added confidence that our results are meaningful. In addition we may note the following reasons why the results for this particular site may be of exceptional value:

- They represent one of the longest such series in the British Isles from a single site.

- The small diurnal and annual range in temperature in Northern Ireland implies a smaller statistical uncertainty in the mean temperature than for a more continental site.

- With a strongly maritime climate, temperatures are coupled to and moderated by those of the Atlantic Ocean. As a result the temperature at Armagh is likely to be more representative of a large region and less affected by local influences than many more continental sites.

- There have been relatively few changes in the siting of the instruments which have been situated at the centre of the Observatory's 20 acre site on the top of a drumlin (small hill) in Armagh.

- The relatively small effect of urban encroachment on the site. The population of Armagh has been roughly constant at 8,000-14,000 people since the early 19th century. In addition, any urban *micro-climate* effect will be minimised by the windy, maritime, conditions.

* The great interest in meteorology of the third director, Thomas Romney Robinson, the inventor of the *Cup Anemometer*, and the longevity of his directorship (59 years) ensured a careful and conscientious approach to recording meteorological data at a time when this was less common than today.

We note that neither of the long composite series, that for Central England and for the North Eastern USA, (see Lamb, 1977), show a pronounced warming in the mid-19th century. Possibly, the Armagh results at this time reflect the greater influence of the Atlantic Ocean on this site, particularly on the high mean mimima for the period 1843-1880.

Thus, whilst the evidence is not conclusive, our results tend to confirm the general correspondence between temperature and the solar cycle length found by Friis-Christensen and Lassen for a more restricted interval, and lead to the conclusion that much of the variability in temperature that has occurred over the past two centuries is of natural origin. That is not to say that the *greenhouse effect* may not be important in the future, or indeed that it has not already assumed the dominant role in climatic change. However, it does imply that we need to take solar variability seriously and to make allowance for it in climatic models.

The Physical link between Solar Activity and Climate

While the evidence presented in Figures 1 and 2 lends support to the case for the modulation of the Earth's climate by solar activity, it has not, so far, been possible to identify the physical mechanism responsible. One of the more obvious candidates would be that the variable brightness of the Sun, which from satellite data is now known to correlate positively with solar activity, results in a significant change in tropospheric temperatures.

However, detailed computations by Lean et al. (1994) show that, if the change in solar luminosity is proportional to the effect seen in recent decades, it would be by a factor of approximately two too small to produce the temperature change believed to have ocurred during the Little Ice Age. Others, (see the IPCC Assessment, 1990), have suggested that the direct effect of solar luminosity changes associated with activity are too small, by factors of five or more, from that required to produce the climate changes observed this century.

More substantial increases in flux occur in the ultraviolet and soft X-rays, during periods of high solar activity. Though these are quite insufficient, in overall energy terms to have a direct heating effect on the Earth's lower atmosphere, Herman and Goldberg (1978) have suggested that they may, through their effects on the upper atmosphere, trigger significant changes at lower levels. A recent paper by Haigh (1994) has considered the effect of solar spectral variability on the stratospheric ozone layer and the consequences for solar radiation reaching the troposphere. Herman and Goldberg (1978) and others have pointed to the possibility that changes in the solar particle flux may trigger changes in cloud formation that in turn will modulate the transmission, reflection and absorption of solar radiation. In conclusion we may remark that, even though the physical mechanism(s) for solar-activity induced changes in climate are still unresolved, there is mounting evidence that a speeding up of the solar dynamo appears to be accompanied by an increase in its efficiency that ultimately leads to an increase in the temperature of the Earth's lower atmosphere.

References

Climate Change - IPCC Scientific Assessment, Houghton, J.T., Jenkins, G.R. and Ephraums, J.J. (eds) 1990, Cambridge.

Bradley, R.S and Jones, P.D. 1993, The Holocene 3,4, 387.

Bradley, R.S. and Jones, P.D. 1992, Climate Since A.D. 1500, Routledge.

Butler, C.J. 1987, J. Hist. Astron. 18, 295.

Butler, C.J. and Johnston, D.J. 1995, J. Atmospheric and Terrestrial Physics (in press).

Friis-Christensen, E. and Lassen, K. 1991, Science 254, 698.

Haigh, J.D., 1994, Nature 370, 544.

Herman, J.R. and Goldberg, R.A. 1978, Sun, Weather and Climate, NASA SP-426.

Lean, J., Skumanich, A., White, O. and Rind, D. 1994, The Sun as a Variable Star - Solar and Stellar Irradiance Variations, proc. IAU Coll. 143, p 236, Cambridge.

John Butler
Dr C John Butler graduated in physics from Edinburgh University in 1963. He subsequently moved to Ireland, firstly as a Scholar in the Dublin Institute for Advanced Studies, and later as Research Assistant at Dunsink Observatory. Since 1973 he has held the position of Research Astronomer at Armagh Observatory where he has worked largely in the field of stellar activity. His interest in climatology stemmed from his surveys of the historical and archival material surviving at Armagh Observatory.

A long-term Comparison of Sunspot Cycle Length and Temperature Change from Zürich Observatory

K. Lassen and E. Friis-Christensen
Danish Meteorological Institute
Copenhagen
Denmark

Summary

Information about northern hemisphere temperature based on proxy data is available since the second half of the 16th century. Systematic monitoring of solar data has not taken place prior to 1750. A critical assessment of existing and proxy solar data prior to 1750 is compared to reconstructed and instrumental temperature series through four centuries. The correlation between solar activity and northern hemisphere land surface temperature is confirmed.

Introduction

Recently the variation of the global temperature, particularly the northern hemisphere land air temperature, has been found to be closely associated with the long-term variation of solar activity during the entire interval of systematic temperature measurements from 1851 to 1987 (Friis-Christensen and Lassen, 1991), Fig. 1. It was shown that the correlation was markedly improved when the sunspot number was replaced by the length of the solar cycle as an index of long-term variability of the Sun, and it was concluded that this parameter appears to be a possible indicator of long-term changes in the total energy output of the Sun. A subsequent comparison with the temperature series reconstructed from proxy data prior to 1880 by Groveman and Landsberg (1979) revealed that there is a good association between the variations in this temperature series and in the solar cycle length record since the beginning of systematic solar observations in the middle of the eighteenth century (Friis-Christensen and Lassen, 1992). This independent result for a separate time interval indicated that the association originally found

224

for the last 130 years has probably been present for at least 240 years.

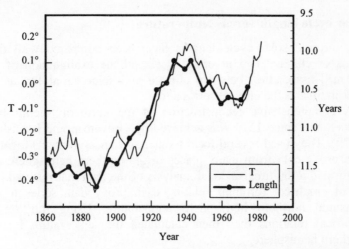

Fig. 1: 11-year running mean of the annual average northern hemisphere land air temperature by Jones et al. (1986) and Jones (1988) relative to the average temperature 1951-1980, and the filtered length of the sunspot cycle.

Regular observation of the number of sunspots, began at the the the Zürich astronomical observatory in 1850 and subsequently reconstructed from less systematic observations back to 1749. Before that year no systematic monitoring of the Sun had taken place. However, several efforts have been made to reconstruct the sunspot variation during the preceding centuries by means of sporadic observations in combination with proxy data. In acknowledgement of the importance of a thorough knowledge of older solar activity data for solar physics as well as for geophysics, including the study of a possible solar influence on the long-time development of climate, we have performed a critical assessment of published solar data covering the period 1500-1750 (Lassen and Friis-Christensen, 1995). In the following we compare a revised series of epochs of minimum solar activity and inferred solar cycle lengths with climate data in an attempt to extend the examination of the suggested association between climate and solar variability as far back as the data series allow.

We have concentrated our effort on the assessment of solar cycle length rather than on magnitude of sunspot number, partly because the cycle length appears to be superior to the sunspot number as an index of solar activity in relation to long-term terrestrial variability, and partly because epochs of minimum solar activity and thereby solar cycle lengths may be derived back in time with greater confidence than sunspot numbers.

Solar cycle length versus temperature

The inferred solar cycle lengths have been compared with time series of climate data in order to extend the examination of the assumed association between climate and solar variability as far back in time as the climate series allow.

A comprehensive reconstruction of the northern hemisphere temperature since 1579 was achieved by Groveman and Landsberg (1979). They used several local temperature measurements together with proxy data from many places in the northern hemisphere and performed a multiregressional analysis of the data that resulted in a set of empirical formulas relating each proxy data series to the measured northern hemisphere temperature. Using this set of empirical relations they then calculated the temperature for the northern hemisphere.

In Fig. 2 is plotted 11-year running average of the annual mean values of their reconstructed temperatures from 1579 to 1860 together with corresponding values for 1851-1987 from Jones et al. (1986) and Jones (1988). The reconstructed temperature values are given as departures from the average northern hemisphere temperature 1881-1975, those of the instrumental series from the average northern hemisphere land air temperature 1951-1980. Also plotted in the figure are the smoothed values of the solar cycle length from 1514 to 1989, with exception of the interval 1641-74, for which reliable data are missing. Naturally, the reconstruction of the northern hemisphere temperature must be less confident than the modern record. Groveman and Landsberg give a standard error of 0.2 to 0.3°C for the single annual averages. Besides this there exist, of course, year-to-year variations due to internal oscillations in the climate, El Niño effects, volcanic eruptions etc. Taking these variations into consideration, the comparison between the temperature record and the solar activity indicates a good association between the long-term variations in the temperature and in the solar cycle length record, although the coincidence may be less obvious during the pre-instrumental period than for the modern instrumental record.

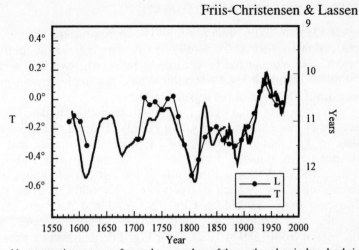

Fig. 2: 11-year running average of annual mean values of the northern hemisphere land air temperature 1579-1860 relative to the average temperature 1881-1975, reconstructed by Groveman and Landsberg (1979) together with corresponding values for 1851-1987 relative to 1951-1980 from Jones et al. (1986) and Jones (1988). Also plotted is the filtered value (1,2,2,2,1 filter) of the sunspot cycle length.

The relation is illustrated in Fig. 3, in which the temperature deviations from the two data series of Fig. 2 are presented together as a function of the solar cycle length.

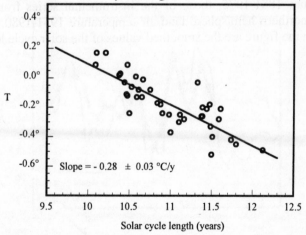

Fig. 3: Temperature deviations from Fig. 2 versus filtered value (1,2,2,2,1) of the solar cycle length.

The graph illustrates how the northern hemisphere land air temperature has varied with solar cycle length since the last decades of the 16th century (the second half of the 17th century excluded). The temperature decreases mono-tonously with increasing solar

227

cycle length. The relationship is approximately linear with regression coefficient (-0.28 ±0.03)°C/y. The correlation coefficient is 0.83. No attempt has been made to reduce the two data sets to a common reference level since this would not imply any systematic change of the slope of the regression line.

A comparison of solar cycle length with phenological data has been presented by Hameed and Gong (1993). These authors combined data of blossoming of plants noted in personal diaries and other documents originating from the area of the Middle and Lower Yangtze River Valley with records of the last day of snow event in the spring season of each year between 1720-1800 kept in the Palace Museum in the Forbidden City. The combined data sets made it possible to estimate the long-term variation of spring temperature in the region from 1580 to 1920. Their Fig. 2 demonstrates a strong co-variation between the spring temperature in Central China and the length of the solar cycle since 1750 reproduced from Friis-Christensen and Lassen (1991).

In Fig. 4 we have redrawn their smoothed temperature curve and shown it together with the time series of the solar cycle length extended back to 1600. The figure demonstrates that the spring temperature in this region of Asia has oscillated in concert with solar activity during the past 300 years.

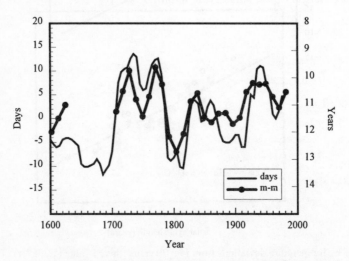

Fig. 4: 5-year running average of spring temperature in the Middle and Lower Yangtze River Valley deduced from phenological data. The curve is redrawn after Hameed and Gong (1993). The ordinate indicates "days before or after an average date". Also plotted is the filtered value (1,2,1 filter) of the solar cycle length.

Prior to 1690 the temperature deviation curve is situated at a lower level than the remaining part of the curve. If real, this fact may be related to the occurrence of the so-called Maunder minimum in solar activity and/or the Little Ice Age. It is notable, however, that the early part of the curve has been computed from a series of diaries ending in 1689 without overlap with the following series based on the dates of last snowfall and beginning in 1720. For this reason, and since solar cycle lengths for the interval 1630-1690 are lacking, the graph in Fig. 5 has been constructed solely from data after 1720. The figure shows how during nearly three centuries an increase of the average solar cycle (smoothed) of one year has resulted in an average delay of the spring time as represented by blossoming of selected plants and date of last snowfall of nearly 7 days [(-6.6±1.0) d/y; correlation coefficient 0.76].

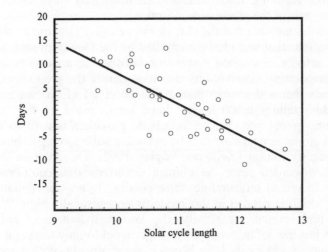

Fig. 5: 'Temperature' deviations from Fig. 4 versus filtered value (1,2,1) of solar cycle length.

Summary and discussion

A revised series of solar cycle lengths has been compared with several mutually independent series of proxy temperature data. Allowing for the greater uncertainty in the determination of an average temperature from the earlier data the comparisons confirm the high correlation between the northern hemisphere land air temperature and the long-term variation of solar activity demonstrated by Friis-Christensen and Lassen (1991) for the interval of systematic instrumental temperature measurements from 1851 to 1987.

THE GLOBAL WARMING DEBATE

The temperature data discussed in the foregoing all refer to the northern hemisphere. The conclusions are, however, believed to be valid on a global level, since it has been shown (Friis-Christensen, 1993) that inclusion of the southern hemisphere land air temperature to yield a global average land air temperature record changes the temperature curve in Fig. 1 by only a minor amount. Inclusion of sea surface temperatures, however, will delay the global temperature relative to the global land temperature by a significant amount.

An explanation of the missing greenhouse warming signal in the observed global temperature might be related to the existence of an effect that could account for a nearly complete cancelling of the effect of the greenhouse forcing, at least up to the present day. Already in the report from the Intergovernmental Panel on Climate Change (IPCC) from 1992 it was considered that the cooling effect of aerosols resulting from sulphur emissions may have offset a significant part of the greenhouse warming.

Our results indicate that the climate does display systematic long-term variations that seem to be controlled by the long-term variation of solar activity. The good correlation between solar activity and global temperature observations also seen during the pre-industrial era implies that a dominant part of the observed global warming during this century could in fact have been caused by the Sun. Simple energy-balance climate models do provide a best fit to the observed global temperature data by assuming solar forcing to be the only necessary forcing (Kelly and Wigley, 1992). This solution was, however, discarded since the climate sensitivity (the equilibrium response in global temperature corresponding to a given radiative forcing) which is needed in this model is unrealistically high. With such a high climate sensitivity, the known monotonicly rising radiative forcing of anthropogenic origin would imply temperature effects that should easily have been observed already. With a more realistic climate sensitivity, however, the variation in the solar constant over long-term (century) time scales should be significantly larger than actually observed to be consistent with the found correlations. A possible explanation of these apparent inconsistencies may imply that solar activity variations do affect climate not only through changes in total irradiance variations but also through other manifestations of solar activity variations (Friis-Christensen, 1994).

REFERENCES

Friis-Christensen E. 1993 Solar activity variations and global temperature. Energy - The Internat. Journ. 18, 1273-1284.

Friis-Christensen E. 1994 Panel discussion on the Solar and Climate Relations. The Solar Engine and its Influence on Terrestrial Atmosphere and Climate. Ed. E. Nesmes Ribes, 405-415. Springer-Verlag Berlin Heidelberg.

Friis-Christensen E. and K. Lassen 1991 Length of the solar cycle: an indicator of solar activity closely associated with climate. Science 254, 698-700.

Friis-Christensen E. and K. Lassen 1992 Global temperature variations and a possible association with solar activity variations. Danish Meteorological Institute, Sci. Rep. 92-3.

Groveman B. S. and H. E. Landsberg 1979 Simulated northern hemisphere temperature departures 1579-1880. Geophys. Res. Lett. 6, 767-769.

Hameed S. and G. Gong 1994 Variation of spring climate in lower-middle Yangtse River Valley and its relation with solar-cycle length. Geophys. Res. Lett. 21, 2693-2696.

Jones P. D., S. C. B. Raper, R. S. Bradley, H. F. Diaz, P.M. Kelly, and T. M. L. Wigley 1986 Northern hemisphere surface air temperature variations: 1851-1984. J. Clime. Appl. Met. 25, 161-179.

Jones P. D. 1988Hemispheric surface air temperature variations: Recent trends and an update to 1987. J. Climate 1, 654-660.

Kelly P.M., and T. M. L. Wigley 1992 Solar cycle length, greenhouse forcing and global climate. Nature, 360, 328-330.

Lassen K. and E. Friis-Christensen 1992 Solar activity parameters used in geo- physical studies at DMI. Danish Meteor. Inst., Tech. Rep. 92-8.

Lassen K. and E. Friis-Christensen 1993 Critical assessment of selected solar activity parameters 1500-1990. Danish Meteor. Inst., Sci. Rep. 93-10.

Lassen K. and E. Friis-Christensen 1995 Variability of the solar cycle length during the past five centuries and the apparent association with terrestrial climate. J. Atmos. and Terr. Phys. 57, 835-845.

Dr Friis-Christensen and Dr Lassen
Dr Friis-Christensen is a geophysicist and head of the Solar-Terrestrial Physics Division, Danish Meteorological Institute. Dr Lassen and he worked as colleagues for many years, before Dr Lassen retired recently.

Section 5

The Politicisation of Science

Political Pressure in the Formation of Scientific Consensus

Sonja Boehmer-Christiansen,
Department of Geography and Earth Resources,
University of Hull
UK

Summary

Neither scientists nor the green lobby alone have driven the climate change story. A whole range of 'political actors', ranging from energy interests to international bureaucracies, has been involved. All found appeals to 'science' useful. This has created serious difficulties for research where the pressure to create consensus must be replaced by the freedom to argue and debate, to test different theories and empirical sources. For the sake of both science and policy, therefore, the greenhouse debate must 'stay on the boil' a bit longer, with scientists and their environmental camp followers treating the rest of us as grown-ups. They need to air their arguments, not just hand out conclusions. It is most unlikely that the debate will be resolved in the short-run by science. Science will remain a servant of politics, and should therefore take great care in what it offers and how it responds to opportunities. Short-termism may not only be the fate of politicians.

A new research environment: or why scientists should be concerned about policy relevance

Government advisors and academic policy analysts rather than bench scientists tend to assume that 'policy-makers' need consensual knowledge in order to make decisions. Observation strongly suggests that nothing could be further from the truth, politics thrives on uncertainty and so does research. Consensus on the facts and measured uncertainties are primarily needed by other researchers engaged in creating 'interdisciplinary' policy advice.

Why then has 'scientific consensus' featured so strongly in the climate change assessments from the Working Group One (WG I) of the Intergovernmental Panel on Climate Change (IPCC), which

234

is based in the UK and supported by the Department of the Environment? This paper argues that science managers, in other words administrators in research councils and research institutions, need to claim 'relevance' in order to get funded. Relevance in turn is seen as being enhanced if there is the appearance of consensus. Demanding agreement at the frontiers of research, is however, profoundly anti-scientific and stifling. Research and policy are likely to suffer from this approach, though politics and funding may prosper.

What tends to be produced in response to such political pressures is not quite scientific consensus, but rather opinion negotiated behind closed doors among a small number of science managers who will then 'market' their findings to users. It cannot be denied that 'decision-making' is easier when all advisors agree on what should be done. The advisors, usually called experts, therefore tend to be carefully selected for shared beliefs and assumptions. On climate change, they tend to be mature scientists who have made their mark as research managers and possess strong, close links to governmental and non-governmental international organisations.

Expert advice is indeed welcome by politicians if this confirms existing policies – such as doing very little because not enough is as yet known. Experts may also support policies pursued entirely on political grounds, but which benefit from being given a scientific gloss: climate change is a prime example. The fields of knowledge which inform the experts, such as natural sciences, economics and accountancy, rarely specify who the policy-makers are, but tend to assume that they are neutral and have no hidden agendas of their own. A great deal of academic policy advice therefore shows no regard for the political process, and little awareness of what non-scientific interests these policy-makers may be pursuing. Parliaments, political parties and the public, are avoided in an attempt to appear 'objective'. An apolitical consensus is delivered by experts to those at the 'top' in return for having their claims to 'policy relevance', and hence their suitability for funding, accepted by postulated 'users' in government. The temptation for politicians and science managers to turn environmental policy into research policy has become irresistible, and it has the added advantage of avoiding the problems of devising an effective regulatory policy.

Research institutions driven by the search for influence and funding will behave tactically. Scientists may persuade politicians who want a quiet life that uncertainties remain too large for regulatory responses. 'More research is needed' is a welcome message if there are no other grounds for action. However, if the relevance of research is then judged by the users, and not by the producers of such knowledge, then the users have the power to lay down research objectives and decide funding priorities. Researchers will have then lost their independence and their integrity is undermined. An alliance is created between users and science managers which is likely to undermine both policy and research, unless the institutions of government are required to search for relevance from a large basket of scientific knowledge.[1]

The ambivalence of IPCC advice

The IPCC evolved between 1985 and 1987. Its leaders were selected by governments and a government could, if it wished, significantly influence membership and recommendations. The Panel in return would act as a mouthpiece for major research global programmes, especially the International Geosphere-Biosphere Programme (IGBP) of the International Council of Scientific Unions (ICSU) and the World Climate Research Programme (WCRP) of the World Meteorological Organisation (WMO). IPCC authors would collect their findings and explain their research needs, and subject those to a highly political process of negotiation, inside the competitive world of scientific institutions. This produced the much-vaunted IPCC 'scientific consensus'. Agreed among a small number of people managing IPCC, the research managers, it was nevertheless the outcome of work done by thousands of scientists attached to, or feeding to, several working groups.

The IPCC was not asked by governments to give advice. Instead, the scientists behind IPCC decided to offer this in the mid-1980s when IGBP and WCRP needed funding. They gave advice, not just on the state of scientific knowledge, but also on the likely impacts of climate change as predicted by grand mathematical experiments called general circulation models and 'realistic' response strategies. The IPCC, at the request of its UN sponsors, quite deliberately trespassed into the world by offering solutions as well as diagnoses.

Once the offer of advice was accepted by world political institutions, much to the surprise of some scientists, the scientific institutions feeding into the IPCC process were indeed required to deliver policy-relevant reports. These gave predictable costs according to timetables, fixed by scientific managers and administrators, often years in advance. The 'scientific consensus' which was created now underlies the Framework Convention on Climate Change, an agreement which will keep politicians, environmentalists, climate modellers and some economic modellers, employed for years to come. Whether effective regulatory policies can also be implemented, is another matter. Legislative proposals will certainly be designed, and for this, a 'scientific consensus' is needed as a baseline.

The IPCC advisory process has made much of statements of the kind that '25 lead authors from 11 countries based on 120 contributing authors from 15 countries and 230 reviewers from 31 countries', though it remains quite unclear what this has to do with scientific truth.[2]

Research has indicated that a small number of governments with strong research interests in atmospheric modelling and space technology (USA, Canada, Sweden, Germany, UK, Australia) used intergovernmental organisations, especially WMO and UNEP, to keep a check on the research agenda emerging from the US dominated ICSU.[3] The aim of both 'independent' and government research bodies was to obtain support for their global research programmes usually described as 'earth systems science'. Heavily based on computer modelling, the collection of vast data sets on emissions and observational measurements, it is very closely linked to technological development in 'telematics', especially in remote sensing. Human data were also required because mankind was defined as the 'villain' from the very start. In my view, the threat of warming (rather than simply climate change which really cannot be defined as there is no baseline) attracted the attention of world politics and hence funding to earth systems modelling (rather than the supporting natural sciences) because a problem discovered by science was marketed concurrently with an impressive mix of technical fixes involving a wide range of expertise and promising to save a range of energy-related technologies that were losing out in the market place.[4]

The inner circle of the IPCC (its Bureau) was in fact dominated by a small group of English-speakers, mainly North Europeans and North Americans who possessed the discretionary power to select and draft their advice to take account of a changing political context – the end of the cold war. Given the contract-based nature of much IPCC research, open dissent from within the IPCC was not likely, and certainly not observed in the UK where the link between government, or rather one small section of the Department of the Environment, and IPCC was particularly strong. All IPCC leadership figures, however, had close links with government via meteorological offices, national research laboratories and environmental ministries. These links were strongest where a domestic alliance in favour of global warming 'being real and dangerous' already existed, as in Britain and Germany. Open debate was prevented because a self-interested alliance in favour of greenhouse gas emission reduction had formed during the 1980s.[5] The next few years will show whether this alliance is strong enough to perpetuate its influence irrespective of major advances in scientific knowledge.

IPCC Policymakers' Summaries were written by scientific civil servants, who were well aware of what their sponsoring bodies wanted. They were also practised in the art of ambiguity. At a minimum they could promise that IPCC WG I would measure the uncertainties and hence allow probabilistic policies. IPCC 'Policymakers' Summaries' dealing with science in particular strove towards giving an impression of consensual knowledge, at least until 1992 by which time the issue had been brought onto political agendas and codified into an international agreement, the Framework Convention on Climate Change (FCCC). However, rather than submitting several interpretations of the available evidence, these also placed a strong emphasis on the remaining uncertainties, a list which appears to have grown longer over time.

For example, in its Updated Opinion for the Rio Conference in 1992, WG I weakened its 1990 emphasis on certainty and predictive capacity by telling governments that:

- there are many uncertainties in our predictions;

- the size of the (observed) warming is broadly consistent with predictions of climate models;

- the observed increase could be largely due to natural variability; alternatively this variability and other human factors could have offset a still larger human-induced greenhouse warming.[6]

The term 'broadly' should be noted, for it hides areas of genuine controversy in need of further scientific research. The IPCC was clearly walking a fine line between promising too much and too little. Too much certainty would undermine the need for diagnostic research, too little would risk losing relevance, political friends, and research grants.

Vested interests and responsibilities

The results of a questionnaire to IPCC participants[7], interviews and historical analysis suggest that significant and contradictory pressures were indeed exerted on the working groups by governments, environmentalists, industrial lobbies and UN bureaucracies. The stakes were far too high for this not to have happened. These interested parties emerged less from the problem, but from the many solutions that simultaneously offered themselves from many intellectual, political and technological stables. WMO wanted to do more climate research and UNEP increase its role and the flow of capital from North to South. The NGOs wanted only small-scale projects, but the World Bank and many governments wanted large ones, both promising to reduce greenhouse gas emissions and test their respective theories of development away from home. In technologically advanced countries, climate change became the 'reality' to underpin the need for ecological modernisation and sustainability to be achieved by science and technology rather than consumption and life styles. In the South, reactions were more complex and difficult, but for Northern environmentalists the response was clear – the destruction of 'nature' would have to be resisted by political pressures, global regulations and bribes, all aimed at reducing 'dangerous' emissions. The control of population sizes in poor countries for the sake of the global environment promised to be easier than reducing consumption in the North.

All the 'interested parties' were pursuing political agendas which they hoped to make more persuasive with reference to 'science', usually meaning knowledge about nature and how humans were harming 'the environment'. So global warming became an increasingly more attractive justification for an impressive policy mix advocated by a strong alliance of interested parties nationally and internationally, but many scientists began to feel uncomfortable about the uses to which their uncertain knowledge was put. They had let a genie out of a bottle and lost control over it.

In particular, global energy markets and their various regulators were attracted to the warming hypothesis. Deeply influenced by the oil shocks of the 1970s, many new players in the global energy markets (nuclear, renewables, efficiency) came to be strongly supported by a small group of mainly European states wanting higher fossil fuel prices for a variety of reasons, including the protection of the competitiveness of nuclear and renewable options in which some had invested heavily in response to rising oil prices. The owners and exporters of fossil fuels and their products, were less keen on carbon taxes. The price of crude oil, the benchmark, collapsed in 1986 and the world was soon flooded with cheap fossil energy. An alliance calling for a rapid reduction of carbon dioxide emission quickly grew strong enough to inspire the negotiations for a treaty.[8] Fuel and energy technology competition thus became a major component of global warming politics, with science at the centre as the arbiter to which all contestants appealed for 'truth'. Quotations from IPCC reports were used selectively by these interests. Some would demand a 60 per cent reduction of greenhouse gases with reference to IPCC, while others would quote the uncertainties in support of the wait and learn more approach. A genuine consensus around 'stabilisation' in developed countries formed, but without being given the force of law. Reductions would be more popular in countries importing fossil energy and relying heavily on nuclear power.

However, by becoming more 'relevant' to policy, including administrators in charge of air pollution control, energy efficiency offices or treasuries (instructed to raise income from new taxes), science did not immediately become more certain. Instead more uncertainties became apparent. Uncertainties were needed to advance a rapidly-blossoming set of research 'missions'. They also gave some hope to the potential losers that this 'concern' was a false alarm instigated either by the green lobby, or the nuclear industry. The IPCC clearly had to keep governments and NGOs with widely diverging policy goals contented enough so that all would continue seeking its advice. Here the FCCC proved a major achievement, for legally-binding emission reductions could not be defined without decades of further research and data collection. Attention had successfully been attracted to selected areas of natural science research by linking a future problem to available (if expensive) technical and institutional solutions. Solutions tied to vested interests were now chasing an elusive problem, the predictability of climate change at the regional and sub-regional level where practical policy has to be made.

Scientific institutions and science policy

The issue at stake for science is how to justify research, and to defend its uncertain findings in highly politicised contexts. Excessive expectations of what science can deliver to the policy debate and the misuse of scientific evidence by policy-makers lacking other sources of authority, threaten to direct resources towards branches of knowledge more successfully claiming 'relevance'. Other, perhaps more important research topics may be ignored and the present neglected for the sake of the future. The subsequent realisations that society has been misled will not enhance public understanding of science. Science policy therefore remains a difficult and highly political arena to which politicians and many scientific institutions pay too little attention. Only among the quantitative social sciences, so keen to copy the successful methodology of the natural sciences, did awareness of accumulating uncertainties lead to restraint about claims to policy relevance. Policy-makers may now ask why they should fund global change research programmes that merely advance discussions inside the ivory tower. But even if the institutions of science do succeed in turning environmental science into science policy, because governments find other responses too costly or politically destabilising, a price may still have to be paid.

The integrity and independence of the scientific community will be challenged and its research priorities will come under scrutiny. Its 'findings' may be discovered not to possess much policy relevance after all. Without more honesty and debate about these issues by scientists themselves, environmental policy is in danger of becoming a highly selective policy for research in the natural sciences, emission measurement and global data collection. Research that becomes too beholden to policy (and too dependent on mathematical models) may lose integrity as well as independence.

But can the managers of science be blamed for playing 'the relevance and mission game'? After all, it is their unenviable task to maintain and enhance the institutions of science and find resources for scientifically rewarding schemes such as the IGBP and WCRP. The onus must therefore fall on political systems which are incapable of funding basic research without appeal to threats, be these military or environmental. It would surely be a pity, if environmental threats were simply to replace security ones as reasons for keeping research laboratories going. A public debate about the many uses of scientific knowledge, not just scientific consensus, is overdue.

Scientific consensus has many uses

The status and influence of IPCC-funded bodies tends to depend on their research budgets and the number of papers produced by 'contractors'. If funders require consensus to be delivered, then science bureaucracies will supply well-presented reports on time. Troublesome contributions will be ignored and old knowledge will be repackaged many times. Research proposals will be made which promise too much and will include delivery dates for consensus and contractual obligations for relevance.

Yet in my experience, the knowledge contained in 'consensual' deliveries packaged for ill-defined 'policy-makers' appears to be demanded not by bureaucrats and politicians but by other academic disciplines who erect grandiose schemes of policy analysis on the 'findings' of science. Responses to uncertain knowledge are, after all, normal in politics and will be based on 'precaution' or risk avoidance, on ideology, faith, wisdom and experience, on opinion and judgement. Genuine research thrives on what is not known 'with certainty'.[9] To improve such 'irrational' behaviour, large areas of academic policy advice largely based on economic rationalism have been developed in recent years. These policy studies (on economic and technological impacts and regulations) need scientific consensus, because without a numerical base for the changes to be expected, their own predictive models relating, for example, to global carbon taxes and land use change, could not be quantified. Consensus about the 'facts' has become the foundation of a large socio-economic and technological research superstructure.

For example, claiming that governments still have problems accepting their responsibilities in the face of 'the strong consensus among experts ... that (the build up of carbon dioxide). ... is threatening to destabilise the world's climate ...', it has been proposed that individual life-time quotas for fossil fuels are to be allocated globally. These can then be traded so that the poor who cannot travel may grow richer by selling their emission rights to those who can afford them.[10] Is this policy proposal any more politically absurd than the allocation of national carbon quotas or global energy taxation?

Basing social science research on the uncertain assumptions of the natural sciences is surely a dangerous way of seeking knowledge, yet it has been the pattern for much of the IPCC related research in its other two working groups, dealing with impacts and response strategies, as well as cross-cutting issues. In my view, this research has ignored one of the institutional imperatives of science: that of organised scepticism. Instead we have appeals to the consensus of other disciplines and 'mission' statements that read like advertising copy. Future climates will be predicted according to timetables, though hedged in with many uncertainties. Future socio-economic behaviour will forecast on the basis of very dubious assumptions and value-free policy recommendation will be made on the naive assumption that science delivers 'facts' to which politics merely adds values.[11] While one cannot but want to agree with the IPCC chairman that 'policy-makers are more likely to seek scientists' advice if scientists are explicitly addressing controversies in the scientific literature and attempting to clarify their implications', the empirical evidence suggests that this has not been done.[12] Indeed, I would argue that IPCC WG I, possibly because of its close ties to government or the personal views of its leaders, has avoided scientific controversy. Many policy-makers, especially those in institutions with vested interests and responsibilities, want clear answers rather than summaries of controversies and research needs. Genuine uncertainty puts the responsibility of decision-making on policy-makers rather than science leaders.

For the political analyst the problem of political pressure on science is less than the impact of such pressures on science where it may well distort research priorities and encourage dishonesty, but with the impact of 'seduced' science on policy and the policy-making process. By demanding scientific consensus too early, policy-makers may well reduce their own freedom of action and make themselves too dependent on 'experts'. True consensus or 'closure' in scientific debates emerges over time and cannot be delivered according to timetables. Seeking agreement on what is known is not the method of science, least of all at the research frontier. Rather it is a political process in which some make concessions and others gain credibility. Agreements can be negotiated about the sharing out of resources and the nature of opinions, not about 'truth'. When opinions or judgements are needed, society has evolved methods of reaching consensus by open debate until everybody agrees, or by voting. To the best of knowledge neither were used in the writing of IPCC statements addressed to 'policy-makers'.

Researchers should not be asked to create consensus at the frontiers of research or to suggests solutions without engaging in much broader debates than were typical for IPCC. Yet the claim that advice was needed did come from the global research lobby in 1985 at the Villach Conference with reference to 'public concern'. In fact, WMO and UNEP had decided not just to study climatology, but also socio-economic impacts and policy and hence 'relevance'. I therefore agree with one of the most outspoken critics of the IPCC consensus, Richard Lindzen, Professor of Climatology at MIT. When addressing the Organisation of Petroleum Producing States in 1992, he argued:

"The notion of scientific unanimity is currently intimately tied to the WG I report of the IPCC... (on which) university representation from the US was relatively small...since funds and time needed for participation are not available to most university scientists...the report is deeply committed to reliance on large models ...(which) are largely verified by comparison with other models. Given that models are known to agree more with each

243

other than with nature (even after 'tuning'), this approach (of creating consensus) does not seem promising.[13]

From his observations in the USA, he claimed that pressure had been brought to bear 'to emphasise results supportive of the current scenario and to suppress other results'.

Why then the 'demand' for consensus from the world of policy? Politicians and administrators in charge of environmental protection are often poorly informed because they lack resources and time to acquire the knowledge needed to make informed judgements. They want to be given simple decision criteria that appeal to their even more distracted political masters, who normally have to fit any 'new' policy into an existing net of commitments and expectations. They prefer to be told that advice is 'scientific' and will not be contradicted by other experts. They want advice that causes least disturbance and brings the greatest political benefit. It is their task to keep voters content, and it is not for science to be contemptuous of this primary political task. The problem of science is how to be most useful without losing credibility and respect, without becoming as self-serving a lobby as so many others.

Global warming and acid rain are excellent examples of why governments fund environmental sciences. Not only do they improve their understanding, but they also gain seats at negotiating tables, identify opposition and endorse preferred policies. All these uses of science are legitimate and advance society's need for science, but they are far removed from research which deserves protection from being directly drawn into disputes about interests. Deliberate attempts to link research policy to the goals of society go back several decades and have not always served science well, for example, in the nuclear field and possibly now in genetics and environmental protection. In these fields scientists will tend to be given social responsibilities which may conflict with their professional ones, and this needs be understood. Scientists using their positions as leaders need to be careful when making policy statements in the name of the 'scientific community' when it is more likely to be a statement of personal opinion.[14] Climate change research finds itself in a difficult, but by no means new situation.[15]

7. Conclusion

The pressure for a scientific consensus on climate change predictions did not come from 'below', but from the science managers who had to attract funding to major global research programmes and believed that 'policy-makers' demanded such a consensus. Pressures for a consensus are indeed strong and come from many directions: bureaucracies, politicians and fellow scientists. Political institutions also thrive on uncertainty. They come to science as a source of arguments, legitimisation and authority for policy objectives which may have very little to do with science. The delivery of a consensus among self-selected scientists and branches of the knowledge, however, delivers much more than a potentially useful knowledge. It is a political resource, which would allow government to participate actively in global diplomacy. Here members of the science establishment could taste 'power' without accountability and may well feel strengthened as representatives of 'a consensus'.

The outcomes in emission reduction policy may bear very little relationship to the 'scientific' justifications, but in the meantime, global warming has significantly shaped science policy in several countries, though not necessarily in the interest of either the environment or society.

What has tended to be forgotten so far is that if societies are indeed the cause of climate change, then societies need be better understood and the political process reshaped to allow much wider participation in policy-making, as well as strong central powers to implement and enforce the general interest. Simply by holding out technical fixes, science may have gained many allies in research and business, but remains unable to suggest practical responses that are also politically acceptable.

References

1. E S Rubin, L B Lave and M G Morgan,1991/2, 'Keeping climate research relevant', *Issues in Science and Technology*, Winter , pp.47- 55. The same issue contains an article pointing out that 100 years ago the settlement of North America was believed to cause climate change.

2. From *Radiative Forcing of Climate Change,* the 1994 Report of the Scientific Assessment Working Group, Summary for Policymakers, UK Meteorological Office, Bracknell. Also cited in *The Globe*, a publication of the UK Research Council's Global Environmental Change Office, April, 1995, p.1.

3. ESRC project Y320 25 30 30 'The formulation and impact of scientific advice on climate change', was completed at Science Policy Research Unit in 1994.

4. S A Boehmer-Christiansen, 1993, 'Science Policy, the IPCC and the Climate Convention: The Codification of a Global Research Agenda', *Energy & Environment*, 4, 4, (Multi-Science, UK), pp.362-407. For a study of this British role in climate change politics, see Boehmer-Christiansen, 1995, 'Britain and the IPCC', *Environmental Politics,* vol. 4 no. 1.

5. The UK government would have closed down coal mines, switched subsidies from coal-fired to nuclear power stations and supported the privatised utilities to dash to gas irrespective of global warming. The German government's support for nuclear power, higher energy prices and the development of 'renewables' similarly benefited from the global warming threat, but was not caused by it. Both countries experienced CO_2 reductions in recent years without regulation and could therefore appear as 'green' leaders in Berlin 1995 when the parties to the Climate Convention met for the first time.

6. WMO/UNEP, *1992 IPCC Supplement*, February 1992. p.5.

7. S A Boehmer-Christiansen and J F Skea, *The operation and impact of the IPCC: Results of a survey of participants and users*, Centre for Science, Technology, Energy and Environment Policy, Discussion Paper no. 16, SPRU,

Brighton, June 1994. Governments, UN agencies, NGOs and industrial lobbies were identified as exerting pressure, with UN agencies as most important for science. 10% of all replies supported vigorous remedial action, 73% saw any type of three types of action (no-regret, high cost, research only) justified by precaution rather than compelling scientific evidence. 6% observed very little impact on the growth of knowledge in their field. There was wide agreement that the concern about climate change had advanced knowledge, and that this advance had been greatest for climate prediction, climatology and oceanography, but least for socio-economic causes and impacts of response strategies. Most respondents expected uncertainties to be significantly reduced in 10-15 years, though much less so for socio-economic issues.

8. Boehmer-Christiansen,1994, 'Global climate protection policy: the limits of scientific advice' (2 parts), *Global Environmental Change*, vol. 4, nos. 2 and 3.

9. Experts Workshop on *Critical issues in the science of global climate change*, 1994, IPIECA, Woods Hole, October. This workshop was sponsored by the petroleum industry. It concluded that 'there are legitimate differences of opinion as to how those uncertainties should be incorporated into policy decisions, but an understanding of the reasons for and effects of the key uncertainties is critical'.

10. J. Hanna (New Economics Foundation, London), Towards a single carbon currency. *New Scientist*, 29 April 1995, p. 50-51.

11. Bert Bolin, in *Ambio Special Issue,* Integrating Earth Systems, vol. 23, no 1, February 1994.

12. Bert Bolin, Next step for climate-change analysis, *Nature*, vol. 368, 10 March 1994.

13. R S Lindzen, 1992, 'The Origin and Nature of Alleged Scientific Consensus', in *Energy & Environment Special Issue*, Proceedings of the OPEC Seminar on the Environment, Vienna, April 13-15, pp.126. IPCC WG I failed to attract Lindzen who has repeatedly attacked its consensus claims.

14. IPCC leaders have made many statements of energy policy which are not 'scientific', but express long time commitments. Bert Bolin (IPCC chairman), for example, has published on

energy policy since 1971; the German climatologists H Flohn collaborated closely with the energy modeller and 'father' of the breeder reactor W Hafele; see *Life on a Warmer Earth,* IIASA, Austria 1981. Sir John Houghton (WG 1 chairman) has addressed the World Energy Council on energy policy, see *Journal,* organ of WEC, July 1993, and is deeply involved in British domestic politics as environmental advisor.

15. N Kaplan, Sociology of science, 1964, in *Handbook of Modern Sociology*, McNally, Chicago, pp.852-881.

Sonja Boehmer-Christiansen
Dr Boehmer-Christiansen trained as a physical geographer, who later turned to international relations and politics, taking a masters degree and doctorate in this area at the University of Sussex. Her research is now in policy studies relating to energy and environment. She has published widely on environmental policy and politics, especially acid rain and climate change, with special emphasis on Anglo-German comparisons. The links between environmental research, environmental policy and environmental technology are of special interest to Dr Boehmer-Christiansen as is the rise of 'eco-alarmism' in the Western world since the beginning of the decline of the US 'empire'. Is there a causal link? Is science misused to defend the 'West', no longer by weapons, but with reference to ecological threats? Dr Boehmer-Christiansen was until recently a Senior Research Fellow at the Science Policy Research Unit, University of Sussex; she is now teaching at the School of Geography and Earth Resources at the University of Hull.

Learning From The Past

Patricia Fara,
Darwin College
Cambridge University
UK

Summary

Climatologists rely on past observations in order to develop
theories on which they can base predictions about future climate
events. The pitfalls of this approach are highlighted by an in-depth
analysis of responses to an earlier inexplicable phenomenon: the
aurora polaris, or northern lights. An explanation as to why
current climate predictions are invariably alarmist is suggested,
tentatively linking this global phenomenon to cycles of research
funding.

Introduction

Three hundred years ago, people – particularly Englishmen –
regarded themselves as favoured inhabitants of God's terraqueous
globe, divinely selected to rule over His creation and use it for
their advantage. They envisaged a stable world, unthreatened by
long-term changes such as global warming, but disrupted on
occasion by unexpected disturbances like comets, earthquakes and
eclipses. Many astrologers and religious prophets pronounced that
visitations were direct messages from God, His warnings to the
sinful of impending millennial catastrophe. In contrast,
Enlightenment natural philosophers established their authority by
predicting the occurrence of these unusual events, thus
reinterpreting them as natural phenomena rather than as
supernatural manifestations. (Park and Daston, 1981; Daston,
1994; Schaffer, 1983, 1987).

To construct laws of nature governing the incidence of rare
events, natural philosophers studied records of similar episodes; in
other words, they learnt from the past in order to predict the future.
Such argument by induction lies at the heart of many of the
forecasting techniques which scientists use today. Scientists can

249

also learn from the past through examining earlier controversies, experiments and belief systems. This type of historical research can illuminate how science has come to acquire such a powerful prestige, and give us a deeper understanding of the processes through which scientific knowledge is generated. Enlightenment faith in the explanatory power of reason has fashioned modern confidence in the scientific approach towards the natural world, but research is not necessarily straightforward progress. Scientists are swayed by financial, political, emotional and religious influences, with the result that yesterday's certainties may be overturned tomorrow.

Although the arguments about global warming are mostly couched in scientific terms, the debate has not always been conducted in the dispassionate style we associate with scientific rationality. This paper reviews the history of investigations into the aurora polaris in order to examine some of the conceptual and procedural difficulties entailed in forecasting natural events.

When natural philosophers of the eighteenth century sought to explain auroral activity, they confronted problems which still challenge modern climatologists, who are studying nature's past as a way of predicting the world's future. Like historians, scientists who analyse constantly changing phenomena (such as the weather, geomagnetic patterns and solar activity) rely on interpreting records which have been produced in the past from within different theoretical frameworks and to serve different ends. Through examining research into the aurora, for which evidential unreliability compounds inductive uncertainty, this paper explores some of the cultural constraints which shape scientific prediction. As Jean Baudrillard points out in his timely study of attitudes towards the coming millennium, "Meteorology is chaotic; it is not a figure of destiny." (Baudrillard, 1994: 113).

The Aurora Polaris

March 6, 1716, was a special day in England. Political chroniclers recorded that military commanders had returned to London after quelling the Jacobite uprising, but they devoted far more attention to the evening's events. All over the country, people stayed up most of the night to watch a display of natural fireworks, an aurora borealis that no-one alive had ever seen over England. At about 7 o'clock, observers agreed, a great light appeared in the sky. Then "it form'd several Columns or Pillars like pure Flame, and afterwards darted violent Flashes towards the South West, which flew with the swiftness of Lightning. At the same time there appear'd several Colours like Rainbows, with surprizing

Corruscations. Sometimes they appear'd sharp, and sometimes wavy, and in this manner continu'd till about Three in the Morning." (Pointer, 1716: 903. See also *Historical Register* (1716) 1: 117; Salmon, 1723: 358).

Edmond Halley, already famous for his cometary predictions, abandoned his dinner party, while other gentlemen leapt out of bed in their nightclothes to join the awestruck crowds. Frightened servants thronged the streets, convinced that the day of judgement had arrived (Halley, 1716: 406-16; Whiston, 1716: 26-53). Still horrified by the government's insistence on publicly executing two Jacobite leaders a few days earlier, people linked recent political disturbances with the celestial spectacles. They envisaged the aurora as armies fighting in the sky, picturing its flashing lights as sparks from weapons and its intense red light as showers of blood (Sarton, 1947; *Nature* (1870) 3: 105, 174-5). Newspapers reported "Giants with Flaming Swords, Fiery Comets, Dragcons, and the like dreadful Figures" (*Weekly Journal*, 10 March 1716). Religious prophets, wrote an evangelical clergyman, "looked upon it as a *bloody flag*, hung out by divine resentment, over a guilty world" (Hervey, 1774: ii, 54).

These descriptions illustrate how people invest natural features with symbolic meanings.[1] Historians often gloss such accounts of heavenly battles as being equivalent to our flying saucers, implicitly colluding with eighteenth-century polemicists who dismissed such language as superstition (Thomas, 1971). But the widespread and continued use of this terminology indicates how its powerful metaphorical significance endured well beyond the end of the seventeenth century. Over a hundred years later, Charlotte Brontë described how one of her heroines "paused to watch that mustering of an army with banners – that quivering of serried lances..." (Brontë, 1979: 381).

Such imagery framed discussions of the aurora, whose repeated appearances fascinated observers for much of the century. The initial dramatic display of 6 March 1716 dominated Royal Society meetings for several weeks, and featured for many years in astrological almanacs (Royal Society Journal Book (copy) 11 (1716): 108-21; Wing, 1739). Like other weather diarists, Gilbert White carefully noted aurorae in his journal, and the topic frequently occurred in scholarly as well as popular publications

---

[1] Scientists now regard the northern and southern lights as linked aspects of a single global phenomenon, the aurora polaris. Because the northern hemisphere is far more densely populated, it is the aurora borealis which carries the more potent imagery (Fara, 1996b).

(Tyldesley, 1976; Briggs, 1967; *Edinburgh Review* 164 (1886): 416-47).

Proponents of natural philosophy sought to convert these northern lights from predictions of disaster into predictable events governed by natural laws. Thus the journalist Richard Steele refuted "the Ridiculous Construction that the Disaffected put on the late Lightning" with his own "Natural" explanation based on "plain Reason, and common Observation" (Blanchard, 1959: 261). In books and poems, in London lectures and country sermons, astronomers and clergymen argued that an omnipotent God had no need for miracles: such uncommon events did not presage disaster, but formed part of His divine plan (Whiston, 1716: 54-78; Pointer, 1738: 198-9; Thomson, 1795: 168-9; Burns, 1981).

In his long account of the spectacular 1716 aurora, Halley mocked the common descriptions relying on battle imagery. He introduced a geometrical vocabulary of radii, cones and areas, and specified the times, angular measurements and geographical directions of the various auroral features. As one of England's most eminent rationalising philosophers, Halley sought to demonstrate that the aurora should not be perceived as a celestial message from God: it was a terrestrial phenomenon which could – in principle – be explained by natural causes and described with mathematical precision (Halley, 1716).

The Scientific Approach

In France, natural philosophers were equally concerned to demonstrate their intellectual mastery over nature. Cloud in Paris had obscured the 1716 aurora which so amazed English observers, but there were many other displays during the century. When crowds panicked during an aurora of 1726, the French government ordered Jean-Jacques Dortous de Mairan, a physician at the Académie Royale, to find a reassuring explanation. He investigated the aurora for at least thirty years, producing the century's most widely known book on the subject, as well as numerous smaller reports (Dortous de Mairan, 1754; Legrand, 1985). He may have been stimulated to extend his analyses by the London earthquakes of 1750, which forcibly reminded people of the unpredictability of natural phenomena. Following two earthquakes, exactly one month apart, millenarianist visionaries prophesied a third earthquake a month later, as God's punishment for a sinful world. A print called *The Military Prophet or a Flight from Providence* satirised the thousands of people who allegedly rushed out of London to escape the predicted third earthquake, which never materialised (Rousseau, 1968). Concerned to displace the authority of such alarmist forecasters, natural philosophers tried to rationalise events like earthquakes and aurorae.

To derive natural laws governing the aurora's incidence – and hence predict future occurrences – natural philosophers depended on collective endeavour. Throughout Europe and North America, diligent sky watchers sent in reports to magazines and learned societies, while natural philosophers exchanged reports with one another through private correspondence networks and international publications. Many of them kept diaries to substantiate their speculations linking the aurora's incidence to other natural phenomena such as rain, earthquakes and tides. Some of them proposed explanatory theories linking the phenomenon with terrestrial magnetism, atmospheric electricity or the Sun's behaviour.

As well as relying on contemporary witnesses, natural philosophers turned to observations recorded in the past. To convert the aurora into a predictable phenomenon, they compiled historical data and searched for regular patterns in its incidence. Halley collected accounts of English aurorae during the previous couple of hundred years, and claimed that there had been a quiescent period during the seventeenth century, followed by a revival of activity in his own time. Dortous de Mairan extended Halley's initiative, collating observations from Aristotle onwards to support two contentions: that after its relative absence during the seventeenth century, the frequency of the aurora had suddenly increased to an essentially constant level; and that similar resumptions of auroral activity after a long period of inactivity had occurred several times in the past.

Dortous de Mairan exemplifies how eighteenth-century investigators developed new ways of using quantitative historical evidence for reconstructing the earth's history – for example, its climate, or its magnetic characteristics. Like his colleagues, he sought public recognition by imposing quantitative order on terrestrial phenomena (Feldman, 1993; Fara, 1996a). By scouring diverse sources, he eventually compiled a set of 1441 aurorae. He tabulated them by month and by year to demonstrate his conviction that auroral activity is determined by the influence of a solar atmosphere extending to the earth. He ended his book with a persuasive query: "And isn't it virtually impossible", he asked, "that such agreement between so many different contributors and observations, should be the effect of chance?"[2] (Dortous de

---

[2] "n'est-il pas moralement impossible qu'un tel accord, entre tant de parties & d'obversations différentes, soit l'effet du hasard?"

Mairan, 1754: 570). Although he posed this question with such apparent self-confidence, Dortous de Mairan recognised two major types of problem which still confront modern scientists building mathematical models of the past: the reliability of the data; and the reliability of the analysis. Several factors limited the completeness of the observations that he could collect. The further back in time he went, the less likely records were to have survived, and the more difficult it became to assign a definite date.

Since there had been no systematic programme of study, many aurorae would have passed unrecorded; indeed, many of them would, like the 1716 aurora over Paris, have been obscured by cloud. In uninhabited regions of the world, no sightings would have been made at all. He was also concerned about the risks of over-reporting: there would be a flurry of observations following a particularly spectacular aurora as people's attention focused on the sky; and observers might mistakenly record an aurora when they had seen a different phenomenon, such as a cometary tail or zodiacal light.

Personal judgement inevitably came into play, as Dortous de Mairan adopted various criteria for tidying up his observations. He excluded all those which were not accurately dated – even though their occurrence was well-corroborated – and made assumptions to compensate for the ones which he presumed were missing. Subjective assessment played a particularly apparent role because, as he complained, earlier writers were less interested in the aurora itself, than in what it presaged. This meant that he had to interpret their records to infer that an aurora had occurred. For instance, while modern analysts might agree that he was justified in accepting accounts using descriptive terms like "Burning spears", they might be less convinced by his argument that Ulysses' report of a bright light on Mount Olympus was actually an aurora. In addition to these shortcomings of his data, Dortous de Mairan had no statistical tests available for validating his work. He relied on verbal rhetoric to convince his readers, arguing that the majority of the observations confirmed his theory, and conveniently ignoring those which contradicted it (Dortous de Mairan, 1754: 166-213, 466-570; Dortous de Mairan, 1761).

The Maunder Minimum

Since then, scientists have developed more rigorous methods for establishing long-term patterns describing the occurrence of the aurora borealis. They have sought to link its incidence with variations in other natural phenomena, particularly sunspots. At the end of the nineteenth century, E. Walter Maunder, head of the

Greenwich Observatory, claimed that there had been a pronounced decrease in sunspot activity from 1643 to 1715 (Maunder, 1894). In response, the Victorian astronomer Agnes Clerke suggested inspecting auroral records, since this period might also be characterised by a profound magnetic calm (Clerke, 1894). Their ideas were revived in 1976 by an American scientist John Eddy, who used existing data catalogues to argue that the Maunder minimum corresponded to the marked absence of reported aurorae asserted by Halley and Dortous de Mairan. He assessed problems of data reliability similar to those which had challenged natural philosophers over two hundred years earlier, including instrument limitations, inconstancy of surveillance and overcast skies. Nevertheless, he concluded that the Maunder minimum was "a real feature" because of the absence of contradicting evidence: "In questions of history where only a dim and limited record remains and where we are blocked from making crucial observational tests, the search for possible contradiction seems to me a promising path to truth" (Eddy, 1976: 1199). Absence of evidence became evidence of absence, and the Maunder minimum became a scientific fact.

Eddy was intrigued by the irony that the Maunder minimum of solar activity coincided with the reign of Louis XIV, le roi soleil. He presented the seventeenth century as an anomalous period in the sun's behaviour, when sunspots and aurorae were infrequent, and when the so-called "little ice age" was at its coldest. But portraying the seventeenth century as an anomaly contradicts fundamental scientific assumptions about the uniformity of nature. One way of resolving this tension between novelty and constancy is to find long term fluctuations extending backwards into time – and hence, by inference, forwards into the future. Scientists have collected an immense variety of data, and used modern statistical techniques, to construct mathematical models of how physical phenomena such as aurorae and sunspots vary over time. Although their methods are, of course, far more sophisticated than those of Dortous de Mairan, these analyses still leave unanswered basic questions about the certainty of models which rely on ambiguous and unrepeatable historical data. How can we be sure that there was a Maunder minimum in the seventeenth century? And if there was one, what does that signify?

The Quality of Historic Evidence

The problems associated with making assertions about what happened in the past are familiar to all historians. For a topic like the aurora, historians of science face a double uncertainty. How much confidence can we place in our knowledge of the episodes we describe? And how do the scientists whom we are discussing establish historical events as scientific facts? Commentators from Giambattista Vico to C P Snow have contrasted the sciences and the humanities, a traditional "two cultures" divide which is increasingly being challenged (Berlin, 1979; Levine, 1987; Marx, 1994). Yet scientists such as astronomers, palaeontologists or terrestrial physicists rely on evidence from the past. Like historians, they are not dealing with experimental observations which can be replicated in a laboratory, but with problematic records of vanished events (Lewontin, 1994; Ginzburg, 1990; Wilson, 1993). Some approaches to constructing predictive laws rely on studying events which are recorded within the same types of sources as those accessed by historians, and so must be apprehended inferentially rather than empirically.

Projects to retrieve geophysical information have recruited not only scientists concerned to construct the largest possible data sets, but also historians proposing various methodologies for making their studies scientific. For example, in 1948, Derek Schove, a mathematical physicist with some historical training, established the Spectrum of Time Project, through which he aimed to construct an international calendar cross-referencing cultural events with records of natural phenomena. In journals and conferences, he solicited information from recondite sources, providing "Rules of the Game" for enthusiastic participants in the chase for obscure accounts, an encouragement perpetuated in the specialised scientific press (summarised in Schove, 1983: 106-9; Siscoe, 1980). Emmanuel Le Roy Ladurie urged his fellow economic and climate historians to place themselves "shoulder to shoulder in interdisciplinary collaboration with the natural scientists" (Le Roy Ladurie, 1979: 295). From the early 1970s, interdisciplinary conferences and publications proliferated, as science specialists collaborated with experts from non-scientific disciplines – such as historians, economists and linguists – in the pursuit of terrestrial history (for example, Rotberg and Rabb, 1981; Schröder, 1985; Pecker and Runcorn, 1990).

Scientists studying the aurora have sought to correlate its incidence with other irregular phenomena, notably the climate and sunspots. Until about fifty years ago, although numerous observation programmes studied short-term variations in the weather, meteorologists assumed that the earth's overall climate had remained constant since Roman times. Subsequent analyses indicated longer patterns of warming and cooling, and while world populations burgeoned against a backdrop of droughts and famines during the 1970s, the United States urged the necessity of international projects. As concern with the environment escalated, funding organisations poured money into attempts to establish long-term meteorological cycles (Lamb, 1982; Geyer, 1992: unpaginated introduction). In order to reconstruct the earth's climate, scientists draw on physical proxy data – for example, tree rings, ice cores and lake deposits. They also rely on cultural evidence, including economic data such as wheat prices and wine yields, as well as historical scientific records of weather-related natural phenomena like rainfall and temperature (Burroughs, 1992; Landsberg, 1981; Bradley and Jones, 1992: 17-268).

Examining how scientists have retrieved and used auroral records exemplifies some of the difficulties involved in this type of investigation. Researchers have scoured a great variety of sources, including poems, the Bible, Norse sagas, mediaeval annals, personal diaries and explorers' accounts. Going back to 5000 BC, they have compiled impressive catalogues of aurorae all over Europe, as well as in China and Japan (Siscoe, 1980). Yet, as Dortous de Mairan was aware, despite such intense collaborative effort, it is impossible to amass a comprehensive collection. Furthermore, using the limited information that can be retrieved presents problems of reliability. The extensive catalogue published by Hermann Fritz in 1873 remains authoritative, yet researchers point to various types of error, some of them not normally associated with scientific endeavours.[3]

Difficulties arise because earlier observers were operating within a different conceptual framework. Older vocabulary makes it difficult for modern researchers to agree on how to interpret historical accounts. John Dryden asserted that God foretold the victory at Sedgemoor in 1685 by "fireworks" and a "streaming blaze" in the sky. Should we credit Halley's insistence that there were no English aurorae during the seventeenth century, or should we follow the assurance of a literary historian that Dryden was indeed describing an aurora (Noyes, 1950: 234; *Notes and Queries* 137 (1937): 326-8)? Schove accused Halley of ignoring seventeenth-century accounts of armies in the sky because they had been dismissed at the time as political propaganda. But one of Schove's contemporaries sided with Halley, judging that the reports referred to a massive thunderstorm (Schove, 1951, 1953;

---

3 As just one example, Fritz resurrected spurious aurorae from Scandinavian mythological sagas, because he relied on creative German translations of nineteenth-century Swedish epics, which were themselves imaginative reconstructions of traditional folklore (Brekke and Egeland, 1983: 10-23; Stothers, 1979; Schröder, 1979).

Thomas, 1971: 103-12). Resolving such issues is not just a nicety of scholarly debate, since solar and terrestrial physicists draw on auroral records for constructing mathematical models of the universe's behaviour.

In addition to these problems of retrieving and interpreting auroral data, critics are concerned about how this information is analysed. They argue that our instinctive faith in nature's periodicity persuades us to make the step from plausibility to proof. After 1843, when the German astronomer Heinrich Schwabe established an 11-year cycle for sunspots, numerous scientists correlated periodic cycles in solar activity with the weather. In 1900, the famous solar scientist Norman Lockyer confidently declared that "The riddle of the probable times of occurrence of Indian Famines has now been read, and they can be for the future accurately predicted" (Eddy, 1981: 150). These simple relationships were subsequently demolished, and shown to be accidental coincidences in limited data sets, but climatologists continue to use statistical methods for relating solar activity to terrestrial weather.

Some experts claim that aurorae merit further historical study because they are the best indicator of solar activity, and because records stretch back far into the past (Eddy, 1981; Link, 1964; Siscoe, 1980). But other scientists disagree, asserting that the ambiguities of the data are compounded by analytical errors (Stothers, 1979; Schröder, 1979; Stephenson, 1990). In particular, they stress that prior assumptions of solar regularity can prejudice the interpretation of ambiguous data. Schove quite seriously discussed an eleven-year sunspot cycle varying in length between eight and sixteen years (Schove, 1955, 1962). His ally František Link, a Czech astronomer, turned to differential calculus, professing that this tactic enabled him to eliminate the "social factor" polluting recorded observations, and successfully constrain the incidence of the aurora within superimposed cycles of 11, 80, and 400 years (Link, 1967).

Climate Predictions and Science Funding

Criticisms of this type of auroral research exemplify those which have more generally been levelled at scientists trying to correlate solar activity with the weather. One tier of commentary focuses on methodology. Sceptics point to the dangers of applying sophisticated mathematical analyses to unreliable data, and accuse scientists of erroneously using small samples or applying inappropriate statistical techniques (Pittock, 1978; Burroughs, 1992: 63-92). Yet more fundamentally, some analysts challenge the very existence of meaningful cycles in solar activity. Eddy has campaigned for more attention to be paid to apparent anomalies like the Maunder minimum, and suggested that large climatic shifts on earth may be due to only minor fluctuations in the sun's radiation (Eddy, 1976, 1981: 166-7). Chaos theorists assert that the atmospheric changes affecting terrestrial phenomena may be inherently unpredictable. Using computer simulations, they have demonstrated that windows of order can appear in chaotic systems, misleadingly giving the appearance of regularity. Exponents claim that meteorologists have been enthusiastically examining "little more than the random noise of an immensely complicated physical system – full of sound and fury, signifying nothing" (Burroughs, 1992: 94-170, quotation 170).

Scientists have also accused their colleagues of being less concerned with statistical validity than in promoting conclusions which seem socially relevant, thus increasing their chance of attracting further research money. In other words, they argue that financial interests are moulding the shape of science. A NASA scientist, Roy Spencer, recently articulated this concern: "It's easier to get funding if you can show some evidence for impending climate disasters. In the late 1970s it was the coming ice age and now it's the coming global warming...science benefits from scary scenarios" (Jones, 1990: 24; Pittock, 1978: 416-7). Eddy and Link both related the low frequency of aurorae in the seventeenth century to the Little Ice Age, and to the possibility that we might be moving into another period of glaciation (Eddy, 1976; Link, 1964; Grove, 1988). Nowadays studies of the sun – including the aurora borealis – are implicated in theories of global warming. Researchers generating dramatic predictions justify their budgets by pointing to the economic necessity of planning for severe disruptions in the world's climate. But dissidents from the alleged consensus on global warming claim that their opinions are being silenced in the cause of presenting scientific unanimity. They maintain that their conclusions are deliberately misinterpreted by protagonists with vested political and financial interests in propagating warnings of disastrous change (Geyer, 1992: 297-315; Lindzen, 1992; Bate and Morris, 1994; Michaels, 1992; Balling, 1992).

Stephen Schneider, a leading US greenhouse theorist, has defended promotional campaigns with alarming candour: "To capture the public's imagination...we have to...make simplified dramatic statements, and little mention of any doubts one might have...Each of us has to decide the right balance between being effective and being honest." (Bate and Morris, 1994: · 49).

THE GLOBAL WARMING DEBATE

Climatology has recently become a volatile political commodity articulated in economic metaphors of resources and expenditure. As we approach the millennium, few people listen to local religious prophets preaching divine retribution on sinful non-believers. Instead, they have become global citizens who heed scientists forecasting ecological catastrophe wrought by mercenary environmental polluters. Grant-awarding bodies and newspaper readers seem equally fascinated by scientific predictions of environmental disaster. Like our predecessors who interpreted battles in the sky as religious omens, or fled from the providential dangers of the predicted third London earthquake, we still relish prophecies of doom (Baudrillard, 1994; Ross, 1991).

Acknowledgements

I should particularly like to thank Roger Bate, Dorinda Outram, Jim Secord and Liba Taub for their helpful suggestions.

BIBLIOGRAPHY

Balling, Robert C. (1992). The heated debate: greenhouse predictions versus climate reality. *San Francisco: Pacific Research Institute for Public Policy.*

Bate, Roger and Julian Morris, (1994). Global warming: apocalypse or hot air? *London: IEA Environment Unit.*

Baudrillard, Jean. 1994. The illusion of the end. *Cambridge: Polity Press.*

Berlin, Isaiah. (1979). The divorce between the sciences and the humanities. In Against the current: essays in the history of ideas, *Ed H Hardy, pp. 80-110. Oxford: Clarendon Press.*

Blanchard, Rae. 1959. Richard Steele's Periodical Journalism 1714-16. *Oxford: Clarendon Press.*

Bradley, Raymond S. and Philip D. Jones (eds.). 1992. Climate since A. D. 1500, *pp. 17-268. London and New York: Routledge.*

Brekke, Asgar and Alv Egeland. 1983. The northern light: from mythology to space research. *Berlin: Springer-Verlag.*

Briggs, J. Morton. 1967. "Aurora and Enlightenment: eighteenth-century explanations of the aurora borealis." Isis, *58: 491-503.*

Brontë, Charlotte. 1979. Villette. *London: Penguin.*

Burns, R. M. (1981). The great debate on miracles: from Joseph Glanvill to David Hume. London: Associated Universities Press.

Burroughs, William J. 1992. Weather cycles: real or imaginary. *Cambridge: Cambridge University Press.*

Clerke, Agnes. 1894. A prolonged sunspot minimum. Knowledge, *17, 206-7.*

Daston, Lorraine. 1994. 'Marvelous Facts and Miraculous Evidence in Early Modern Europe', in James Chandler, Arnold I. Davidson and Harry Harootunian (eds.), Questions of Evidence: Proof, Practice, and Persuasion across the Disciplines, *pp. 243-74. Chicago and London: Chicago University Press.*

Dortous de Mairan, Jean-Jacques. 1754. Traité physique et historique de l'aurore boréale. Paris: L'Imprimerie Royale.

Dortous de Mairan, Jean-Jacques. 1761. Conjectures sur l'origine de la fable d'Olympe, en explication & confirmation de ce qui en a été dit dans l'un des éclaircissemens ajoûtés au Traité physique & historique de l'aurore boréale. *Paris.*

Eddy, John A. 1976. "The Maunder minimum", Science 192, 1189-1202.

Eddy, John A. 1981. "Climate and the role of the sun", in Robert I. Rotberg and Theodore K. Rabb (eds.), Climate and history: Studies in interdisciplinary history, *pp. 145-67. Princeton: Princeton University Press.*

Fara, Patricia. 1996a. Sympathetic Attractions: Magnetic Practices, Beliefs, and Symbolism in Eighteenth-Century England. *Princeton: Princeton University Press.*

Fara, Patricia. 1996b. "Who owns the aurora borealis?". History Workshop Journal, *in press.*

Feldman, Theodore S. (1993). The ancient climate in the eighteenth and early nineteenth century. In Science and nature, *ed. Michael Shortland, pp. 23-40. Oxford: British Society for the History of Science.*

Geyer, Richard A. (ed.). (1992). A global warming forum: scientific, economic and legal overview. *Boca Raton: CRC Press.*

Ginzburg, Carlo. (1990). Clues: roots of an evidential paradigm. In Myths, emblems, clues, *pp. 96-125. London: Hutchinson Radius.*

Grove, Jean M. 1988. The Little Ice Age. *London and New York: Methuen.*

Halley, Edmond. 1716. "An account of the late surprizing appearance of the lights seen in the air, on the sixth of March last; with an attempt to explain the principal phænomena thereof", Philosophical Transactions, *29, 406-28.*

Hervey, James. 1774. Meditations and contemplations, *2 vols. Paisley.*

Jones, Derek. (1990). The greenhouse conspiracy: An edited transcript. London: Channel 4 Television.

Lamb, Hubert H. (1982). Climate, history and the modern world. *London and New York: Methuen.*

Landsberg, Helmut E. 1981. "Past climates from unexploited written sources," in Robert I. Rotberg and Theodore K. Rabb (eds.), Climate and history: Studies in interdisciplinary history, *pp. 51-62. Princeton: Princeton University Press.*

Le Roy Ladurie, Emmanuel. (1979). The territory of the historian. *Sussex: Harvester Press. (transl. B and S Reynolds).*

Legrand, Jean-Pierre. 1985. "J.-J. Dortous de Mairan et l'origine des aurores", La vie des sciences, *2, 487-509.*

Levine, George. (1987). One culture: science and literature. In Science and literature, *ed. George Levine, pp. 3-32. Wisconsin: University of Wisconsin Press.*

Lewontin, Richard C. 1994. "Facts and the factitious in natural sciences", in James Chandler, Arnold I. Davidson and Harry Harootnian (eds.), Questions of evidence: Proof, practice, and persuasion across the disciplines, *pp. 478-91. Chicago and London: Chicago University Press.*

Lindzen, Richard S. (1992). Global warming: the origin and nature of alleged scientific consensus. Paper presented at the Vienna OPEC Seminar on the Environment, 13-15 April 1992.

Link, František. (1964). Manifestations de l'activité solaire dans le passé historique. Planetary and Space Science, *12, 333-48.*

Link, František. 1967. "On the history of the aurora borealis", *in A Beer (ed.),* Vistas in astronomy: volume 9, *pp. 297-306. Oxford: Pergamon Press.*

Marx, Leo. 1994. "The environment and the "two cultures" divide", in James R Fleming and Henry A Gemery (eds.), Science, technology and the environment: multidisciplinary perspectives, *pp. 3-21. Akron, Ohio: University of Akron Press.*

Maunder, E. Walter. (1894). A prolonged sunspot minimum. Knowledge, *17, 173-6.*

Michaels, Patrick J. (1992). Sound and fury: the science and politics of global warming. *Washington: CATO Institute.*

Noyes, George R. (1950). The poetical works of Dryden. *Boston: Houghton Mifflin.*

Park, Katharine and Lorraine Daston. 1981. "Unnatural conceptions: The study of monsters in sixteenth- and seventeenth-century France and England", Past and present 92, *20-54.*

Pecker, J. C. and S. Runcorn (eds.). 1990. The earth's climate and variability of the sun over recent millennia: geophysical, astronomical and archaeological aspects. *London: Royal Society.*

Pittock, A. Barrie. (1978). A critical look at long-term sun-weather relationships. Reviews of Geophysics and Space Physics, *16, 400-20.*

Pointer, John. (1716). A chronological history of Great Britain: or, an impartial abstract of the most remarkable transactions, and the most considerable occurrences, both civil and military, domestick and foreign, and particularly of all promotions, during the first year of the reign of His Majesty King George. *London: for Bernard Lintott.*

Pointer, John. 1738. A rational account of the weather. *London: for Aaron Ward.*

Ross, Andrew. (1991). Strange weather: Culture, science, and technology in the age of limits. *London and New York: Verso.*

Rotberg, Robert I. and Theodore K. Rabb *(eds.). 1981.* Climate and history: Studies in interdisciplinary history. *Princeton: Princeton University Press.*

Rousseau, George S. (1968). The London earthquakes of 1750. Cahiers d'Histoire Mondiale, *11, 436-51.*

Salmon, William. (1723). The chronological historian: containing a regular account of all material transactions and occurrences, ecclesiastical, civil, and military, relating to the *English* affairs, from the invasion of the *Romans,* to the present time. *London: for W Mears.*

Sarton, George. (1947). Was Peiresc the first (in 1608) to offer a rational explanation of the rains of blood? Isis, *38, 96-7.*

Schaffer, Simon. (1983). Natural philosophy and public spectacle in the eighteenth century. History of Science, *21, 1-43.*

Schaffer, Simon. (1987). Newton's comets and the transformation of astrology. In Astrology science and society, *ed. Patrick Curry, pp. 219-43. Woodbridge: The Boydell Press.*

Schove, Derek J. (1951). English aurorae of AD 1660/61. Journal of the British Astronomical Association, *62, 38-41.*

Schove, Derek J. (1953). London aurorae of AD 1661. Journal of the British Astronomical Association, *63, 266-70.*

Schove, Derek J. (1955). The sunspot cycle, 649 B. C. to A. D. 2000. Journal of Geophysical Research, *60, 127-46.*

Schove, Derek J. (1962). Auroral numbers since 500 BC. Journal of the British Astronomical Association, *72, 30-5.*

Schove, Derek J. (1983). Sunspot cycles. *Stroudsberg, PA: Hutchinson Ross Publishing Co.*

Schröder, Wilfried. (1979). Auroral frequency in the 17th and 18th centuries and the Maunder minimum. Journal of Atmospheric and Terrestrial Physics, *41, 445-6.*

Schröder, Wilfried (ed.). 1985. Historical events and people in geosciences. *Frankfurt-am-Main: Peter Lang.*

Short, Thomas. (1750). New observations, natural, moral, civil, political and medical, on city, town, and country bills of mortality. *London: for T Longman and A Millar.*

Siscoe, G. L. (1980). Evidence in the auroral record for secular solar variability. Reviews of Geophysics and Space Physics, *18, 647-58.*

Stephenson, F. R. 1990. "Historical evidence concerning the sun: Interpretation of sunspot records during the telescopic and pretelescopic eras", Philosophical transactions *A330 (1990), 499-512.*

Stothers, Richard. (1979). Ancient aurorae. Isis, *70, 85-95.*

Thomas, Keith. (1971). Religion and the decline of magic. *Harmondsworth: Penguin.*

Thomson, James. (1795). The seasons. London: for T Chapman.

Tyldesley, J. B. (1976). Gilbert White and the aurora. Journal of the British Astronomical Association, *86, 214-8.*

Whiston, William. (1716). An account of a surprizing meteor, seen in the air, March the 6th, 1715/16, at night. *London: for J Senex.*

Wilson, Adrian. 1993. "Foundations of an integrated historiography", in Adrian Wilson (ed.), Rethinking social history: English society 1570-1920 and its interpretation, *pp. 293-335. Manchester and New York: Manchester University Press.*

Wing, V. (1739). An almanack for the year of our lord God 1738. *London.*

THE GLOBAL WARMING DEBATE

Patricia Fara

Patricia Fara studied philosophy at Oxford University. Later, she ran a small but international publishing business, before returning to academic life to study for a PhD. She now lectures in the history of science at Darwin College, Cambridge, and is the author of several books.

Climate Change: Forcing a Treaty

Frits Böttcher
The Global Institute for the Study of Natural Resources
The Hague
The Netherlands

Summary

The theory of global warming, for which there is little evidence, has come to dominate the world's environmental agenda to such an extent that an international treaty is based on it. This remarkable feat came about through the well-orchestrated efforts of an inner circle of science-policy makers within the IPCC, who dominated discussion in order to achieve the necessary 'scientific consensus' for politicians to take action. The paper explains how all this was achieved, and traces the global warming campaign from its inception in the 1980s to the Berlin conference of 1995.

Introduction

Having read the preceding chapters the reader is confronted with a crucial question. How could it happen that a subject, still shrouded in scientific uncertainty, obtained the status of the most important global environmental issue? During the past ten years global warming has been embraced by ministers for the environment, with their civil servants and governmental agencies, by environmental pressure groups and especially by the media. A related question is: how could a subject as complex as climate change trigger the signing of an international climate treaty after less than five years preparation? It is an event unique in the annals of international negotiations.

A conjunction of many circumstances led to this remarkable situation. But the dominating factor has been the intense co-operation between a small group of scientists, politicians and diplomats[1], which culminated in the Rio conference of 1992, with the forcing of a Climate Treaty.

THE GLOBAL WARMING DEBATE

The main purpose of my article is to analyse this joint effort. But first of all I would like to mention briefly a number of other circumstances, leading to a lack of balance in the scientific and political treatment of the global warming subject.

- The study of global climate change has emerged as a relatively new multidisciplinary branch of science, dealing with an extremely complex subject. The main disciplines involved are: physics, chemistry, biology, meteorology and geology. Most participating scientists are specialists, who restrict themselves to isolated parts of the whole field. Only a few scientists have a comprehensive view of the subject.

- The present state of knowledge in this relatively new branch of science is far from mature. However, a major obstacle to a scientific debate of all the uncertainties is the Intergovernmental Panel on Climate Change (IPCC), a powerful body of civil servants and scientists, who dominate the discussion. Their objective is to achieve a consensus, needed by the politicians for their decision making.

- Within that community of a few hundred people, the predictions based on computations with GCMs (General Circulation Models) play a predominant rôle. This is unwise because the GCMs are unsuitable for predictions for three reasons:

1. GCMs are based on crude approximations.

2. The physical basis of the models is inadequate.

3. Artificial flux adjustments are used to prevent the models from producing totally unrealistic results. These "fudge factors" artificially supply or remove heat and water over the entire ocean. Otherwise the combined ocean-atmosphere systems would show a large imbalance in the way heat and moisture are exchanged between the ocean and the atmosphere.

The conclusion of Bengt Dahlström, of the Swedish Meteorological Institute, concerning their shortcomings is,

"Bearing in mind the ... weaknesses of present global climate models, it cannot be ruled out that the calculations might be producing misleading results". [2]

268

This warning, given in 1993, has been repeated in several recent reports.

Moreover, the supposition that the Earth's climate can be written down as a huge collection of mathematical equations, to be dealt with by a computer, grossly underestimates the extreme complexity of the atmosphere-oceans-biosphere system. Indeed, the climate system may be inherently chaotic.

- Large groups of specialists have jumped on the band wagon by initiating research projects concerning the impact of a possible climate change. Such investigations form a fashionable, but vulnerable, type of research – dependent on the reliability of the climate change predictions.

- The discussion of the so-called greenhouse effect and the possible consequences of global warming is obscured by misunderstanding and confusion, due to the complexity of the atmosphere-oceans-biosphere system and particularly due to the fact that the subject lends itself to spurious logic and unclear thinking[3].

- The enormous influence of water vapour as the major greenhouse gas is usually underestimated or even ignored, whereas the rôle of carbon dioxide is often exaggerated for political reasons.

- The global warming predictions seem to fulfil the subconscious wishes of many people to anticipate a doomsday.

- For ministers of the environment, the subject is extremely attractive. It is far easier to talk about a hypothetical worldwide threat in the long-term future than to solve mundane environmental problems. The call to "save our planet" is a good vote-catcher.

- The threat of global warming is supposed to be anthropogenic, caused by the burning of coal, oil and natural gas. The issue is closely connected with the world-wide energy production and consumption, particularly in the industrialised countries. This energy connection has led to heated debates in the political arena, for instance between ministers responsible for the environment and some of their colleagues, between political parties, between developing countries and the rest of the world

THE GLOBAL WARMING DEBATE

and last but not least within the community of industrialised nations.

- Alarming predictions have little to do with science but much to do with politics. Disbelievers are stigmatised as reactionaries while believers are seen as progressive. The distinction between disbelievers and believers is bringing different types of environmentalism into collision. On the one hand we have an environmentalism based on scientific knowledge and insight into the roots of prosperity. On the other we have environmentalism based on pseudo-science and feelings of guilt and fear.

- An important element in the alarming predictions is the "scare-them-to-death approach". I learned that expression from an American climatologist, who told his audience in the early seventies that such an approach was the best way to obtain funds for the large computers needed for climate research.

In 1990, the scientific director of the Royal Netherlands Meteorological Institute openly criticised some of his colleagues for surrendering to such temptations. His article in the journal of the British Meteorological Society started with the following warning:

"I worry a lot these days. I worry about the arrogance of scientists who blithely claim that they can help solve the climate problem, provided their research receives massive increases in funding. I worry about the lack of sophistication, the absence of reflection, and the way climate modelers covet new supercomputers. I worry about the scientific and technological advances being promised for the next ten years. I worry about the eagerness with which we tend to prostitute ourselves in order to please politicians who might be seduced into financing our craving for expansion. I worry that our claims will backfire on us. I worry that they will hurt our chances of obtaining adequate support for the long-term commitments needed in climate monitoring and ecosystem research". [4]

The Joint Effort of Scientists and Policy-Makers

The roots of the pressure on policymakers by scientists can be traced back to the early seventies when American climatologists used the "scare them to death approach" to obtain the funding for their climate modelling. Later in the seventies, after the publication of their first reports, they called in the help of two UN bodies: the World Meteorological Organisation (WMO) and the United Nations Environment Programme (UNEP).

The WMO was founded in 1949 and unites all the meteorological institutes of the world. Combined, they have a budget of $5 billion. UNEP was founded after the UN conference on the environment, held in Stockholm in 1972.

The WMO is a member of the International Council of Scientific Unions, (ICSU), the federation of international scientific unions, such as the world-wide unions of physical societies, of chemical societies and of geological societies. Representatives of the WMO persuaded the ICSU that climate research should become one of its specific fields of attention, and consequently representatives of WMO, UNEP and ICSU met in Villach (Austria) in October 1985 to discuss this newly discovered threat to mankind. Seldom has a scientific meeting had such an influence on the policy makers. The participants concluded that,

"although quantitative uncertainty in models results persist, it is highly probable that increasing concentrations of the greenhouse gases will produce significant climatic change".

The conference statement mentioned that,

"the understanding of the greenhouse question is sufficiently developed that scientists and policy-makers should begin an active collaboration to explore the effectiveness of alternative policies and adjustments".

It recommended that UNEP, WMO and ICSU take action to "initiate, if deemed necessary, consideration of a global convention".

The scientists who attended the meeting had insufficient evidence for the statements they made, and hence were irresponsible.

This pressure on governments and the UN had two immediate results. It strongly influenced the discussions in the World Commission on Environment and Development and it initiated the formation in 1988 of the Intergovernmental Panel for Climate Change (IPCC), a joint venture of the WMO and the UNEP, set up as "an intergovernmental mechanism aimed at providing the basis for the development of a realistic and effective internationally accepted strategy for addressing climate change". The term mechanism, with its relationship to machinery, is quite appropriate to describe what has happened since 1988. Two IPCC reports[5,6], published in 1990 and 1992, became the cornerstones of a UN action which assumed climate change to be the great threat of the next century.

The World Commission on Environment and Development and its Brundtland Report

I will come back to the IPCC later, because the chronological order requires me to deal firstly with the rôle of the World Commission on Environment and Development (WCED). This commission was called into existence by the General Assembly of the UN in 1983. Its main task was "to propose long-term environmental strategies for achieving sustainable development by the year 2000 and beyond".

Its report "Our Common Future"[7], published in 1987, is usually named the Brundtland report, after the Norwegian prime minister and former environment minister Gro Harlem Brundtland, who chaired the WCED.

The concept "sustainable development", mentioned as a major goal of the programme, understandably plays an important role in the Brundtland report. On page 43 the following definition is given:

"Sustainable development is development that meets the needs of the present without compromising the ability of future generations to meet their own needs".

It is not surprising that widely different interpretations of this fashionable concept are in circulation. Usually it is supposed to mean that the planet is handed over to the next generation environmentally in the same, or even in better condition, than we inherited it from the previous generation. But the Brundtland report goes much further:

"Living standards that go beyond the basic minimum are sustainable only if consumption standards everywhere have regard for long-term sustainability. Yet many of us live beyond the world's ecological means, for instance in our patterns of energy use. Perceived needs are socially and culturally determined, and sustainable development requires the promotion of values that encourage consumption standards that are within the bounds of the ecological possible and to which all can reasonably aspire."

The expression "patterns of energy use" hints at CO_2 emission and climate change. The Brundtland report was written three years before the first IPCC-report appeared. Its foreword mentioned:

"Scientists bring to our attention urgent but complex problems bearing on our very survival: a warming globe, threats to the Earth's ozone layer, deserts consuming agricultural land".

The Brundtland report states that, "the greenhouse effect, one such threat to life-support systems, springs directly from increased resource use". And it concludes, based on this brief reference to the Villach meeting, that global warming,

"could cause sea-level rise over the next 45 years large enough to inundate many low-lying coastal cities and river deltas. It could also drastically upset national and international agricultural production and trade systems".

By paying no attention to other voices than the Villach "consensus", the Brundtland Commission contributed greatly to spreading the idea that global warming was a major problem facing mankind.

The Toronto Conference
In June 1988, in a follow-up to the Brundtland report, Canada sponsored an international conference on "The Changing Atmosphere: Implications for Global Security". The conference focused on climate change. One of its principle purposes was to bridge the gap between scientists and policy-makers. It was attended by more than 340 individuals from 46 countries, including two heads of state, more than 100 government officials, scientists, industry representatives and environmentalists.

The Toronto Conference issued a statement which began with the portentous words:

"Humanity is conducting an unintended, uncontrolled, globally pervasive experiment whose ultimate consequence could be second only to a global nuclear war. It is imperative to act now".

The statement went on to predict that, given the high rates of likely warming, "no country would benefit in toto from climate change". As initial action, the Conference recommended:

- a 20 percent reduction in global CO_2 emissions from 1988 levels by the year 2005,

- development of "a comprehensive global convention as a framework for protocols on the protection of the atmosphere," and

- establishment of a "World Atmosphere Fund" to be financed in part by a levy on fossil fuel consumption in industrialised countries.

The Toronto Conference was not officially government-sanctioned, because the government participants attended in their personal capacities. Hence the Conference Statement was not binding on anyone. It was drafted by a committee composed mostly of environmentalists and discussed in less than a day and environmental activists dominated the scene. Many participants did not fully appreciate the political difficulties of addressing the climate change issue.

The attitude in governmental circles towards the conclusions of the Villach and Toronto meetings varied from enthusiastic approval in some countries to suspicion in others. Some officials considered the conclusions were the result of environmental activism rather than sound science. In an attempt to bring back governmental control to an increasingly important political issue, a number of governments had already requested WMO and UNEP to establish the Intergovernmental Panel on Climate Change with the mandate of providing "internationally co-ordinated assessments of the magnitude, timing and potential environmental and socio-economic impact of climate change and realistic response strategies". Thus it was that the year of the Toronto Conference (1988) also saw the birth of the IPCC.

The Influence of Individual Scientists

Another important event in 1988 was a hearing of the US Senate Energy Committee on the greenhouse effect. It was a good example of the unprecedented rôle played by some individual scientists in influencing policymakers. I should like to discuss this aspect before continuing the IPCC story.

In the summer of 1988 the US suffered from a heatwave. The testimony of James Hansen, a NASA climate modeler, to the Senate Energy Committee that "the greenhouse effect has been detected and it is changing our climate now" made front page news, coming as it did at the height of the heatwave. Senator Max Baucus commented: "I sense that we are experiencing a major shift. It's like a shift of tectonic plates". James Hansen should have known better because every meteorologist knows that regional heatwaves have nothing to do with climate change. They occur in a region when the distribution of high and low pressure centres shows little change for a number of weeks. During such a period the jet stream in the upper atmosphere hardly changes. Such a "blockage" seems to be a chaotic phenomenon. In The Netherlands there have been thirty heatwaves so far in this century.

According to the Royal Netherlands Meteorological Institute, there is no explanation for the puzzling occurrence of a heatwave. American meteorologists could have confirmed this. But thanks to Hansen's testimony, climate change burst on to the political stage in the US.

Even George Bush used it immediately in his election-speeches a few months later.

"Those who think we are powerless to do anything about the greenhouse effect are forgetting about the White House effect. As President I intend to do something about it".

After his election, Chief of Staff John Sununu convinced the new President to adopt a different view.

John Sununu is one of the key players in the story. He knew enough about physics and chemistry to understand how weak the scientific basis of the climate predictions was and hence he became the major "obstructionist", the spoil-sport in the greenhouse game. He opposed any initiative that might require the US to take steps to reduce its greenhouse emissions.

After his resignation as Chief of Staff in 1991 it became clear that his attitude was shared – mainly for other than scientific reasons – by a Congressional majority. During the presidential elections in 1991 Governor Clinton and particularly Senator Gore were the advocates of controlling CO_2 in their successful campaign. Since then they have experienced how large is the opposition within their own Democratic party against measures aimed at reducing CO_2 emission. In 1993 they tried in vain to introduce a modest energy tax, the so-called BTU-tax.

The Activities of the IPCC

Meanwhile the IPCC was up and running. It held its first meeting in November 1988, electing professor Bert Bolin of Sweden as chairman and establishing three working groups: Working Group I on science, chaired by the United Kingdom, Working Group II on impacts, chaired by the Soviet Union and Working Group III on response strategies, chaired by the United States.

On December 6, 1988 the General Assembly of the UN adopted the establishment of the IPCC, urging governments, inter-governmental and non-governmental organisations, and scientific institutions to treat climate change as a priority issue. This decision triggered an escalation of speculative scientific thinking. In spite of many uncertainties in the underlying scientific theory and in spite of the deficiencies in the computer models used for climatic predictions, a small but vociferous group of scientists claimed that there was sufficient evidence to predict disastrous climatic developments for the next century.

Throughout 1989, the three IPCC working groups held frequent workshops and meetings. Two persons played a dominant rôle: chairman Bolin and Sir John Houghton, the chairman of Working Group I. Their dynamic leadership was to be of great importance in achieving a so-called consensus for the conclusions of the first IPCC-report. At the first meeting (Washington, February 1989) of Working Group III James Baker (US) called upon the Secretary of State to take "prudent steps that are already justified on grounds other than climate change". This approach became well-known as the "no-regrets" policy.

In May and June 1990 the IPCC Working Groups finalised their First Assessment Reports. During a plenary IPCC meeting in Sundsvall, Sweden in August the reports were approved.

A few hundred scientists had contributed to the scientific report of Working Group I. It gained acceptance by governments as the authoritative statement on climate change, although most of the scientists involved had only limited knowledge of a few aspects of what was being reported.

The Intergovernmental Negotiating Committee (INC)

The plenary IPCC meeting in Sundsvall was followed a few months later by the Second World Climate Conference (SWCC) in Geneva. Its first part was the scientific component, followed by a ministerial meeting which reflected the growing political interest in the climate issue.

The SWCC Ministerial Declaration stressed the need to stabilise emissions of greenhouse gases, but was unable to decide when or at what level stabilisation should be achieved.

At the SWCC the differences among developing countries were striking. The oil-producing states questioned the science of climate change and made a plea for a "no-regrets" approach. On the other hand, small islands and low-lying coastal states, united in the Alliance of Small Island States (AOSIS) argued for strong response measures.

Both the IPCC and the SWCC called for negotiations on an international climate change convention to begin as quickly as possible. Intensive negotiations led to the proposal for anIntergovernmental Negotiating Committee (INC) to prepare the envisaged convention. On December 21, 1990 the UN General

Assembly adopted resolutions, establishing the INC under the auspices of the General Assembly.

The INC was to complete its work in time for the convention to be signed at the United Nations Conference on Environment and Development to be held in Rio de Janeiro, June 1992.

Only 18 months were available for the drafting of the Climate Treaty and some critics said, the INC was "doomed to success", because no country could accept responsibility for a failure of the negotiations without risking adverse publicity.

At the first plenary session of the INC in February 1991, the obstacles to a world-wide agreement seemed almost insurmountable. The complexity of the climate issue, the continuing scientific uncertainty and the wide range of diverging views had to be considered. The INC had to find a compromise that could be supported by at least a majority of participants.

One of the major obstacles was the position of the United States, arguing that only a vague Framework Convention could be formulated. Further scientific research and a better assessment of the economic costs and benefits of possible options were necessary, they said, before quantitative targets and timetables could be adopted. The US was strongly supported by Saudi Arabia, Kuwait and a number of other developing countries. On the other hand, some industrialised countries especially Germany, The Netherlands and Denmark, entered the negotiations with rather ambitious objectives. Under pressure from these countries, the European Union contemplated a tax on CO_2 and energy.

Despite all these obstacles and after cumbersome negotiations and stalemates the INC finally reached its goal, thanks in large part to chairman, Jean Ripert (France). He prepared a draft convention, acceptable to all countries. It shows all the characteristics of a last minute compromise. The agreement was reached in May 1992. With the adoption of the Framework Convention on Climate Change, the INC laid the foundation for a new field of law: International Climate Law. And it also prepared a new UN body: The Conference of the Parties (COP). This led to the most publicised event of all.

The Rio Declaration and the Climate Treaty

The major tangible outcome of the United Nations Conference on Environment and Development (UNCED), Rio de Janeiro (June 1992) consisted of three documents. They were the final result of painstaking negotiations in many preparatory committee sessions during the previous three years:

- *Agenda 21*, a 750-page detailed plan of action for the Earth's future.

- *The Rio Declaration on Environment and Development*, a short document, containing 27 simply formulated principles.

- The *United Nations Framework Convention on Climate Change*, (UNFCCC) shortly named "The Climate Treaty", a 30-page document with a complicated text.

Environmental organisations have unanimously condemned the three documents, because of their vague wording and lack of commitments.

But the UNCED meeting has ensured that the environment, linked to economic development, will continue to be an item on the international agenda.

I will discuss the two documents which impinge on the subject of this report: the Rio Declaration and the Climate Treaty.

The Rio Declaration

The Rio Declaration starts with an anthropocentric principle, stating that "human beings are at the centre of concerns for sustainable development". This principle reduces the "save our planet" slogan, used by politicians and environmentalists, to the dimension "save us". This is emphasised in the second principle, giving the states "the sovereign right to exploit their own resources pursuant to their own environmental and developmental policies".

It is understandable that many fanatical environmentalists complain that the Rio Declaration starts from the classical and Jewish-Christian tradition that human beings are not an integral part of nature, but have a position of dominance over the rest of nature. Yet, the Rio Declaration is modern in the sense that humans are supposed to have the responsibility to transfer the planet in a condition acceptable for coming generations. That is the reason why the expression "sustainable development" appears eleven times in the Declaration, although a definition of this fashionable concept is lacking.

Reading the Rio Declaration one wonders now and then how such a vague principle can be used as a manageable instrument in the practice of decision making. In this connection it is already difficult to apply it to the second part of principle one, stating that human beings "are entitled to a healthy and productive life in harmony with nature". What is a productive life? And does not productivity go against sustainability, particularly in developing countries?

In the discussion on sustainability it is often overlooked that humans have been changing the planet continuously in the past 10,000 years. In some cases it is evident that this has led to disastrous environmental results. The oldest example is the soil erosion in the Mediterranean and Near East regions due to deforestation and misuse of land for agriculture, starting several thousand years BC. But such extreme examples are easier to judge in hindsight than the majority of other actions, where the question arises: which changes should be seen as not sustainable? The Netherlands are an example of a country where nothing remains of the original environment of only a thousand years ago.

An impressive description of this continuous process of change (God made the world, but the Dutch made Holland) has recently been given by the geologist Peter Westbroek in his book[8]: "converted from an inhospitable wilderness into an artefact, an environment adapted by human shrewdness to human demands".

He even dares to think of a futuristic situation in which, due to the explosive growth of the world population, the entire earth might be "converted into a cultural domain – a kind of park, a giant laboratory, or a great work of art". This is not the sort of sustainability of which some ideologists dream.

The Rio Declaration is an interesting document from an idealistic point of view but it will probably have little practical influence before the end of the century.

The Climate Treaty

From a scientific point of view it is remarkable that the Framework Convention on Climate Change (usually called the Climate Treaty) starts from the concern "that human activities have been substantially increasing the atmospheric concentrations of greenhouse gases, that these increases enhance the natural greenhouse effect, and that this will result on average in an additional warming of the Earth's surface and atmosphere and may adversely affect natural ecosystems and humankind". At several places in this phrasing scientific suppositions are presented as scientific certainties.

The preamble of the convention also notes that there are many uncertainties in predictions of climate change, particularly with regard to the timing, magnitude and regional patterns thereof.

But the whole document leaves no doubt that, in the minds of those who adopted it, there is only one possible climate change: global warming in the next century.

THE GLOBAL WARMING DEBATE

Global cooling, a fashionable subject only twenty years ago, is not even mentioned as a theoretical possibility while climate change due to natural disasters is neglected completely.

At the signing of the Convention by the European Community a special statement was issued to the annoyance of President Bush of the United States. The core of that statement was the following announcement:

"The Community and its Member States reaffirm the objective of stabilisation of CO_2 emissions by 2000 at the 1990 level in the Community as a whole. They will continue their ongoing work to implement the necessary measures to achieve this and – for this purpose – are working on 'a Community Strategy to limit carbon dioxide emissions and to improve energy efficiency'".

It was a sturdy statement, but three years after the signing of the Climate Treaty, the objective of the European Union appears to be unrealistic and little progress has been made towards its implementation.

The Energy Connection and the Policymakers' Dilemma

In spite of the warnings about carbon dioxide emissions the increasing global energy demand will inevitably lead to a rapidly increasing use of fossil fuels in the coming decades. Coal, overtaken in the 1960's by oil as the world's major source of primary energy, will gradually regain its position as the most important source. Because 84% of the world production of coal is used to provide energy in the countries that produce it, it is illusive to believe that a Climate Treaty can prevent the increasing use of coal in developing countries. In the industrialised countries coal can be partly and temporarily replaced by natural gas and oil to stabilise the emission of carbon dioxide or at least reduce the growth rate of the emissions. But world-wide it would be as difficult to prevent the increase of CO_2 emission as it would to prevent the growth of the world population. China, for instance, is expected to surpass the CO_2 emission of the entire OECD in the first half of the next century. Recent prognoses by both the World Energy Council[9] and the International Energy Agency[10] foresee a considerable increase in the use of fossil fuels in the coming decades, leading to a large increase in CO_2 emissions, particularly in the newly-industrialised countries.

We have to take into account that energy is for the economy of states and communities what carbon dioxide is for the living plant:

one of the vital conditions. This fact should be considered very seriously as a "look before you leap" warning for those politicians and economists, who advocate a drastic energy tax as an easy fix, forgetting the subtle web of economic relations.

In this connection I think there are indications for what I would like to call the policymaker's dilemma. It is caused by the fact that the predictions of the IPCC concerning a possible global warming, due to carbon dioxide and other greenhouse gases, have introduced a new element in the discussion on the role of fossil fuels. Gradually coal has become again the black sheep of the fossil fuel family. But even the other fossil fuels are considered a necessary evil. The only positive aspect of this development is that once again the emphasis is laid on energy conservation and on efficiency improvement of power plants and other users of fossil fuels. For policymakers it is not difficult to accept these two principles, as long as the measures fall in the category of what is usually indicated as a no-regrets policy.

The policymaker's dilemma, however, is whether or not under the present circumstances much more radical measures should be taken, even if economic disruption would follow.

Article 3 of the Climate Treaty refers to the dilemma in the following words:

"The Parties should take precautionary measures to anticipate, prevent or minimise the causes of climate change and mitigate its adverse effects. Where there are threats of serious or irreversible damage, lack of full scientific certainty should not be used as a reason for postponing such measures, taking into account that policies and measures to deal with climate change should be cost-effective so as to ensure global benefits at the lowest possible cost".

My first comment is that it will be very difficult to determine whether measures "ensure global benefits at the lowest possible cost". And the expression "lack of full scientific certainty" raises the question how much scientific uncertainty is acceptable for policymakers to take action in spite of the uncertainty. This is an extremely important element in the policymaker's dilemma. Imagine if ten years ago – when scientists forecasted several metres of sea-level rise as possible – governments had undertaken costly programmes for the construction of sea-walls. Now it is becoming clear that if global warming occurs, a fall of sea-level rather than a rise is more likely, as snow deposits at the poles increase.

A widespread, but wrong idea – ventilated by some ministers of the environment – is that the cost of preventive measures are akin to paying a fire insurance premium. "Although the chance is small that your house burns down, you nevertheless pay an insurance premium" is a comparison frequently drawn. It is a wrong comparison, because one pays an insurance premium not to prevent one's house burning down, but to claim compensation in case it happens. A correct comparison with the fire risk would be to consider how much one is prepared to pay for fire prevention measures. The decision about such costs could be based on a cost-benefit analysis, balancing the effects of a possible disaster against the cost of constructing safeguards against it. Also in the case of natural disasters such a cost-benefit analysis has to be made. It is a kind of arrogance to believe that expensive measures would make it possible to keep nature wholly under control.

An oft-used argument for not postponing drastic measures is that we cannot wait for sufficient scientific evidence because it might then be too late to prevent a disaster. Since the Brundtland report and the Ministerial Declaration of the UN Economic Commission for Europe meeting (Bergen, 1990) it has been widely accepted that policies to achieve sustainable development must be based on the precautionary principle.

That principle is included in the quoted article 3 of the Climate Treaty: "environmental measures must anticipate, prevent and attack the causes of environmental degradation". In the case of the predictions concerning a sea-level rise or fall we have indicated already how unwise it can be to hasten the application of the precautionary principle in case of considerable scientific uncertainty.

Lack of knowledge concerning technologies, available now and in the future, can also lead to a wrong application of the precautionary principle. In the case of CO_2 emission it should not be ignored that carbon dioxide produced in power plants and in other installations could be removed and stored in exhausted oil or gas fields, deep in the oceans or otherwise.

The Berlin Conference 1995

In April 1995 more than a thousand delegates from 120 countries met in Berlin for the first "Conference of the Parties", usually indicated as "The United Nations Climate Conference". One of the very few tangible results of this conference marathon of eleven days was the decision to choose Bonn as the seat of the Permanent Secretariat.

During the preparative negotiations in the preceding months it had become clear that hardly any progress could be expected during a conference, dominated by large controversies between both individual countries and groups of countries.

For instance the US delegates refused to back a Berlin Mandate that would include targets and timetables for industrial nations to cut their emissions of greenhouse gases.

For outsiders the results were so disappointing that a German journalist summarised them in seven words: the mountain was delivered of a mouse. This old fashioned expression of Latin origin should, however, be supplemented by a customary Dutch expression. Its translation in English reads: this mouse will appear to have a tail, which means "this won't be the end of the matter", because the IPCC continues its insidious activities.

What Happened After the Berlin Conference?

Since the most important decision during the Berlin meeting was the decision to meet again in Tokyo in 1997, most countries are following a policy of wait-and-see. Within the European Union the stalemate situation continues. A majority of the members are against decisions on targets and timetables for the reduction of CO_2 and other greenhouse gases. The original 1990 plans for a CO_2 tax or energy tax or a combination of both have been abandoned because of the majority opposition. Instead, preparations are presently being made for a harmonisation of the existing fuel taxes. Critics already refer to the new proposals as the green cloak of hidden taxation.

REFERENCES

1. *Negotiating Climate Change; The Inside Story of the Rio Convention.* Edited by I. M. Mintzer and J. A. Leonard; Cambridge University Press 1994

2. Dahlström, B. *The Earth's Climate*, p.48; published by Elforsk AB, Stockholm 1993

3. Böttcher, C. J. F. *Science and Fiction of the Greenhouse Effect and Carbon Dioxide*, pp. 25-31, published by The Global Institute for the Study of Natural Resources, The Hague 1992

4. Tennekes, H. 'Weather', *Journal of The Royal Meteorological Society Vol. 45* 1990: p.67

5. *Climate Change: The IPCC Scientific Assessment,* Edited by J. T. Houghton, G. J. Jenkins and J. J. Ephraums, Cambridge University Press 1990

6. *Climate Change 1992: The Supplementary Report to the IPCC Scientific Assessment,* Edited by J. T. Houghton, B. A. Callander and S. K. Varney, Cambridge University Press 1992

7. World Commission on Environment and Development (WCED); *Our Common Future,* Oxford University Press 1987

8. Westbroek, P. *Life as a Geological Force,* W. W. Norton & Company 1991

9. *Energy for Tomorrow's World* Report of the World Energy Council, St. Martin's Press, London 1993

10. *World Energy Outlook,* 1994 Edition, International Energy Agency, Paris 1994

Dr C. J. F. Böttcher

Frits Böttcher became professor of physical chemistry at Leiden University in 1947, becoming professor emeritus in 1980. He was the first president of the Science Policy Council of The Netherlands (1966-1976). He headed The Netherlands Delegation to the OECD Committee for Science and Technology for 12 years (1963-1975). In that period he was chairman of the OECD examiners for science policy of three countries: Austria (1970), Switzerland (1971) and Ireland (1972). He has been president or member of the Supervisory Board of a number of large and middle-sized Dutch companies.

Böttcher was one of the founding members of the Club of Rome in 1968 and member of its Executive Committee from 1972-1978. He has been an honorary member since 1986.

Böttcher's scientific work has mainly concentrated on chemical thermodynamics, electric polarisation and relaxation, and the physico-chemical aspects of biomedical problems. Böttcher's publications include more than one hundred papers in scientific journals and a monograph, "Theory of Electric Polarization"(first edition 1952, second edition in two volumes 1972 - 1978). He has given numerous lectures in Europe, The United States and Japan.

He is Chairman of the Board of Trustees of the Global Institute Foundation for the Study of Natural Resources.

Mission Statement

The European Science and Environment Forum is an independent, non-profit-making alliance of scientists whose aim is to ensure that environmental debates are properly aired, and that decisions which are taken, and action that is proposed, are founded on sound scientific principles.

The ESEF will be particularly concerned to address issues where it appears that the public and their representatives, and those in the media, are being given misleading or one-sided advice. In such instances the ESEF will seek to provide a platform for scientists whose views are not being heard, but who have a contribution to make.

Members are accepted from all walks of life, all branches of science; the only requirement being that they are recruited to the ESEF through an existing member. There is no membership fee. Members will be expected to offer their services in contributing to ESEF publications on issues where their expertise is germane.

To maintain its independence and impartiality, the ESEF does not accept outside funding from whatever source, the only income it receives is from the sale of its publications. Such publications will automatically be sent to members. Copies will be sent to selected opinion formers within the media and within government.

ESEF Members

Dr Sallie Baliunas USA

Dr Robert C. Balling USA

Prof. Dr A. G. M. Barratt UK

Dr Jack Barrett UK

Mr Roger Bate UK

Dr Sonja Boehmer-Christiansen UK

Prof. Dr Frits Böttcher The Netherlands

Mr Charles Bottoms UK

Prof. Norman D. Brown UK

Prof. Dr K. H. Buchel Germany

Dr John Butler UK

Mr Piers Corbyn UK

Prof. Dr. A. W. C. A. Cornelissen The Netherlands

Mr Richard Courtney UK

Dr Candace Crandall USA

Dr A. J. Dobbs UK

Dr John Emsley UK

Dr Patricia Fara UK

Prof. Dr Hartmut Frank Germany

Prof. Dr Eigil Friis-Christensen Denmark

Dr Alastair Gebbie UK

Dr T. R. Gerholm Sweden

Prof. Dr Gerhard Gerlich Germany

Mr Peter Henry UK

Prof. Dr Hans-Eberhard Heyke Germany

Dr Vidar Hisdal Norway

287

THE GLOBAL WARMING DEBATE

Dr Sherwood Idso USA

Prof. Dr Zbigniew Jaworowski Poland

Dr Tim Jones UK

Prof. Dr Wibjörn Karlén Sweden

Dr Terence Kealey UK

Prof. Dr F. Korte Germany

Mr Johan Kuylenstierna Sweden

Dr Alan Mann UK

Dr John McMullan UK

Prof. Dr Helmut Metzner Germany

Dr Patrick Michaels USA

Sir William Mitchell UK

Dr Asmunn Moene Norway

Prof. Dr Dr hc mult Paul Müller Germany

Dr Genrik A. Nikolsky Russia

Prof. Dr Harry Priem The Netherlands

Dr Ray L. Richards UK

Dr Michael Rogers UK

Dr Tom V. Segalstad Norway

Dr S. Fred Singer USA

Dr Willie Soon USA

Prof. Dr H. P. van Heel The Netherlands

Dr Robin Vaughan UK

Prof. Dr Nico Vlaar The Netherlands

Dr Gerd-Rainer Weber Germany

Sir Geoffrey Wilkinson UK